A BIT OF HEAVEN FOR THE FEW?

An oral history of the
hospice movement
in the United Kingdom

A BIT OF HEAVEN FOR THE FEW?

An oral history of the hospice movement in the United Kingdom

David Clark, Neil Small, Michael Wright, Michelle Winslow & Nic Hughes

Observatory Publications

First published in 2005 by
OBSERVATORY PUBLICATIONS
International Observatory on End of Life Care, Institute for Health Research,
Lancaster University, Lancaster, LA1 4YT, UK

observatory-publications@lancaster.ac.uk
www.eolc-observatory.net

British Library Cataloguing-in-Publication Data
A British Library CIP Record is available

ISBN 0-9544192-0-0

Designed and typeset in Frutiger by BBR Solutions Ltd, Chesterfield.

Printed on acid-free paper in the UK by Bath Press Ltd, Bath.

Buy this and other Observatory Publications titles from www.eolc-observatory.net.

Contents

vii   Acknowledgements

1   Introduction

13   Chapter 1: Personal motivations

42   Chapter 2: Hospice growth and spread

72   Chapter 3: Hospice teamwork: towards an integrated community

89   Chapter 4: Diversification: the rise of hospice organisations and professional associations

116   Chapter 5: Spirituality and hospice care

134   Chapter 6: Pain, symptoms and the hospice response

155   Chapter 7: The family is not an optional extra: bereavement care as an integral part of the hospice

177   Chapter 8: Finished and unfinished business

199   Appendix 1: Dramatis personae

218   Appendix 2: A timeline of hospice developments

222   Appendix 3: The work of the Hospice History Project

226   Consolidated bibliography

231   Index

Acknowledgements

This book is the product of interviews and research carried out over about 10 years, from the mid-1990s. Two of the authors, David Clark and Neil Small, were involved in the work from the outset, and the team gradually expanded to include Michael Wright, Nic Hughes and Michelle Winslow. Along the way, many individuals and organisations have assisted us in developing our endeavours. Michael Worboys was the first to seriously encourage the idea. The Wellcome Trust then showed unwavering support for our work, as it developed from modest beginnings into what came to be known as the Hospice History Project. Two grants from the Wellcome Trust (numbers 043877/Z/95 and 058078/Z/99) enabled a huge amount of interviewing and other data collection and analysis to take place (see Appendix 3), and support from the Trust's People Awards programme (grant number 071072/Z/03/Z) has supported the production of this book and an accompanying exhibition.

Over the years several other colleagues and students conducted oral history interviews for the project upon which we have drawn here (see Appendix 1) and we thank them all for their involvement: Lorna Campbell, Clare Humphreys, Gerry King, Kirsten Lund, Paul Lydon, Marcia Meldrum, Sara Morris and Silvia Paz. In addition, Sophie Page Hall gave particular assistance with Chapter 7. We have also enjoyed considerable institutional support for our work on hospice history and we acknowledge here the universities of Sheffield, Leeds, and Lancaster in this respect. We are also grateful to our colleagues in the Trent Palliative Care Centre at Sheffield and the Institute for Health Research at Lancaster for their ongoing interest and supportive reflections. At Lancaster, John Welshman was generous in reading through an earlier version of the manuscript and we are grateful to him for his comments and guidance at that time.

So much oral history material has meant a huge amount of transcribing, and a great deal of this tricky task has been done by Margaret Jane. Her knowledge and understanding of the subject matter have added hugely to the quality of these transcripts and we also thank her for significant work on the manuscript, as well as for administering and supporting the project generally over many years. Several others have given assistance in various ways and we thank them also: Denise Brady, Jill Cooper, Marjorie Coultard, Derek Doyle, Keith Telford, Jo Frost, Avril Jackson, Christine Kearney, Mandy Pratt, Cicely Saunders, Robert Twycross and Eric Wilkes. Prue Dufour, whose untimely death occurred just as we were finishing the book, was also helpful to us in various ways; she will be greatly missed by many in the world of hospice care.

At BBR, Chris Reed and Amanda Thompson have had a major role in bringing the book to completion. Their editorial input, typesetting and design work, and above all unstinting support for the concept have been hugely important and we thank them for everything they have done. Some of the photographs appear by kind permission of *Nursing Times*; others have been provided by our respondents, whilst some come from the extensive archives of the International Observatory on End of Life Care. We have made every effort to ascertain the copyright status of the photographs, but should anything have been overlooked and can be pointed out to us, Observatory Publications will be pleased to correct this in a subsequent edition.

Finally, we must acknowledge wholeheartedly and with huge appreciation, all of those who gave up their time to be interviewed and whose stories and experiences are recounted here. We thank them for their various comments on the penultimate draft of the manuscript and we hope that they will feel content with what we have done here. Sadly, some of our respondents have died in the intervening years since we first met and talked with them; we trust that in capturing their hospice involvement in these pages, some small contribution is made to their memory.

Our book has been written as a five-way collaboration. Its chapters have been worked and reworked in the light of our individual interests and varied perspectives on hospice history. Yet, after many months of writing and editing, we still have a sense of a 'work in progress'. This is not *the* oral history of the hospice movement in the United Kingdom, but rather *an* oral history that has been constructed at a particular time, with the materials we have to hand. It is not fully comprehensive and there are those whose voices – for various reasons – we have been unable to include. Nevertheless it is wide ranging, many stranded and provides a significant first step in making sense of an important aspect of our country's modern history. We could not have written it without the wonderful help and support we have received from so many. Its limitations, needless to say, are entirely our own.

David Clark, Neil Small, Michael Wright,
Michelle Winslow and Nic Hughes
October 2004

Introduction

The late-twentieth-century development of hospice and palliative care in the United Kingdom has had an influence far wider than the specific field of medicine and health care in which it might at first appear to be contained. Indeed, within a short period of time, hospices of various kinds have become part of the landscape of death and dying in modern culture. Noted for their openness about terminal illness, their pioneering approach to the relief of symptoms associated with advanced disease, their support for patients and families, and their concern for the bereaved, hospices seem somehow synonymous with what it might mean to 'die well' in our society. Moreover, such achievements have been made not only as a result of the efforts of professionals in health and social care, but also through the involvement of local communities, 'lay' people, charitable giving and the efforts of volunteers in many capacities. This book seeks to explore these developments through the words, experiences and perceptions of some of those involved in what has come to be known as 'the modern hospice movement'. It is a work of 'oral history' captured through narratives of recollection, and is intended to provide a further perspective on our growing understanding of what must be regarded as an important aspect of modern British social history.[1]

By the mid-twentieth century several changes were occurring in western medicine and health care. Specialisation was advancing rapidly; new treatments were proliferating; and there was an increasing emphasis upon cure and rehabilitation. At the same time death in the hospital, rather than at home, was becoming the norm; and the dying patient or 'hopeless case' was often viewed as a failure of medical practice.[2] Nevertheless, concerns about improving care at the end of life were beginning to surface in the 1950s. In the UK attention started to focus on the medical 'neglect' of the dying patient and articles on the subject began appearing in the professional journals of doctors, nurses and social workers. Four particular innovations have been identified.[3] First, a shift took place within the professional literature on the care of the dying and this saw idiosyncratic anecdote begin to give way to more systematic observation. New studies by doctors, social workers and social scientists provided evidence about the social and clinical aspects of dying in contemporary society. By the early 1960s leading articles in authoritative medical journals such as *The Lancet* and *The British Medical Journal* were drawing on the evidence of research to suggest ways in which terminal care could be promoted and, at the same time, how arguments for euthanasia might be countered. Second, a new view of dying began to emerge which sought to foster concepts of dignity and meaning. Enormous scope was opened up here for refining ideas about the dying process and exploring the extent to which patients should and did know about their terminal condition. Third, an active rather than a passive approach to the care of the dying was promoted with increasing vigour. Within this, the fatalistic resignation of the doctor ('there is nothing more we can do') was supplanted by a new determination to find imaginative ways to continue caring up to the end of life – and indeed beyond it, in the care of the bereaved. Fourth, a growing recognition of the interdependency of mental and physical distress created the potential for a more embodied notion of suffering, thus marking a profound challenge to the body-mind dualism upon which so much medical practice of the period was predicated.

As we shall see in the chapters that follow, it was the work of Cicely Saunders, first developed in St Joseph's Hospice in Hackney, East London that was to prove most consequential. For it was she who began to forge a peculiarly modern philosophy of terminal care. Through systematic attention to patient narratives and by listening carefully to stories of illness and disease, she evolved the concept of 'total pain'. This view of pain moved beyond its physical dimensions alone to encompass the social, emotional, even spiritual aspects of suffering – captured so comprehensively by the patient who told her: *all of me is wrong*.[4] But it was also linked to a hard-headed approach to pain management. Her message was simple: 'constant pain needs constant control'.[5] Analgesics should be employed in a method of regular giving which would ensure that pain was prevented in advance, rather than alleviated once it had become established; and they should be used progressively, from mild, to moderate to strong.

When Cicely Saunders founded St Christopher's Hospice in Sydenham, South London, in 1967, it quickly became a source of inspiration to others. A free-standing and independent organisation dedicated to the care of those close to death, three features allow us to call it the first 'modern' hospice: it aspired to combine excellent clinical care, education and research. St Christopher's therefore differed significantly from other homes for the dying that had preceded it and it sought to become a centre of excellence in a new field of care. Its success was phenomenal and it soon became the stimulus for an expansive phase of hospice development, not only in the UK, but also around the world.

From the outset, ideas developed at St Christopher's were applied differently in other settings. Within a decade it was accepted that the principles of hospice care could be practised in many locations: not only in specialist in-patient units, but also in home care and day care services. Likewise hospital units and support teams were established that brought the new thinking about dying into the very heartlands of acute medicine. By the mid-1980s, a process of maturation was in evidence. Around 100 hospices had been formed in the UK, complemented by home support services and the first hospital palliative care teams; funding from the National Health Service (NHS) and from the major cancer care charities was becoming available. Within the professional lifetime of the founders of the modern hospice movement, a remarkable proliferation had occurred; at the same time the *definition* of hospice care started to come into sharper focus.

In particular, after 1974, the term 'palliative care' was used increasingly. This was the concept devised by the Canadian surgeon, Balfour Mount, who had visited St Christopher's in 1973 and then returned to Montreal to explore how *hospice* ideas could be integrated into *hospital* medicine, starting up the palliative care service there in 1975.[6] The debates and discussions that followed saw 'hospice' and 'palliative' care preoccupied with their aims and purposes, seeking clarity about their status within medicine and health care and undergoing an extended process of self-reflection.[7] In the early decades, modern hospices can be viewed as part of a particular sort of social movement, focused on a single issue – the improvement of the care of the dying. This was in turn supported by wider forces: consumerism and increasing discernment among the users of health and social care services; demographic trends which created substantial numbers of individuals able to volunteer their labour in local hospices; and greater affluence which led to an increase in charitable giving. This movement may well have contributed to a new openness about death and bereavement that was in evidence in the late twentieth century (in the UK, for example, the first person ever to be seen to die on television, was in the care of a hospice).[8] Inspired by charismatic leadership, it was a movement which condemned the neglect of the dying in society; called for high quality pain and symptom management for all who needed it; sought to reconstruct death as a 'natural' phenomenon, rather than a clinical failure; and marshalled practical and moral argument to oppose those in favour of euthanasia. Indeed for Cicely Saunders and her followers such work served as a measure of the very worth of our culture: 'A society which shuns the dying must have an incomplete philosophy.'[9]

At the same time other interests were at work. In particular professional recognition of this emerging area of expertise seemed desirable if the work was to spread and the influence of hospice philosophy was to go beyond the confines of the voluntary movement that bore its name. This

occurred in the UK in 1987, with recognition of the specialty of palliative medicine by the Royal Colleges of Physicians and of General Practitioners, and was subsequently seen by some as a turning point in hospice history.[10] But whilst modernisers claimed that specialisation, the integration of palliative care into the mainstream health system, wider 'coverage' of services and the development of an 'evidence-based' model of practice and organisation were crucial to long-term viability, others mourned the loss of early ideals and regretted an emphasis upon patients' physical symptoms at the expense of psychosocial and spiritual concerns and the needs of the wider family and community. In short, there were claims that forces of medicalisation and routinisation were at work and even that the putative 'holism' of palliative care philosophy masked a new, more subtle form of surveillance of the dying and bereaved in modern society.[11]

During the 1990s, however, a growing commitment to the evidence-based approach was emerging and two forces for expansion were also clearly visible. First was the impetus to move palliative care further 'upstream' in the disease progression and to make it available to those at earlier stages of a life-threatening illness, thereby seeking integration with curative and rehabilitation therapies and shifting the focus beyond terminal care and the final stages of life.[12] Second, there was a growing interest in extending the benefits of palliative care to those with diseases other than cancer, in order to make 'palliative care for all' a reality.[13] By the end of the twentieth century therefore, the work of hospice and palliative care was delicately poised. For some, integration with the wider system was a *sine qua non* for success; for others it marked the entry into a risky phase of new development in which early ideals might be compromised.

Modern hospice care and palliative care have a shared

and brief history. The evolution of one into the other marks a transition which, if successful, could ensure that the benefits of a model of care – previously available to just a few people at the end of life – will in time be extended to all who need it, regardless of diagnosis, stage of disease, social situation or means. This controversial theme echoes through many of the sections of this book. At the same time, understanding the history of hospice and palliative care also helps to illuminate wider discussions relating to euthanasia and the 'right to die' movements as well as questions about the meaning of illness, suffering and disease in society. To that extent the history of hospice and palliative care amounts to a subject of much more than specialist interest. To understand that history is not only to engage with the transformation of medicine in the latter part of the twentieth century, it is also to begin to make sense of how we die in the modern world.

An oral history of the hospice movement: approaching this book

The oral history of the modern hospice movement presented here has been produced with a variety of readers in mind. Primarily, we hope it will be of interest to the kinds of men and women whose voices and experiences are captured within it: those who have contributed in diverse ways to the growth of the modern hospice movement and the caring services delivered by hospices. It should also be relevant to students of hospice and palliative care and to those preparing to work in the field, for whom an understanding of origins may serve as a helpful frame of reference for individual goals and plans. It may well be read by those who have benefited in some way from hospice services and

we hope it will provide insights into why and how hospices do what they do. Finally, it may be read by anyone with interests in social movements, modern health care, death, dying and the relief of suffering in society. By and large, we have tried to keep our approach fairly simple. We have avoided excessive use of technical language and have not given too much space to the wider historiography and sociology of hospices, though some of that material is referred to in footnotes, where additional detail and explanation on specific matters can also be found. By such means, we have tried to give priority to making sense of hospice history through the words, spoken in interviews, of men and women who have been actively involved in it as participants.

To understand this better, it is worth sharing some thoughts about what oral history is, how it relates to other ways of exploring the past, and the particular way we have used this approach here. Our book is built around transcripts of interviews carried out with those who have been involved in hospice care in the UK. Our subjects were usually interviewed in their homes or at their place of work, and the interviews recorded for later transcription. We have selected parts of those transcribed interviews to explore themes we have judged important in the development of hospice care.

Each of these processes requires a little elaboration.

Why oral history?

There is a long tradition of collecting stories people tell about their lives. Oral history is compiled from such stories, often of personal experiences and opinions, and organised around subject matters, meanings and themes. Oral histories help balance our reliance on written histories, whether these are found in books, diaries or other documents. It has often been used to make available the voices of people who have not written about their lives or experiences and who might otherwise go unacknowledged by history. But in this book, in many cases, we are reporting the words of well-known leaders in a particular field. Indeed several have written about their work, and some have been the subject of the writing of others. In all cases there exist documentary materials relating to the organisations in which they have been involved. Taking this into account, we wanted to present a different image from that which already exists. We asked our respondents to consider their careers, or work, as a whole and to describe this in the context of their lives. The invitation to talk freely about themselves in this way was not such a common experience for most of those involved (though a few had been interviewed many times before) and was, in the main, welcomed. This approach allowed the interviewers involved to ask questions about *what*, *why* and *how*, not only eliciting factual information but also discovering motivations for individual and group actions, and reflections on events that had taken place. In this way, it was possible to explore context – what was happening at specific points in time – in society, in their profession and in their own lives. What impetus prompted them to become involved with hospice care, and what had they found most challenging and rewarding? By such means our oral history also sought the 'big picture': the shape of their work in their lives as well as personal assessments of the influence of their work on the lives of others. All of the authors of this book were involved in the interviewing, to various degrees; and in addition some other colleagues worked with us as interviewers – part of a growing network of collaboration.[14]

Why these people?

Our project began in 1995 with a series of interviews with Cicely Saunders and with Eric Wilkes. Given what we have already said in this introduction, Cicely Saunders was an obvious and vital choice. Eric Wilkes had also founded a hospice, St Luke's in Sheffield, and was the author of a policy document that was of key importance in the development of hospice care in the UK.[15] In addition he was the inspiration behind the Trent Palliative Care Centre from which our Hospice History Project was first launched. Both of these original interviewees were then asked to suggest a list of others whom we might approach. We also looked at what had already been written about hospice development and identified suitable informants from the literature. For a while, in each of our subsequent interviews we asked the same question – 'who else should we talk to?'

This self-referential form of 'snowballing sample' was initially part of a deliberate intention to study a particular 'elite' – that is, people were invited to contribute because of their recognised achievements within the field of hospice and palliative care.[16] Our selection of interviewees has not been exhaustive, though it is ongoing and we continue to add to the oral history archive. It has not proved possible to capture the stories of all those who have played a key role in hospice development in the UK, though many are represented here. Sadly, some died before the opportunity could be arranged to talk with them, and others have died in the period since they were interviewed. Some of our interviewees are nationally and internationally known, inspirational leaders. We have also sought the voices of others whose influence in hospice care might be less widely recognised but who have, nevertheless, helped shape the services delivered in a local area and may indeed be very well known there. In addition there are those who have not been in conventional leadership roles – the long-serving nurse, the volunteer and others. All of these sorts of contributions can be found in the pages of this book and over time we hope the Hospice History Programme at the International Observatory on End of Life Care will increase the number and the range of people whose stories are collected and made available for study (see Appendix 3).

Hospice care has also been shaped by its patients and their families. It must be noted that these voices are absent from the narratives we present here, although their contributions are recognised indirectly through our respondents' stories about patients and families and the inspiration gained from their care. We are already addressing this, through an allied Hospice Narratives Study, which records the voices of patients and family members in receipt of hospice care. This may be the subject of another volume in due course.

Much of the early thinking and many subsequent developments in hospice care have built on international collaborations, but in this book we mainly restrict our focus to events and people in the UK. We have also concentrated in the main on hospice care for adults, though brief mention is made of the work of children's hospices.

Some readers may note an absence of critical and dissenting voices: those antagonistic to hospice philosophy and practice; those who have been disappointed by their involvement in hospice work; those who doubt the hospice 'project' and its ability to deliver on its claims; or those who see unwelcome consequences in the hospice approach. These and other notes of dissension have been sounded in various writings.[17] But we have not sought views from outside the core group of hospice people interviewed here. However, even those closest to hospice development can be critical at times of aspects of care or of the perceived direction of change. They can be supportive of hospice ideals, impressed by the achievements but neither blind to some of the failures, nor dismissive of the challenges still to be faced. We have included some of these reflections as they relate to various themes explored here.

This is a history that preserves the words of those involved, that seeks to represent the balance of what is said and that reconstructs individual narratives into themes which reveal aspects of hospice development. We have described and sought to explain. We have not attempted judgements nor come to evaluative conclusions, though our final chapter does draw on interviewees' perceptions of work still to be done and the extent to which there remains an 'unfinished agenda' for hospice and palliative care.

This is, in consequence, *an* oral history and not *the* oral history of hospice care in the UK. No doubt other authors and researchers, different interviewees, or even other selections from our own interviews would have produced narratives subtly different from this one. Likewise, if we had asked different individuals to participate, our story might have other emphases as well as different milestones and examples.

How reliable is oral history?

There are questions surrounding this method of historical research. In particular it may be asked, how accurate is an individual's recall of events? Memory is, of course, always selective and any life story is, by its nature, subjective. Those we interviewed may have been inclined to tell us what they thought we wanted to hear. For example it may be that some gave accounts in which things seem much more planned out than they were at the time – or conversely they portray something as happening by chance when another view would see clear reasons for an action. A further challenge is that some might exaggerate their own role whilst others will underplay their contribution.

Yet, oral history is a widely used research method. It is an approach to the past that has a broad presence in scholarship, including work about the history of health and social care.[18] Researchers have found that recall is a problem, but this is true for recent events as well as more distant ones. The biggest problems are getting dates wrong or foreshortening the period between separate events, that is, merging events together. Here we are fortunate in looking at hospice care because there are other sources for much of this detailed work, such as when it relates to events in the public world, and we can therefore check for accuracy. It is also evident that before we interviewed them, a number of the people gathered their thoughts in an 'aide memoire' and even produced relevant documentary material for us. They knew what our approach would be, indeed we had asked them (when appropriate) if they could provide a curriculum vitae and that, in itself, gave some landmarks for their accounts. The accuracy of opinions and attitudes of course is not so easy to check. It may be that what people report as feeling 'then' is more to do with what they are feeling 'now'. We think that the life history approach helps in this – focusing the person on what this new project or that challenge meant in the context of all the other things that were going on in their lives at a particular time.

We can also consider how consistent people are across the story they tell us. In several cases we also have accounts from others of the same events – for example, there are a number of interviews with people in the early team at St Christopher's. There are also written accounts with which to cross-reference. It can be particularly rewarding to consider interviews alongside the letters or articles and reports written at the time of the events they are reflecting. In several places we take this approach in footnotes, drawing on the published literature of the time and also on the published letters of Cicely Saunders.[19]

If there are problems in oral history as an approach, there are also strengths and advantages. An interviewee may well fail to recall accurately the 'facts', but the significance of an event or experience will nevertheless remain vivid in the memory. It is this individual perspective that oral history is so good at bringing forth. How past events are understood, both at the time and with hindsight, will influence decisions and actions which then ripple out to shape the decisions and actions of others. Oral history is not necessarily 'historical truth' (a difficult thing to claim whatever the method used); rather it has a *different credibility*.[20]

It is useful to remind ourselves that all sorts of history, in all sorts of times, has had to come to terms with the problems of evidence. The oldest serious historical work to come to us from the ancient world, Thucydides' *History of the Peloponnesian War*, was written in part to reject the romantic myths of the past purveyed by the poets. Thucydides complained that even though he checked his data as carefully as he could, the truth was still hard to discover. 'Different eyewitnesses give different accounts of the same events, speaking out of partiality for one side or the other or else from imperfect memory'. That was written around (the evidence is not definitive), 400 BC.[21]

How did we select what is presented here?

Producing a volume such as this from the considerable amount of material contained in the overall programme archive requires a particular approach to the extraction of material and to its subsequent presentation. There are generally thought to be three ways to present oral history in written summary.[22] First, one tells the story of an individual's life. Second, one can select and group material from different individuals that engages with the same theme; when grouped together one can see how experiences were similar and can highlight contrasting stories. Third, some oral history is used to shape and illustrate a particular historical interpretation the writer is trying to construct; that is oral history used illustratively. We have chosen the second approach.

The interview transcripts from which we draw here have been examined to see how they can be organised in themes.[23] These themes sometimes turn out to be related to structural things – the development of particular organisations dealing with end of life and bereavement care, including charities such as Marie Curie Cancer Care, Macmillan Cancer Relief, Help the Hospices, the National Council for Hospice and Specialist Palliative Care Services, and Cruse Bereavement Care. Sometimes the themes relate to changing ways of seeing what can and should be done to improve care for the dying and the bereaved – developments in responding to pain or the evolution of ways of understanding bereavement and loss are examples. Often our respondents talked of why they were involved in hospice care, and we have sought to group together different conceptualisations as to motivation. Underpinning the motivations of several, but also underscoring many of the practice innovations and organisational responses, are various notions of the spiritual, and we explore what this means to some of those we interviewed. Not surprisingly there is a lot of overlap. Almost within the same sentence a person might speak of something they did, why they did it and the sense of significance they think it has had. In the same way in any one extract of talk a person may say something relevant to several of the chapters of this

book. The voice of the past can be fragmented, inconsistent, even contrary at times. Beyond a limited amount of 'tidying', we have not substantially edited the spoken transcribed words of our informants.[24] Reading oral history can therefore be a little messy at times: when individuals develop their own picture in their own words, we are reminded that few express themselves in perfect sentences or by means of organised and logical steps. But oral history is also vivid, revealing and at times inspirational to read and we hope that readers will share some of the excitement in it that we have found.

What does oral history explain?

We often give a shape to our experiences by creating stories out of them. An oral history of the hospice movement creates the possibility of these stories coming together to reveal how the movement developed an understanding of a new way to care for dying people in society and drew attention to the care of the dying as a matter of public interest. Oral history can help to explain that link between the individual story and the story of the group. It allows insight into the differences in perspective, varieties of motivation and a changing sense of achievement. Its strength is to locate persons in time – in terms of life story and contingent events – and also in terms of wider factors that shape experience and understanding. It also allows a circle to be completed, showing how the actions of others moved hospice care forward. Oral history is the route to understanding subjective selves in time and in space.

How to approach the book

This is the sort of book that might see the reader having to cross check things in order to put the narratives into historical context or to have some background on the individuals talking or the organisations they are describing. The chapters do not contain a strict chronology of dates; interviews refer concurrently to events that happened at different times. We have not found it possible to build an oral history around a process of 'periodisation', whereby particular times could be labelled or characterised in a specific way (though this has been done in other material that has emerged from our programme).[25] An example of this absence of periodisation can be seen in Chapter 1, where a number of individuals identify the disquiet they felt during professional training or early career about an absence of concern for the patient as a human being. This concern refers to experiences over a long time period. It is salutary to realise that accounts of patients being treated as objects and the absence of recognition that they should be involved in decisions about their own care come from across the whole period, from the 1940s to the 1970s. For this reason we have adopted the 'anthropological present' as a device for much of our data presentation. We refer to our informants in the present tense and so we have avoided the contrivances of a narrative always told in the past tense. But it should be noted that we began the process of interviewing in 1995 (dates when each interview took place can be found in Appendix 1 and are often reinforced in notes to particular quotations) and so the 'reach' of our interviews is considerable. To that extent readers will find much here that resonates with contemporary issues in hospice care as well as that which illuminates past events and developments.

As an aid to the reader, we have provided in the appendices and indexes a variety of information to assist in making sense of the oral testimony presented here. These include: a brief biographical sketch of each person whose words we use; a timeline with significant dates in the development of hospice care; further details of the work of the International Observatory on End of Life Care and its Hospice History Programme; and a consolidated bibliography of all secondary sources. We have made extensive use of endnotes to give brief details of some of those mentioned in the text and to elucidate particular points, as well as to refer to key publications and reports or events relevant to our history and to provide information about key websites; and there are more detailed elaborations in supporting text and in the illustrations we have chosen.

Summary of chapters

Our book is organised into particular themes, though as we have explained these are often intertwined and overlapping in the material we present chapter by chapter and section by section.

Chapter 1 explores the process of becoming involved with hospice care. It begins with a recognition that for many of those we interviewed the experience of caring for patients and listening to their wants and needs is central to their whole story. Both personal and professional experiences are considered, along with a sense of religious calling, the strength of a perception of social need and concerns about the shortcomings of current provision.

Chapter 2 deals with how hospice care developed from small beginnings to become established throughout the UK.

How did local groups get started? How did they raise the necessary funds? How did these new organisations develop imaginative ideas about the sorts of service that best fitted their resources and could meet local need? This chapter also looks in some detail at how staff were recruited to run the new hospice services.

Chapter 3 examines the development of teams and the meaning of teamwork in hospices. Working together in teams has been crucial in setting up hospices and in providing the integrated care that is one of their features. It has also helped shape the particular style of education offered in and by hospice organisations. Teamwork is, of course, not without its potential for tension and conflict, and this is explored at the end of the chapter.

Chapter 4 focuses on the emergence of professional palliative care organisations. It begins with the work of Macmillan Cancer Relief and Marie Curie Cancer Care. The chapter goes on to look at umbrella organisations including both multidisciplinary bodies with a broad scope of concern and organisations that focus on a single issue or activity. Professional associations are also considered, before the chapter concludes with a consideration of the impact of these changes on hospice and palliative care development more widely, and specifically the effects outside the hospice movement.

Chapter 5 examines the spiritual dimension of hospice care. The motivating force of Christian faith in developing hospices is acknowledged, along with the wider development of a broader concept of spirituality. The meaning of the spiritual when related to care and suffering is explored. There is also an examination of how individuals seek and find their own sources of spiritual support. This chapter then goes on to look at the nature of hospice chaplaincy and finishes with

reflections about individual patient care and the importance of the spiritual dimension.

Chapter 6 seeks to unpack the pain and symptoms that are at the heart of so much hospice care delivery. It acknowledges the hospice contribution to a wider view of 'total pain' and explores the various approaches that have been developed for the relief of suffering in terminal illness, drawing on narratives about specific patients. Some of this has involved overcoming obstacles to the use of powerful narcotics in the relief of pain, as well as the development of new policies and technologies for pain relief. The chapter also shows how ideas about pain relief, first developed in hospice and palliative care settings, began to influence practice in mainstream settings and to be adopted in the international policy context.

Chapter 7 looks at the development of understanding about bereavement and at the implications for hospices in terms of the focus on care for the family. This chapter includes a review of theoretical understandings about ways of responding to bereavement. It considers the way that professional experiences of an absence of concern with the impact of loss and grief prompted innovation and it recognises that there has been much mutual learning, with good practice in one hospice being replicated in others.

Chapter 8 addresses unfinished issues concerning the ongoing development of hospice and palliative care. We explore this from two perspectives: the biographical and the structural. Several of those we spoke to concluded their interviews with some account of what they felt they had achieved personally in this work; what they still hoped to carry out; and in some cases what was left unfinished. Others talked more widely about work still to be done in order to fully realise the goals of the hospice movement: extending palliative care beyond the care of those with cancer and reaching out to those disadvantaged in their access to services by other circumstances, as well as thinking critically about the role of hospices within the spectrum of health and social care services. There were also many reflections on further challenges and future directions for local hospice provision. In this final chapter we consider these different reflections on unfinished business.

Finally, we offer some comments about our choice of title for this book. The phrase comes from an interview with Richard Hillier, but he has since pointed out to us that the words were originally those of Graham Thorpe, a physician colleague at Countess Moutbatten House, Southampton. Graham Thorpe once posed the question to Richard Hillier: 'Should we be offering a service to South Hampshire or "a little bit of heaven to a few"?' By this he was referring to the problem of how to serve an entire population with an appropriate service, rather than delivering something exceptional to only a minority of those in need. It is a question which continues to exercise hospice and palliative care services. We show in the book how the ideas of the first modern hospices were quickly taken up in many settings. We map out the growth and the achievements along the way, as well as the tasks and challenges that remain.

Notes

1. For a general introduction to the development of hospice and palliative care in the British policy context, see D. Clark and J. Seymour, *Reflections on Palliative Care* (Buckingham: Open University Press, 1999). For a popular account, focused on hospices, see M. Manning, *The Hospice Alternative. Living with dying* (London: Souvenir Press, 1984).
2. See C.J. Gavey, *The Management of the 'Hopeless' Case* (London: H.K. Lewis, 1952).
3. D. Clark, 'Cradled to the grave? Pre-conditions for the hospice movement in the UK, 1948–67', *Mortality* 4 (3): 225–47, 1999.
4. C. Saunders, 'The symptomatic treatment of incurable malignant disease', *Prescribers' Journal* 4 (4), October: 68–73, 1964.
5. C. Saunders, 'Drug treatment of patients in the terminal stages of cancer', *Current Medicine and Drugs* 1 (1), July: 16–28, 1960.
6. Balfour Mount later reflected on this in a piece about the Royal Victoria Hospital Palliative Care Service, which became operational in 1975: 'The term "hospice" has pejorative connotations in French and Spanish. What then, could we call the proposed program? The answer occurred to me one morning while shaving. "There are Dialysis Units, Coronary Care Units, Intensive Care Units ... why not 'Palliative Care Units?' PCU? Perfect!"' This designation offered a neutral and somewhat ambiguous alternative. 'To palliate' has its origins in the Latin *pallium*, or cloak. This term initially meant to conceal or hide. More recently, however, it had come to mean 'to mitigate the suffering of; to ease'. See B. Mount, 'The Royal Victoria Hospital Palliative Care Service: A Canadian experience' in C. Saunders and R. Kastenbaum (eds.), *Hospice Care on the International Scene* (New York: Springer, 1997: 73–85).
7. See for example: C. Saunders, 'What's in a name?', *Palliative Medicine* 1 (1): 57–61, 1987.
8. This took place in the BBC series, *The Body*, first shown in 1998; the patient was in the care of a home care service in Ireland.
9. C. Saunders, 'And from sudden death ...', *Frontier*, Winter 1961, no page numbers.
10. N. James and D. Field, 'The routinisation of hospice: charisma and bureaucratisation', *Social Science and Medicine* 34 (12): 1363–75, 1992.
11. D. Clark and J. Seymour, *Reflections on Palliative Care* (Buckingham: Open University Press, 1999).
12. A good example of this can be seen in the recognition given to palliative care in the New Labour government's strategic vision for cancer reform. See Department of Health, *The NHS Cancer Plan: A plan for investment, a plan for reform* (London: HMSO, 2000).

13. This was a particular argument of a key government report that appeared in 1992. It was produced by a combined committee of doctors and nurses reporting to the Minister of Health and sought to deal with the overall 'positioning' of hospices in relation to a widening array of palliative care provision. See SMAC (Standing Medical Advisory Committee)/SNMAC (Standing Nursing and Midwifery Advisory Committee), *The Principles and Provision of Palliative Care* (London: HMSO, 1992).

14. See Appendix 1 for more details of the interviewers and the interviewed.

15. Working Group on Terminal Care [The Wilkes Report], *Report of the Working Group on Terminal Care* (London: DHSS, 1980).

16. See A. Seldon and J. Pappworth, *By Word of Mouth: Elite oral history* (London: Methuen, 1983).

17. Some examples include: C. Douglas, 'For all the Saints', *British Medical Journal* 303: 579, 1992 and S. Fordham, C. Dowrick and C. May, 'Palliative medicine: is it a really specialist territory?', *Journal of the Royal Society of Medicine* 91: 568–72, 1998.

18. See J. Bornat, R. Perks, P. Thompson and J. Walmsley, *Oral History, Health and Welfare* (London: Routledge, 2000).

19. D. Clark, *Cicely Saunders – founder of the hospice movement. Selected letters 1959–1999* (Oxford: Oxford University Press, 2002).

20. A. Portelli, 'What makes oral history different?' in R. Perks and A. Thomson (eds.), *The Oral History Reader* (London: Routledge, 1997: 68–69).

21. Thucydides, *History of the Peloponnesian War* (Harmondsworth: Penguin Books, 1954).

22. See P. Thompson and R. Perks, *An Introduction to the Use of Oral History in the History of Medicine* (London: National Life Story Collection, British Library, 1993).

23. In doing this we have made use of computer software specifically designed for the purpose, as well as intensive detailed readings of interview transcripts.

24. We have made only minor changes, removing obvious deviations, repetitions and hesitations and, occasionally, changing a word or phrase into a less colloquial one to help in comprehension. Occasionally extracts from the same interview are repeated to illustrate different themes in different chapters.

25. See for example: D. Clark, 'Palliative care history: a ritual process', *European Journal of Palliative Care* 7 (2): 50–55, 2000.

1 Personal motivations

'There's a real desire to do something to make things better for somebody else' **Cicely Saunders**

The development of hospices in the UK can be seen as a force shaped by the commitment and imagination of many individuals, found in varied settings and circumstances at different times. So as we begin here to articulate a history of hospices, it is helpful to try to make sense of the motivations and preoccupations of some of those involved. Why would a person become part of a fledgling hospice initiative? In what circumstances would a decision be made to reorient an entire career to work with dying people? How might someone feel moved to set out upon a whole life-changing course in order to be involved in this endeavour? Hospices and the hospice movement have attracted charismatic leaders who have found ways to integrate a particular vision into a whole programme of activity, wherein the person and the cause are sometimes difficult to distinguish. Such leaders have had the ability to inspire others, and the hospice world has numerous examples of individual lives transformed by an ethics of care and of service. From the accounts of such men and women we are able to learn something about the values that have underpinned hospice development and the ways in which these have been altering over time.

In this opening chapter those involved in hospice care, in a variety of ways, describe the circumstances that have motivated them. In some cases we found such motivation to be quite clearly articulated; in others it proved more difficult to explain; and for some, becoming involved in hospice care occurred with no sense that it would later prove to be so significant. A number of those we interviewed spoke freely about their intentions and motivations, others found these less clear or easy to describe. Sometimes, motivation was inferred rather than explicit. As with many of the things we do and the directions we take, it was often unclear why a decision had been made to do this rather than that. Yet it was clear from many accounts that involvement in the hospice world has been something of special significance.

We detected differences between those who professed a clear sense of motivation and those for whom there had been a less obvious route into hospice work. We could also distinguish between those who were involved in setting up new services from the outset (obvious 'pioneers'), and those who joined existing teams ('consolidators'). In the contributions that follow we can also see some clear themes that help us to understand individual motivations: experiencing the death of a family member or friend; professional experience of the care of the dying, including learning from bad practice; looking around for help; building on good experiences; seeking mentors and being driven by an intellectual curiosity; a sense of religious calling; contact with a key person who may point the way to hospice work, or being 'recruited' by people already committed; and motivation stemming from a wider view of social justice. For some of our informants, the hospice represented a welcome institutional home, separate from but working alongside the NHS. Others felt a commitment both to hospice care and to the NHS and were pleased to bring the two together in their work.

In practice it is often the case that many of these motivational themes merge together. We see how a person's professional and personal life are interconnected, how both may be informed by a spiritual dimension, or how they are expressed in the need to effect some practical change in the society in which they live. Presenting motivation as if it is something contained and focused is at best artificial, and at worst misleading. We should be wary of making the complex too simple, or indeed of the reverse – sometimes things are as straightforward as they initially appear!

The complexity of motivation is well illustrated in the sections that begin this chapter. Here, arising out of encounters with patients, we find a strong sense of what needed to be done and also a vision about what might be achieved. We start with an extended consideration of the experience and work of Cicely Saunders and go on to look at other examples of learning from the patient. This is a perspective that lies at the very heart of hospice history. With examples mainly drawn from the 1950s and 1960s, we then go on to look at the sorts of prevailing attitudes found by those who wished to communicate with and learn from their patient. We consider how they sought to combat these largely negative attitudes. Our respondents describe situations where being more empathic often involved only small changes in approach. They acknowledge that it is not always easy to listen and that even the best listening does not solve all problems. Towards the end of the chapter we gain an insight into lessons learned at crucial moments in the care of terminally ill people and we see something of the changing character of caregiving, as responsibilities increase, as organisations alter and as workload pressures change. We conclude with a return to the question about what being involved with a hospice can achieve and we restate the centrality of the wish to do what one can for individuals who are in great need – a theme not only of this chapter but of all of those that follow.

The vulnerable friendship of the heart

In interviews and in her publications Cicely Saunders has described very special and profound relationships with two particular patients: David Tasma in the late 1940s and Antoni Michniewicz in the early 1960s.[1] Each of these men, when they died, left her with a particular kind of legacy. In the case of David Tasma, it was a sense of how things might be done differently when caring for dying people. With Antoni Michniewicz it was a profound grief that motivated her through a new sense of authenticity born of loss. Each tells us much about the power of personal experience in shaping her philosophy of hospice care. These stories, and the lessons learned from them, have an enduring resonance that is all the more significant when we consider the international influence of Cicely Saunders' ideas.

Cicely Saunders began training as a nurse at London's St Thomas's Hospital in November 1940, but spent most of the next three years rotating around accommodation that the hospital had occupied outside the city for the duration of the war: Hydestile, near Godalming; Park Prewett, near Basingstoke; and Botley's Park, in Chertsey. Many of the patients were servicemen, some having routine operations but others with war injuries. Resources were few, and she describes how this made a virtue out of a necessity:

Cicely Saunders: nurse training in the 1940s led on to social work and then medicine.

We didn't have any of the drugs that we've got now, none of the psychiatric drugs at all, no anti-TB drugs, didn't even have penicillin until D-Day, by which time I'd been invalided out. So we really had nothing to offer but ourselves and meticulous nursing, and so that really made me realise how important relationships are in any medical sphere. And I always enjoyed the patients.

In 1944 problems with her back led to Cicely Saunders' 'invaliding out' of nursing and soon afterwards she returned to academic studies at Oxford. On completion she trained as a lady almoner (a medical social worker) and then resumed work at St Thomas's. There, in 1947, she encountered a patient, David Tasma, who was to play a crucial role in her life and in her thoughts about how to improve care for the dying:

Well I was aware that there was this chap of 40 who'd got an inoperable cancer and had just had a palliative operation, and I knew he was single and on his own, a Pole who'd left Poland quite a long time before and he was just living in digs, so I knew he'd run into trouble. So I got to know him reasonably well and then I followed him up in out-patients. I met him in July '47. Then in January '48 he collapsed at home and his landlady rang me and I said, 'I'll come and see him tonight but meantime, you know, "get his family doctor in".' And I went to see him at his digs that evening while he was waiting to go into another hospital and it was then that he asked me was he going to die and I was the one who told him, which of course a social worker shouldn't have done. But you couldn't be anything else but honest with him.

David Tasma was admitted to Archway Hospital, in Highgate, London. Cicely Saunders began to visit him regularly. Quite quickly the relationship shifted from a professional one to a close friendship:

He suddenly said to me one evening, 'Can't you say something to comfort me?' I found myself saying the Twenty-Third, the Shepherd's Psalm, and then the *Venite*, the Ninety-Fifth, which I'd sung lots of times in choirs, and then 'I will lift up mine eyes to the hills', which I also knew by heart. And then I said, 'Well, shall I read you something?' because I'd got a little book of psalms and the New Testament in my handbag, and that was when he said, 'No, I only want what is in your mind and in your heart.'

The two talked about what sort of thing might have helped him:

Not necessarily so much better on symptoms, because he didn't have a terribly difficult dying, but somewhere that could have helped him with what I was trying to do, which was to assure him that he was a worthwhile person, dying at the end of what he thought of as a rather empty life.

One subject of their conversations was the idea of a home that could have welcomed him, rather than that very busy surgical ward:

When I organised him a solicitor to come and help him make his will … it was then he said, 'I'll leave you money, I'll be a window in your home.'

The poetic words of David Tasma wanting 'what is in the mind and the heart' and offering to be a 'window in the home' have been oft repeated throughout the hospice movement in the intervening years. What was emerging for Cicely Saunders at the time was a way of achieving that particular combination:

The balance between everything of the mind – all the research, the science, the understanding of family dynamics and so on – but matched with the vulnerable friendship of the heart.

David Tasma: 'I only want what is in your mind and in your heart.'

Cicely Saunders' time with David Tasma was vital in identifying three basic principles, which remained of crucial importance to her in the years that followed. First, the 'openness to challenges' in getting ideas into practice; second, the insight of 'the mind matched with heart, science and spirit'; and third the recognition that each must make their own journey and exercise the 'freedom of the spirit' that David Tasma had demonstrated.

A dozen years later, as the 1960s got underway, Cicely Saunders was now qualified as a doctor, publishing actively on the subject of terminal care, making plans for her own hospice and working at St Joseph's, Hackney:

1960 was quite a year because it was the year we were working out the Christian foundation and the medical foundation at St Christopher's and what kind of a community we were going to try and set up, to give something of the security that the nuns of St Joseph's gave their patients.[2]

Then, in February of 1960 Antoni Michniewicz was admitted as a patient to St Joseph's:

He was just an interesting and challenging patient, an ex-Eighth Army, very patrician Pole … in July … when his daughter passed her exams and – he was a widower – and she went to tell him and I went to congratulate her, and she said, 'Oh my father has so much fallen in love with you, doctor.' He said, 'I don't know how to express it, please don't be offended,' and I said, 'Well, no, I'm honoured' and just something happened. And then we had just a few weeks of becoming incredibly close, with the rigorous discipline of being his doctor, and so I never pulled the curtains round more than I would have done anyway for any other patient, and yet we managed, I did allow myself to sit and talk with him at five o'clock in the evening, and sometimes I just couldn't help taking an hour. And that was a very intense and totally, I suppose I would say, spiritual relationship. In a way it was unfulfilled, and in a way it was fulfilled. And when he died, I was absolutely devastated. But before he died I was able to get across to him that he was a giver as well as me, because he was saying, 'I can give you nothing … nothing but sorrow' … but just before he died, just before he lost consciousness, he gave me the most incredible smile.

It is clear from her summing up of the impact of this relationship what it gave to Cicely Saunders:

… tremendous satisfaction that such a special person should love me and also very much a depth of spiritual things … the day after, I went back and there was another patient in his bed and I remember standing at the door and thinking 'I can't go in: it hurts too much', and then looking at the crucifix and letting it hold me, and getting around.

St Joseph's Hospice, Hackney

The Irish Sisters of Charity became established in Hackney, London in 1900 in response to a request from a local Jesuit priest, Father Peter Gallwey who sought their involvement with the local community. Five Sisters arrived from Dublin to carry out work they had pioneered in Ireland, caring for the sick and dying, and helping to alleviate the plight of the poor in the East End of London. During the first five years, the Sisters' work focused primarily on visiting families and homes in Hackney and Hoxton, but the idea of founding a hospice was Peter Gallwey's long-held dream and the Sisters of Charity were likewise convinced of the need for an institution that would care for the dying poor of the area. In 1904, an anonymous benefactor bought the Cambridge Lodge estate where the Sisters had lived since the previous year and presented it to them for use as a hospice, which they opened in January 1905, with 12 beds.

Increasing applications for care soon encouraged expansion and many building projects and expansions followed, so that accommodation was available for 75 patients by 1975. One significant addition was Our Lady's Wing, opened in 1957 and which provided an excellent, modern facility in which newly qualified physician and research fellow, Cicely Saunders, was able to develop her early work on the care of the dying. In 1976, the Macmillan Home Care Service was established; a Day Centre opened in 1984; and in 2005, to mark its centenary, the hospice opened extensive purpose-built accommodation for in-patients.

That's what I owe very much to Antoni, because he gave me the authenticity of having really been there, been really close to somebody who was dying; and being very close within bereavement made me realise the potential that there is in that area … the power of powerlessness is something that you can go on learning about endlessly; so that you move from purely clinical into philosophical and theological insights, and there's no end to discovery there.

Antoni gave me not only the authenticity but the head of steam to do it, because there's a real creativity in bereavement – I mean, think of the people who lose a child and start a leukaemia research charity and so on. There's a real desire to do something to make things better for somebody else.

After Antoni died … there was a kind of a ladder out of the very dark hole of grief, in which one upright was 'Oh, my love, how happy you are' and the other was 'Oh God, I am so grateful'. And every time I'd manage to come back to seeing those again there was another rung on the ladder, and I was a little bit further out. But I still need that ladder sometimes, even after all these years.[3]

These stories of Cicely Saunders' encounters with love and death provide a preface to much of what will follow. They introduce, in her words, 'the vulnerable friendship of the heart' and the associated 'power of powerlessness'. That power she describes as something which can be learned about endlessly and which can move a person's insights from the clinical into the philosophical, and from there to the theological. As we shall see later, hospice history when told in the words of its makers is often about bricks and mortar, about committees and balance sheets, about science and technology. But it is also about love and loss, about the heart, the imagination and the soul and it is no accident that we have chosen to begin with these.

Antoni Michniewicz, who died in St Joseph's, Hackney, February 1960.

Learning by listening to the patient

Through the deaths first of David Tasma in 1948 and then of Antoni Michniewicz in 1960, Cicely Saunders was able to learn so much about the self and about the tasks ahead. Her accounts remind us of the distinction between caring 'for' and caring 'about' patients. They show how the voice of the patient has guided the hospice movement from its outset to the present day. Indeed, Cicely Saunders identifies three members of the long-stay ward at St Joseph's – Alice, Terry and Louie – as the 'founding patients' of St Christopher's in that they took such a keen interest in hearing about and discussing her emerging thinking for the new hospice. So it was also that the name of the first modern hospice was suggested by another special patient, Barbara Galton (or Mrs G), as Cicely Saunders explains:

Mrs G, that paralysed patient who I knew so well as a student – as her body became weaker and she was blind as well as paralysed, and she didn't even know which side she was lying on because she lost her position sense, and yet her spirit just went on growing. And she was the one who gave us the name St Christopher's. When I said I'm going to call it hospice, she said, 'Well what does that mean?' So I said well it's come to mean a stopping place for travellers. And she said, 'Travelling – well you'll have to have St Christopher, won't you?' So that's why we did.[4]

One of the crucial contributions of hospice care was to reframe understandings of the nature of pain and the optimum strategy for responding to it – we shall see evidence of this in Chapter 6. Here we see a merging between the understanding of the challenge and the shape of the response:

Well there was one patient who, when I said to her, 'Well, Mrs Hinson, tell me about your pain' – this was the day after she was admitted – and she said, 'Well, Doctor, it began in my back; but now it seems that *all of me is wrong*', and she talked about one or two more symptoms, and she said, 'I could have cried for the pills and the injections but I knew that I mustn't. Nobody seemed to understand how I felt and it seemed as if all the world was against me. My husband and son were marvellous but they would have to stay off work and lose their money, but it's wonderful to begin to feel safe again.' So she's really encapsulated the whole thing in the answer to one question.

Other patients echoed similar problems:

… just saying, 'Well it was all pain but now it's gone and I'm free', a feeling of being absolutely held in, or Stephanie whose tape recording I used in the 'Week's Good Cause Appeal'[5] when we started the fund-raising for St Christopher's, [who] says, 'The pain was so bad, if anybody came into the room I'd say "Don't touch me, don't come near me," but now it seems as if something's come between me and the pain. It feels like a nice thing wrapped round me.' And I've got a lovely slide of her laughing in bed and another one of her later on when she's beginning to look very yonderly and beginning to sort of let go, but she's alert and very much herself. She's quite free of pain.

Whilst Cicely Saunders found that progress was being made, it was also important to be cautious:

… dying can be very hard work and I think it's very important that you don't idealise it, and you realise how profound the difficulty of parting and of helplessness and dependence can be … all the time we've been learning more sophisticated things we can do to deal with symptoms, but I think the basic giving, of trying to help people search their own way, is basically the same … I think the power of powerlessness is something which you learn when you're with people who're dying and basically helpless. And that of course is a deeply Christian insight.

In this extended consideration of the experience of Cicely Saunders we have explored how, at the origins of the modern hospice movement, the intimate experience of patient care was linked with scientific curiosity and spiritual commitment to fashion a personal motivation that resonated with others. Cicely Saunders was pointing to a new way of thinking about patients' needs and a new way of relating as a professional and as an individual: '… you can't be with dying people and remain strict within boundaries, because there aren't any boundaries when you're dying'. Her aim was to be: '… a propagandist for patients. I was trying to get patients to speak, to be a voice for the voiceless'.[6]

Something of the significance of this can be gleaned from a consideration of the context of prevailing care practices in the late 1950s and early 1960s. We continue by exploring this further, specifically the criticisms that emerged around the theme of how bad things were when it came to 'listening to the patient'. We then explore stories of how to be more empathic, of lessons learned and of some of the challenges that come from adopting such an approach.

How bad things were

If one of the innovations coming from emerging thinking about the care of dying patients and their families in hospices was the power of listening to the patient, it is important to put this idea in the context of prevailing practice at the time. Of course not all professional carers were bad at listening to the patient and not all hospice staff were gifted in this area. But there was a culture of professional dominance and of distance within medicine and health care in the 1950s that could be seen as an impediment. Here we recount examples given from nursing by Jean Radley, from Colin Murray Parkes about what went on in medical school, and from Eric Wilkes and Tim Lovel about hospital doctors and general practice.

Jean Radley began her general nurse training in Manchester in 1959:

I started nursing in an era where you were not allowed to talk to the patients really, you couldn't, if you had half an hour spare – well you very rarely had half an hour spare, did we? But five minutes, if you were talking to a patient the ward sister would soon descend, and say, 'Have you nothing to do?' and say 'I can find you a job ...' as though that wasn't important. So for my generation of nurse ... we had to get around to the fact it's essential to talk to the patients, or to listen to them.

Colin Murray Parkes identifies a culture in the 1950s and

St Christopher's Hospice, Sydenham

Established in 1967, and often considered to be the first of the 'modern' hospices – combining clinical care, teaching and research – St Christopher's is widely known throughout the world of hospice and palliative care. Its opening represented the culmination of years of pressure, persuasion and persistence by Cicely Saunders, the recognised 'founder' of the modern hospice movement. St Christopher's was deliberately established outside the NHS so that specialist ideas and practices could be developed and then channelled back into the mainstream through the education and training of professionals. It concentrated initially on in-patient care, before home care, day care, respite care, bereavement and counselling services soon developed in a hospice model which was then replicated in various areas around the country and elsewhere. Always committed to education, it developed extensive teaching facilties, a substantial library and an extensive information programme.

1960s of keeping a distance from patients and links this both to the way medicine was taught and to a more fundamental perception as to the proper concerns of medicine:

Consultants were handling obviously very distressed patients by distancing from them, or rather by not handling them. I became aware, fairly early on in my medical career, that there was this sort of distancing process, and the very thing that I'd learned in medical school as a means of thinking about what goes wrong in the body – that's a sort of detachment from the human being and thinking about what's going on under the skin – was being used as a defence to prevent the doctor from actually getting too emotionally involved, getting too close to his patients.

Eric Wilkes recounts two stories from early in his medical career that, for him, were typical of the times in the 1950s:

The senior surgeon, for whom I had a tremendous affection, was a marvellously bad communicator in very much a sort of James Robertson Justice tradition of fiction.[7] I remember one tiny little man who was obviously not at all well and the diagnosis in his case – and it shows you how long ago it was – was a rectal cancer and syphilis, and [the surgeon] announced, by the patient, who was standing there with about 20 students around him, and the nurses and the registrars in their white coats, 'Carcinoma of rectum is a common disease, syphilis is a common disease; this man has both.'

… a concert pianist came into neurological out-patients and his doctor had said he was getting increasing problems with his playing, and what was it? And the consultant neurologist was a marvellous technician, demonstrated beautifully the early symptoms of Parkinson's disease in this man, which was the reason for his deterioration, and at the end of this brilliant demonstration, the patient said to him, 'What is going to happen to me?' And the consultant replied with a smile, 'I'll write to your doctor.'

Tim Lovel's examples are from a little later but the experience is very similar to that of Eric Wilkes:

I remember a surgeon at the Radcliffe Infirmary [Oxford] would turn to a patient and say 'Have you a pain?' and the patient would say what it was; and the consultant would turn to the secretary, 'Says he has a pain'; 'Have you been sick?' – 'Says he's being sick.' Anything more calculated to put off a patient would be difficult to imagine.

It was not just hospital doctors who had this approach to patients. Tim Lovel describes examples from general practice:

I've seen doctors who've waved the patient to a seat and then kept them virtually to await their pleasure, while the doctor reads the notes and says, 'Ah, yes, you're Mr – em … em – Smith and you've come about', going through them while the patient just has to passively wait until the doctor deigns to actually look at them rather than the notes. Some of my East Enders, who came down from London, used to say that they had never seen their doctor's face. He had a big bell which he would hit with the flat of his hand, the patient would come in, he'd be looking down at his prescription pad, he would say 'yes', and the patient would say what was wrong, and the doctor would write a prescription, tear it off, hand it up with one hand and hit the bell with the other hand, and they never saw what he looked like.

Learning to be empathic

Sometimes what was needed was not major or drastic change. Tim Lovel describes some small things that could make a great difference:

I developed little habits like shaking the hand of every patient I met, and quite often their hand would just stay gently in mine, even though I wasn't holding on to it, they seemed to get something from that, that personal contact. I would always sit on a chair or on the edge of the bed, as close as I conveniently could, to the patient. In out-patients I always insisted on the desk being pushed away against the wall, never ever sitting behind a desk, but sitting – so I could turn to a desk if I needed to write – but sitting facing the patient.

On a single, one-day, visit to St Christopher's in 1970, Tim Lovel found a particularly congenial environment in which to develop this approach:

When I went to St Christopher's, we were each issued with a most important piece of equipment, before going on teaching ward rounds, and that was a chair. Everybody on the ward round was given a chair, and talking to the patient didn't start until everybody was sitting down, at eye-level with the patient, and then the person taking the ward round would start to talk. And when you'd finished with that patient and thanked her, you all picked up your chairs and went on to the next bed and you all sat down again.

How listening to the patient helped inform understanding

Listening to the patient could both prompt new ways of thinking and add depth to existing understanding. Cicely Saunders here discusses how at St Joseph's, Hackney in the late 1950s her understanding of pain developed in this way and how she found the patient's voice could be used to educate others:

Very soon I realized, and this was partly my social work training, that you learnt about people by listening to them, so the idea of making tape recordings of very much a question and answer type, and of getting people to describe what their pain was like, this would be a help to be able to get across so that people would listen. I knew from what patients were saying that this wasn't just a physical problem and I knew from my previous nursing and social work that anxiety

and depression were major components. I was certainly alert to the fact that family problems were difficult, very often adding to distress and I also felt that a search for feeling that they were wanted, and were still important people was a spiritual pain. So out of what one patient said, very neatly describing her pain to me, developed the idea of 'total pain' with those four components.[8] And that seemed to me to be a structure that, although it was a whole package as far as the patient was concerned, it was almost an internal checklist for you when you were listening to them to spot what were being the main problems of their suffering.

Richard Hillier, talking of his early years as a doctor in the mid-1960s, working with dying patients and their families, identifies the richness of being with someone at this time:

Thomas Hardy said something about experience not being about numbers but about depth. I mean anyone who looks after somebody in their own family who dies, gets an enormous amount of experience with one patient. And I think those of us who started were seeing things in a lot of depth and learning a tremendous amount.

Talking can help illuminate difficult areas

Tony Crowther, a general practitioner (GP) who was involved with the work at St Luke's, Sheffield from its outset, and who served as its Medical Director from 1986, points out the value of engagement and of seeking understanding:

We get a lot of patients who come in and say,[9] 'Right, I've come in; I really want putting down now.' And don't ask me why, but I get away with – and I've only developed it myself, I haven't been taught – I just say, 'Right, well now it's ten past four: six o'clock do you?' And then I smile, and the patient looks a bit aghast, and we say, 'Well, OK, let's talk about … what you're actually saying is you want help, with what's happening.' 'Yeah, that's really what I want.'

'Everybody on the ward round was given a chair, and talking didn't start until everybody was sitting down, at eye-level with the patient.'

Jo Hockley, a nurse with long experience in both England and Scotland of hospice and palliative care, also speaks of seeking the voice of the patient in the context of the need to achieve symptom control and of the importance of seeing the patient in their family situation:

I don't believe you can really come alongside somebody unless their symptoms are well controlled ... I suppose it's literature I've read, it's my experience with patients that has made me have this opinion now and I think one of the most important aspects – it's a wee bit like birth, if they have the family around, and to have the family around there's got to be openness between what the patient understands is happening to them and the family being able to talk to the patient. So that would always be my aim with somebody, that even if it was only for the last day, there would be that recognition of being together and understanding the full intent – because sometimes, you know, it takes that time, if I'm only involved with somebody for 10 days, which is what the situation often would be in the hospital, I wouldn't have necessarily a long time to get to know the patient as well as the family, to bring them together.

Tony Crowther develops the point about the difficult issues that can arise when there is a need to balance the impact of symptoms with the level of awareness of the patient. Reconciling two profound needs can be complex and challenging:

The patients teach us an awful lot ... the staff teach us an awful lot. I mean we see groups of patients who just accept that they're dying and there's no problem and we look after them and they die. We have other patients who, because of the enormity of their ... usually physical problem ... I would be letting them down if I did not ... make them slightly less aware of what's happening to them. Now that sounds probably difficult to understand. What I'm meaning is, there are some patients that the very horror of their illness, wrapped

up with the slowness of their dying process, maybe the disease is extremely localised ... I feel, as a doctor, I have a duty to make sure that when that patient's horrors are likely to get even worse, of making that patient, with the knowledge of the nursing staff and the knowledge of the relatives, less aware of what's happening. Now I am aware that that's walking a tightrope. On the other hand, if we don't walk a tightrope we will let patients down, in my opinion. What is important is that it's done openly; it's done with the knowledge of the patient, if possible, but more often with the knowledge and approval of the relatives and, above all, the staff.

We will conclude this section on learning from the patient with two reservations. First, Richard Hillier is aware that sometimes privileging the voice of the patient and promoting patient choice is just helping clinicians out of a problem they are not keen to address:

I'm not saying you should do what patients like, I mean I'm not against choice, but I think choice is a marvellous expression now

Tony Crowther: 'The patients teach us an awful lot ... the staff teach us an awful lot.'

used, which actually is about absolving one's responsibilities onto someone else. 'You choose,' we say, because we don't want to make the decision for them, and I think one has to be careful about that.

Finally, linked with the important caveat about not idealising the process of care in the hospice and its impact on dying, we have to recognise that – however much is learned and however much progress is made – it is still possible to encounter insights like this one reported by Richard Hillier:

… a patient said to me a little while ago, he said, 'You know, Doctor …' he said, '… you hospices try and tart death up …' he said, '… and make it look good,' he said, '… and I'm telling you, it's bloody awful …' and he said, '… it's always going to be like that.'

Personal experience

All of the caregiver experiences we have introduced so far have emphasised the voice of the patient or a relationship with the patient. We now look at some of the features of motivation that link more specifically with events in a person's life or the significance of certain professional activities.

A medical student with Cicely Saunders, Tom West was doing his final exams in the late 1950s when his father was diagnosed with terminal cancer. Here he offers an alternative formulation to that of Cicely Saunders herself, on the question of who was the 'first' modern hospice patient:

He became very much iller and my mother rang up Cicely Saunders … and she came down straightaway and helped to keep father at home for the last three weeks of his life. And so I claim that, rightly, that my father was the very first terminal cancer patient that Dr

Cicely Saunders … ever looked after. And so Pa is the first patient in the worldwide hospice movement …

After time working as a medical missionary,[10] Tom West returned to the UK to become Deputy Medical Director at St Christopher's in 1973:

After qualifying I did my three house jobs and then … joined the Church Missionary Society … and was sent to West Africa … I think it was a remarkable preparation for my hospice work, because I learnt something about teamwork which I believe stood me in very good stead in the hospice later, and I learnt something about courage: it takes courage to do an operation you've never done before; it takes courage to deal with dying people and their families. And I did actually learn something about prayer; it was helpful to have a prayer said before one began a difficult operation, even if the patient having a spinal anaesthetic was the first and loudest to say 'Amen', at the end of the prayer.

In the mid-1970s Prue Clench (later Prue Dufour) was working as a nurse on a radiotherapy ward in Bath; here she identified much good practice:

We could have patients for six or eight weeks on the ward before they died, and we could let people go home for the weekend and keep the bed and have them back again. Some of the ideas of hospice care were already there. The most outstanding gap was that symptom control was simply totally lacking … and I suppose as a slightly older person, and because I'd had a lot of sadness in my own life, patients very readily talked to me, and shared how they felt … I became much more aware that, although we were trying so hard to care for them and there was a great commitment there, we were missing the boat of what really mattered for so many people, and their fears about being drugged and dropping their tea all over their top sheet. And we might say it didn't matter but it mattered very much to them … when in fact you have met with a lot of parting yourself, then you feel the pain of other people … And just like everybody else the whole world over, I wrote to Cicely Saunders … Somewhere along in my nurse training I must have either read Cicely's articles in the *Nursing Times*[11] … because how did I know to write to her? But I did, I wrote her a long, foolscap, handwritten letter. And being Cicely Saunders … she wrote me a long handwritten letter back telling me how things could be different on Ward Nine. And it ended up with: 'Why not come and do a month's course [at St Christopher's]?'

In a strikingly different example, Sheila Cassidy was working in Chile in 1975 after the overthrow of the Allende government, and was involved in treating a fugitive from the police for a bullet wound:

A week later I was arrested at gunpoint by the secret police and the maid in the house where I was arrested was shot and killed, and I was taken and tortured to make me divulge the information about the chap I had treated … and also the people who had been involved, who were a lot of church people … I spent three days in a torture centre, three weeks in solitary confinement … really facing the fact that they might actually kill me … detention camp for five weeks, then eventually I was released … So I have a very traumatic history, and also an experience of powerlessness, of fear, isolation, which I think has given me a particular bond with the dying.[12]

After returning to the UK, Sheila Cassidy got a job in the radiotherapy department of a hospital in Plymouth:

… and found to my great surprise that I actually loved working with cancer patients and had a great empathy for them … when a local hospice in Plymouth was being opened I was offered the job … I remember speaking to one of the Plymouth consultants who was involved in the planning for the hospice and he said, 'We didn't know who on earth would run it. And then you came and it was obvious.' And there was a funny thing, I had met up with Robert Twycross[13] (some time before, in 1978) … because at that time I

didn't know anything about hospices and Twycross looked at me and said, 'I knew you would come.' And I said, 'What do you mean?' and he said, 'Oh, with your background you were bound to end up in hospice.'

Mary Butterwick, founder of Butterwick Hospice in Stockton-on-Tees, speaks of the personal experience of her husband John's death from a brain tumour in 1979. Here the shortcomings of his care produced first a change in understanding and then a series of steps to act upon that understanding on behalf of others in her community:

By the time they told me what his illness was he was in a coma and couldn't respond; nobody told me anything more than that, that he was dying and that within hours he would be dead … He died on his own with none of us there because, you know nobody thought fit to phone us.

My life changed from that night, and after working through a great deal of pain I had to learn how to forgive because I felt that these people could have done so much different for him. Not medically, I'm not knocking the medics, I never knock the medics: we need the medics in the world, but it taught me how much more we are than that as a human being and that we do have feelings, we do have emotions.

She became a volunteer for Stockton Voluntary Services and through this appreciated how common were the experiences she had encountered:

The *Evening Gazette* [the local evening newspaper] was doing something and I was asked just to watch this video and it was about a young girl that had basically had terminal cancer diagnosed. She was a young woman with a young family and a husband and she didn't know where to go, she didn't want to tell her husband, she couldn't tell her kids and where did she go to talk about her illness and that and, oh my goodness here we go again, you know. And to cut a long story short, I volunteered to kind of help start this steering group and we did start one again, as I say, a group of cancer patients where they could bring their families.

This mutual help group for people coping with cancer was followed by a response to the needs of the bereaved:

I got asked to sit on a steering group to bring Cruse into the community[14] and I was on the first group in Middlesborough to bring Cruse into Middlesborough and then I realised that this was really for me … I thought, 'Right, I must be one of these counsellors,' because, you know, I've got so much inside of me, you know. Well, basically I did their training, their first lot of training in this community.

From here Mary Butterwick went on to establish the John Butterwick Trust and then the Butterwick Hospice.

Finally, in this section we look to an observation made by Paul Williment who became involved as a volunteer, home care team administrator, expert computer advisor and, following his ordination in 1989, part-time Catholic Chaplain at St Gemma's Hospice, Leeds. For him it is not specific aspects of the hospice that should be emphasised but rather the special characteristics of a hospice as a whole. He uses a most interesting description of a hospice as a 'thin place':

I think working with people who are very ill is quite a privilege. A hospice is a kind of thin place really between two realities and I think thin places are very special because they keep you in touch with what's really important … the living relationships, you know that's the core of what's important and a lot of the things that perhaps we might feel are important in the general race for life retreat into a more appropriate perspective and that's a good thing.

Hospice founder, Mary Butterwick: 'My life changed from that night.'

Professional experience

We now see how earlier encounters in clinical work left unresolved questions that might be addressed by work in the hospice context. In 1961, in his first house job in the radiotherapy unit of a London hospital, Tony Crowther visited St Joseph's, Hackney at the invitation of Cicely Saunders:

We did this ward round, and I'll always remember, she introduced us to a patient with cancer of the stomach who was reading a book, sitting up in bed, totally inoperable carcinoma. And we came away from the bed, and I was the bright-eyed, bushy-tailed houseman who said, 'Excuse me, Dr Saunders, but I haven't seen any fridges for blood or drip sacks to give blood, and yet that man with a cancer of the stomach may have a massive haematemesis,' which is what we had been taught in pathology … And she said, 'Well it's unlikely, but if he did, he'd have an injection of morphine and he would either die of his haemorrhage comfortable and unaware of what was happening, or if he didn't die from it, then we would think about it and consider transfusion the next day.' And I thought, 'Wow! What common sense. That's humanity, that's normality.' 'Cause I'd only been taught resuscitation and putting drips up and saving lives, and I thought, 'Wow, that is brilliant.' And ... I suppose, forgot about it.

Then in the early 1970s, about seven years after moving from London to Sheffield, at a social gathering, Tony Crowther was asked:

'Have you heard about this new nursing home that's going to be built, St Luke's Nursing Home?' And I said, 'No, I haven't.' And [his acquaintance] said, 'Well it's going to be where ... they look after terminally ill patients.' And of course I immediately flashed to St Joseph's and Cicely Saunders and the chap with the carcinoma of the stomach, and I thought, 'Wow! That's just my cup of tea.'

Some people we talked to felt pulled towards hospice care; others were pushed away from their current work environment. While Tony Crowther embraced the possibility of a new experience, a sense almost of home-coming, Richard Hillier describes the impact of encountering assumptions about common practice in the hospital where he was working early in his medical career:

On my first day in my first house job ... we were doing the ward round with the guy I was taking over from, and our boss. And there was a girl behind the curtains, who was a young girl with carcinoma of the breast, making an awful noise. And my boss said to the chap who was just about to leave: 'Can you give her a grain of morphine', which is 64 milligrams of morphine. And she had a grain of morphine, the noise stopped, and at the end of the ward round she was dead. And I said, 'Did we, was that our fault?' And he said, 'Oh no, no, no, she was very seriously ill.' And I said, 'But, you know, I didn't think she was that ill, I mean ...' I said '... I know I'm new

here, but ...' And he put his hand on my shoulder in a very sort of avuncular way and he said, '... sometimes these cases are very, very difficult and it's really important, it's a good lesson to you, just keep them comfortable and it doesn't matter what you give them.' And I said, 'Really?' And he said, 'Oh, yes,' very assuredly.

But it was not just the assumptions and practice of others that did not feel right:

Once or twice during that job, I got it terribly wrong. I remember telling somebody, a family, that the, a patient was going to die, and them absolutely breaking up, and I couldn't stand it really, and I just said to Sister, 'For God's sake, let me out of this,' and I walked out and left it to her. I told another man he was going to die, and he didn't. And these were pretty awful really; I mean they're stories which any young doctor can tell. And I honestly think I switched off then. I didn't really, I mean I was humane to them and I was good to them, 'cause I enjoyed that sort of thing, and I was nice to them, but I didn't ... and I was kind, I was the kind of hospice kindness; I would sit down and listen to them, and talk to them, and put my hand on their hands if necessary, and I wasn't afraid of them, but I was kind, I was nice and kind. But I didn't have a clue what I was doing really.

Richard Hillier subsequently moved into a more research-oriented position:

And then I worked for the MRC [Medical Research Council], and I've said this in front of Cicely ... I was reading a new journal called *The Journal of Hospital Medicine* in which there were two articles[15] by ... Cicely Saunders, one about communication, the other about pain; and I couldn't put it down ... And that really was a stunning experience for me because suddenly there was somebody talking about what I felt in my heart, but had never ... but had thought was wrong, you know, and that was an extraordinary experience for me. And I just ate the article really, and I told everybody about it ...

From here, Richard Hillier moved into general practice, where he 'tried out' the sense of confirmation of his own feelings that he had got from these 'stunning' articles. Yet, as we find again and again in stories of hospice care, it is the encounter with a particular patient that brings all things together:

There was a patient I remember … vividly. I can remember all about him more than any other patient there, who was dying … he was the first person I tried to make this work, and, blimey, it did work. You know, I mean we talked very openly about the whole thing, in a family where there'd been barriers up everywhere, and to my amazement, you know, the whole thing settled down. He had pain and symptom problems and I just copied it like a recipe really, and sort of to-ing and fro-ing and working with him … And between us we managed the symptom control. And I was very open with him and said, 'I used to make a mess of this.' And he'd say, 'Oh, you're doing alright this time, Doctor. Do you think we could have a bit more of this and that?' And it was a very powerful, powerful experience, and I was very sad when he died. But he made me think, 'God, this is fantastic,' you know, 'this is more useful than anything I've done. This is real, I mean I haven't seen this, ever,' you know, I thought, 'This is terrific.'

Of course, Richard Hillier had not found a magic answer:

So that was really tremendous; and then nothing. The others after that were all fairly straightforward, until I got to Portsmouth when we began to get more of them, and I began to find that it wasn't so easy … There were symptoms I was mismanaging, and I couldn't get pain under control, couldn't do this, couldn't do that. And I scoured the article, you know, to see what I was doing wrong and I couldn't find anything. So I thought, 'Well, this is ridiculous, I must go and work with this lady.' So I wrote to her and she invited me over and

I went to work there. And at that point I thought, 'I can do this,' I thought, 'This is fantastic.' And I went back home after I'd worked with Cicely to my wife, and I said, 'Ah, this is just something else really, this is terrific.'

For Tom McGinley in Northern Ireland, frustration with the quality of care for dying people in general practice proved a stimulus to further training and an enduring involvement in hospice care:

I came to this part of the world about 1960, spent a few years in the hospital, and then went into general practice. It became apparent very soon that I was very, very unhappy with the standard of care for people who were dying, first and foremost. In my six years at university, a six-year course then, I had never seen anybody die, we weren't really allowed to talk to people who were dying, we weren't even allowed to sit at their bedside when they were dying, and we were told that our objective at university was to learn how to cure people. So in my early years in general practice I was very, very unhappy, and very – really very – no great confidence in dealing with it, and I suppose what really was the trigger of my real interest was when a terminally ill young boy of about 18 or 19, who was dying of cancer, and I wasn't able to – not only deal with his pain relief that he needed, but he wanted me to talk to him about dying and about death, and I failed him completely. Then, at that stage, Dame Cicely Saunders had started the hospice in St Christopher's, having spent a number of years at St Joseph's. So, I went – started to go to St Joseph's then, maybe a few weeks every year, with my holidays spent there … I remained a full-time partner in general practice because I had a feeling that – right, if I was ever going to be involved in hospice that it was better to stay in general practice.

In other instances, it is a sense of not doing things well that stimulated a move elsewhere. Sharing a flat with Cicely Saunders during the years of evolving ideas and early fund-raising, Gillian Ford recalls that 'Most of the work was done in the kitchen … on bits and pieces of paper.' Even in these early days Cicely Saunders was highly motivated:

… already intent on this vision of doing something for people who had late stage disease and who were being neglected by those caring for them, and particularly those with cancer … The way she's described it is: the ward round which passes by the end of the bed because the person who has got untreatable … (in curative terms) … late stage disease – it was a reproach. Nothing more could be done: 'Let's hope they don't ask me anything.' And of course there was the tradition of 'not telling'. Finding some anodyne statement … on which one could turn one's heel.

For Eric Wilkes, experiences as a GP and working in a cottage hospital in the small town of Bakewell in Derbyshire in the 1960s had a major influence on his thinking.

I remember one … villager I admitted to die … He obviously knew he was very ill and he wanted to share it with me, and I didn't feel I was ready to share it with him so I hedged and I said, 'We'll do our best and we'll see what happens,' and all the meaningless palliative[16] phrases which attempt to conceal a doctor's embarrassment. And there was a look on his face which was not contempt, but which was fear, which I had not dealt with. I had dealt with it in words, but the non-verbal communication was a disaster. And I said to myself, 'You must not go on like this because … you may get no second chance.'[17]

Gloria Day describes a series of experiences gained while working as a nurse in a Sheffield general hospital that preceded her discovery of the hospice and its different ways of working. Even with excellent nursing practice there was something missing in the hospital care of dying patients:

Death was just something else, it was almost like to be ignored, you know, it was pushed in a corner; it was pushed in a side ward; it was pushed out of the way. Relatives came and they seemed to be grieving a lot, I was often in a position where probably I didn't see the relatives, or if I did it was, well, give them a quick cup of tea and say, 'Oh, I'm really sorry' and then just get out of the, you know, 'Goodbye and farewell'. And it all seemed very haphazard … and if they were crying, I mean, there were times when … my compassion would be there, and I'd be saying, 'Oh, please don't cry, please don't get upset,' but I didn't know what to say after that, I just didn't know what to say. So it was often left with, 'Well, here's the certificate and, er, goodbye then,' and that was it.

I can remember feeling anger at times … I was in Casualty once and they brought in a very young road traffic accident who was dead and we had to see the girlfriend and the father, and I remember the father making a comment to the girlfriend and I could have thumped him and I thought, 'There is something more than this,' and he said, 'Oh, you'll get over it.' And I thought, 'No, you can't possibly get over something like this, you can't,' and I felt, I wanted to thump him, this man. And I knew then, you know, there were incidents that happened to make me realise I wasn't, I didn't cope, but I knew I wasn't alone – neither did anybody else.

We sometimes talked to colleagues and they'd said, 'Ooh, I felt awful, I gave that person nothing, I gave that family nothing,' and I used to think, 'There must be something more that we could do.' I thought my nursing practice was excellent, I did everything, my patients didn't do without anything, they had everything that I could get them within my means. But I knew there was something I was definitely not giving them and that was it.

At the same time, some also talked of more positive motivations. Eric Wilkes found how good practice could be sustained and spread:

One of my favourite stories was when I had a schoolmaster who had a brain tumour and he wasn't very good at feeding himself because he was in the late stages when I admitted him to the cottage hospital, and the senior sister at the cottage hospital was spending half an hour of her busy working day, not managing the ward, not organising, but feeding him soup. And I went up to her and half jokingly I said, 'What are you, the senior sister, doing here feeding him soup?' And she said, 'He taught me French!' And I've never forgotten that …

The problem then was clear:

How can we help Sheffield look after its dying patients … as well as we're doing it in Bakewell, where they're surrounded by visitors, they're surrounded by relatives, they're surrounded by friends, they're looked after by a doctor who may be pretty ignorant, but at least he's familiar and, to some degree, involved in their fate, rather than cocky young men … (in those days, not many women) … who are totally changing jobs every six months anyway?

The appeal of research, of meeting people pushing at the edge of their discipline, of trying to merge different intellectual approaches, of contributing to high-level policy discussion – these too were key influences we identified in some interviews.

After qualifying as a doctor Ann Gilmore had developed an interest in psychiatry and geriatrics, working in Glasgow on a three-year study of elderly people living in their own homes:

All along the way I've had research interests, I'm very academic so … something would occur and I would say, 'Oh, that's an interesting thing,' and I would go and do it, and I would find that nobody else had done it so there was hardly any literature on something that I had done, so, once again, that puts you at the front of things and … I was a United Nations Fellow, was a World Health Organisation consultant. I was interested in terminal care and did one of the early papers in terminal care, about 1972. I did a survey of GPs in Glasgow, about how they dealt with the terminally ill. That was '72[18] … As a result of that, I was put on an international planning committee for a conference in thanatology, which is the study of death and dying and grief and bereavement and ritual, and everything that leads into it, which is not a popular movement in Britain, it's almost, virtually unheard of, but it's very big in France, and very big in the States and South America. And I met all the top people in this. Really top people: Kübler-Ross,[19] you know, she and I were buddies, you know.

In the late 1950s when considering subjects early in a research career in psychiatry, John Hinton found that:

Some of the problems came back from the medical career, sort of resurfaced a little bit. I'd been very conscious during my period as medical registrar, and in neurology, of the problems of people who were dying, helped by the fact that one of the consultant physicians I worked for did take an interest in seeing that people who were dying were looked after well: Clifford Hoyle[20] was his name, and so I had always found it fairly easy to let people who were dying or seriously ill talk to me. I really didn't see why other people had so much problem about it. And they said, 'Well you can do it, you can carry on and talk to him,' even if I was just a sort of junior member of the team.

Colin Murray Parkes describes an academic curiosity that was met, in part, through a study of stress. In 1956 he began studying as a trainee psychiatrist at the Maudsley Hospital in London:

I got interested in bereavement as part of the Diploma in Psychological Medicine – the DPM. And as part of that we all had to do a research project and write a short dissertation. And because of my interest in stress, I decided I wanted to do something in that field, so I started looking around for people who were suffering stress. And there were a couple of patients on the ward where I was working at the time, who had both suffered bereavements, so I thought, 'Well, that sounds like a good stress.' In fact, I remember drawing up a sort of shopping list of stresses. I wrote down all the major stresses I could think of, and bereavement kept popping up as the top one. It was a major life event which didn't occur sufficiently frequently for many people to get used to it. It was something which you could study because it occurred at a particular time and place. It was something that was a subject of statistics and records and things that you could access.

This interest in bereavement as stress then linked with a broader concern and with a sense of dissatisfaction with the practice he had already encountered:

I met Cicely Saunders. I'd actually met her once before we went to America and she and John Bowlby[21] and I had dinner together … She was working at St Joseph's Hospice at the time, studying pain relief but also interested in the wider psychosocial aspects of caring for the dying. This was a subject I was interested in, in my area, as I've already talked about my dissatisfaction with medicine and with the way in which it seemed to me that doctors and nurses were handling the major stresses that patients and families were going through. So when I met someone who, although she didn't pretend to any specialist knowledge, was very interested in psychosocial care of the dying, that was obviously something we wanted to know more about. And I said, right from the start, that if I could be of any help to her I'd be very pleased to do so.

Colin Murray Parkes adds to that level of intellectual engagement and clinical experience a recognition of the prevailing times. That he would develop these interests tells something about his own biography; that these would engender some social momentum and wider following is to do with factors outside the individual:

I think that we were both products of the history of the times. So I think Elisabeth Kübler-Ross, Cicely Saunders and perhaps myself too, to some extent, although we're often seen as innovators, we were actually doing what the world was ready for. There was a sense in which people were getting very dissatisfied with these machines for dying that we were creating. The more the technology of medical care progressed, the more inhuman it became and the more people with serious illnesses began to feel that they were cogs in a machine.

Religious calling

The theme of a religious or spiritual calling to hospice work has been referred to by various commentators and explored in detail in the particular case of Cicely Saunders.[22] At the end of the 1960s, when considering his career options as a doctor, Robert Twycross was facing some choices. His eventual decision to work in hospice care can be explained in various ways:

Most people, religious or not, have some feeling that there is some sort of direction in life. You know the famous expression that some people use, 'When one door shuts another opens', and that sort of thing. And I suppose the fact that I'd had this little voice, which I heard after an interview (for a job unrelated to hospice), 'That takes you one step away from St Christopher's …' and maybe there was something pulling me towards St Christopher's, though what that was – whether it was Cicely's charisma or whether it was divine calling, you know, I must leave that to you. I mean, being religious I could of course wrap it up and say, 'Well, I was definitely called to this work,' but I'm not sure that I should because, you know, I think a measure of religious maturity, if I can claim such, is to be a little bit agnostic at times. I think other people writing of me will probably undoubtedly say, 'He had a clear calling …'

Mary Baines had trained as a doctor with Cicely Saunders and in the late 1960s was working as a GP in the area of South London near to where St Christopher's was located. She began work at the hospice in 1968 and continued there until her retirement in 1996:

I don't think it was anything I particularly wanted to do. Although I suppose if you had asked me at the time I'd have said, well it will be something I'd do for a few years and then go back to general practice, and that it would be an extra experience. I'm sure as well that there was the challenge and the newness. And I was a fairly academic doctor … But the career that has happened to me … I, in my wildest dreams, would not have guessed … Well I think, I don't know whether you will believe this or not, but I think there's no doubt that that was a call of God to do this … a number of us have felt that as well … It wasn't that I wanted to, it wasn't that I was unhappy, it wasn't at that stage that it offered me a better future. It certainly wasn't more money. It certainly wasn't more security.

Contact with someone else

For others there was a sense, not of God, but of another person spotting a certain potential, and that seeming to be right. In 1980, at the end of an unsuccessful interview for a job unrelated to hospice work, the interviewer said to Rita Beattie:

'We're planning to open a hospice here [in Northern Ireland] …' and she said, '… and I can see you're the person to run it.' When she said this, she didn't realise what bells began to ring within me. It was as if something was being prophetic. So I told her about my interest in hospice care, and my years that I had spent in London and how I'd enjoyed the time, and I was interested. So she said, 'If you're interested, come back and talk to me.'

Three years later the hospice was established and seeking staff:

So I went for interview and … one of the people on the panel was the lady I had met three years previously. I couldn't believe it because I didn't know what her involvement, or whatever … And I walked out of the interview knowing the post was mine.

In the late 1960s Derek Doyle was working as a doctor in Edinburgh after a decade spent in Africa. He recounts meetings with the matron at his hospital:

A remarkable lady: Miss Ann Weatherill. The name is now famous in Scotland … she had immediately recognised that Edinburgh could probably do with a hospice. We won't call it a palliative care unit: it was to be a hospice. Now she'd been down and seen Cicely in, I think, around '67, now I'm talking about '68 only within one year of St Christopher's opening. Now, of course, like everybody, I'd read about St Christopher's. I'd seen *The British Medical Journal*, I'd seen the articles and had myself by no means thought we must get this started, but I thought there's a lot to be said here. This is definitely highlighting a huge deficiency within our care, and I don't mean within the Health Service, but within our care … In short, Miss Weatherill one day said to me, 'What do you think about a need for a hospice?' And I said it was a good thing. And I never wanted to get involved in it but she nagged me for one whole morning as I was moving between the wards, she kept meeting me, and in the end (it's a joke now), I fobbed her off and said, 'Oh very well I'll come for a coffee with you and your cronies tonight if you like.' And that was it: 1968, the end of that year, we'd formed a founding committee and, eventually, in 1977 … St Columba's – to be the Edinburgh hospice.

Ann Weatherill and St Columba's Hospice, Edinburgh

Dr Derek Doyle, writing in January 2004, recalls:

Ann Weatherill was born and brought up in Yorkshire and trained as nurse in the Royal Infirmary of Edinburgh. When war broke out she went into the Royal Alexandra Nursing Corps and saw service in Europe and North Africa where she was in charge of a large base hospital. After the war she elected to work near her widowed mother so as to look after her, giving up chances of promotion to senior nursing/administrative posts. When free to take up appointments wherever she wished she was appointed to be Matron of Berwick Infirmary, where senior consultants were distinguished surgeons and physicians from Edinburgh. From there she moved to Edinburgh as Matron of Corstorphine and Beechmount hospitals, associated hospitals of the Royal Infirmary of Edinburgh, with 132 beds between them.

In 1967, the year St Christopher's opened, she visited it, already convinced Edinburgh too needed a hospice. The following year she brought together a small group of citizens to plan such a place, remaining on that planning group but never wanting to chair it or dominate it in any way though her presence was always obvious. Like many of us she found the slow process of gaining public attention and support a much longer and more painful process than had ever been foreseen. She retired in 1977 the same year as her dream came to fruition but, perhaps reluctantly but certainly wisely and graciously, decided not to be the hospice's first Nursing Director choosing rather to continue to lecture about it, make all the vestments for an Anglican chaplain, plan its beautiful chapel and be a powerhouse behind the scenes. Few people knew she was the one with the original vision for a hospice in Scotland. Inevitably and understandably she found it difficult to see others doing what she had wanted to do, and difficult to accept that it was basically a secular unit with an ecumenical basis of belief. It is doubtful if she ever thought it would have any influence beyond its own walls, even into all the other hospitals of Edinburgh and its university. To her death she said she regretted that it had had to grow to so many beds and, as she saw it, lose its 'homeliness'.

Her final years, increasingly affected by ill health, were devoted to the Anglican Franciscan Order of which she was a tertiary, fulfilling a lifetime ambition to take holy orders of some sort. She died in March 1995, her ashes being sprinkled as she had wished, in the grounds of St Columba's outside the chapel overlooking the hospice and its beautiful grounds.

The idea of hospice care seemed to resonate with Derek Doyle's earlier work in Africa and with a sense he had of himself as someone who gets things going; but we also see that this was underpinned by a sense of religious motivation:

That opened, and by then everybody had assumed that I would be Medical Director. It had never crossed my mind, never ever, until the very last year. The whole of my life, was [working] with incurables in a sense. People didn't come to you with early disease in Africa, they came with gross disease. Even my surgery was, and now to use our correct word, was palliative surgery. I mean I was making them comfortable, even with big surgery. I wasn't curing anybody that I could set out to cure. Even with the children I was making life more comfortable. I wasn't curing people, I wasn't deliberately doing that. If some were cured it was very fortunate and fortuitous but all my life, I now look back, I realise that I was dealing with people that were extremely disadvantaged, that were disabled in one way or another, and I was trying to just ease in some modest way. Secondly, I'd always been involved in starting, creating, whether it was setting up a committee or a body here, I mean I did that at school and university. I've always enjoyed creating something, or getting a bunch of people together and saying, 'What do you think of this as an idea?' And I suppose I've always enjoyed being the evangelist, the 'missionary', but not in a religious sense necessarily, because that matters to me but it's not an overwhelming thing. People think that this is a great driving force, I don't think it is. I think it's a sort of underpinning ethos.

Robert Twycross recalls meeting Cicely Saunders while he was still a medical student at Oxford and highlights both what was happening outwardly and what the subconscious was also doing, inwardly:

... there was an international conference organised by the SCM, the Student Christian Movement, which was in Bristol in the first few days of 1963, which was the big freeze-up. It froze on Christmas Eve and, unlike this year,[23] it didn't unfreeze on New Year's Day, it continued freezing for a couple of months. And we somehow managed to get to Bristol despite the amount of snow between here and there. And in this international student conference, in addition to the keynote addresses and that sort of thing, there were workshops. And one series of workshops was on 'Health and Healing' and it was groups – group discussion – and there were sufficient senior members to have a senior member sitting in, I think, with each discussion group. And the senior member in the group I was in happened to be Cicely Saunders. And obviously she said a few things which happened to resonate with me ...

So 18 months later ... less than 18 months later, Cicely Saunders came to speak [at Oxford] on 'The Management of Pain in Terminal Cancer'. That meant that I went into her black book as a doctor, or a future doctor, who might well be interested in hospice care. And that meant that a couple of years after I qualified, which must have been ... the exactitude doesn't matter, does it ... but let's say some time in 1968, she wrote and said would I be interested in applying for a Clinical Research Fellowship, and I wrote back saying, 'Well, it's very nice of you, but I've decided to take my MRCP [Member of the Royal College of Physicians], so I've got to finish that.' And I sort of forgot about it. And then a couple of years later, when the Research Fellow they appointed died tragically, I think within two years of taking up his post,[24] I got another letter in December 1970 saying would I like to consider applying for the Research Fellowship now, which I did.

For some people there is a sense of having a vague interest shaped by someone already established in hospice work. Here we see indications of how a core group reached out and drew in people who thought they were dipping their toe into the water. This is motivation by proxy – being carried along by the drive of others, but it required a susceptible subject.

Having moved from London to Sheffield in the early 1970s, Ros Beetham describes how her husband passed on a note in a copy of *The British Medical Journal* about a new hospice, St Luke's, which was being developed around the corner from their new home:

My husband said, 'Are you interested?' [in being a volunteer] and I said, 'Not really ... I don't know what a hospice is, I'm not really looking for anything to do.' But I wrote to Eric [Wilkes – Medical Director], a rotten letter, because I've seen it ... saying I'd like to be a volunteer, we'd moved here, etc ... I didn't say anything much about myself. But he invited our family to tea ... being Eric. And, I thought, 'That's nice, volunteers are treated well.' So we went to tea at his home, and had a very nice time. And then some time later we were invited to a party of the Friends of St Luke's. Now this is all before the hospice opened, and it would be in early '71. So, again, thinking, 'Charming, aren't they?' went along like a lamb to the slaughter. But I didn't know that. And in the middle of this party, of whom there were already the chosen few ... staff ... the administrator, Colin Bibby, who was a solicitor ... began to ask me some very personal questions ... I didn't get the gist of this at all until he asked my views about volunteering, about which I knew nothing whatsoever.

Again we can see a connection with the personal characteristics and self-perception of Ros Beetham:

The only thing that related to that was the fact that I'd always been innovative in what I'd done. And I'd ... land up doing all sorts of 'people type' things that nobody had done before. So this conversation about volunteers went something like this: 'Would you be interested in becoming our voluntary help organiser?' So I said, 'I don't know what you're talking about, but I like a challenge.' 'Oh, right, well we would like you to be our voluntary help organiser at St

Luke's.' 'I have a couple of children and I'm not prepared to give up looking after them.' 'That's fine, we have a crèche and you can work any hours you like. All we need you to do is to set up a service, and then you can go home and pop in from time to time.' Which I never let him forget. So I said, 'Alright, then …'

These were early days in hospice development and much that was being tried was based on improvisation and assumptions of goodwill and competence:

So I'd got this job, about which I still knew nothing. We didn't have any sort of brief. In those days nobody knew what this was about. And, looking at the background at that time of volunteering, this was a stage where nothing was formal, and that mostly people were invited to come and work without any sort of looking at them seriously to see what they were capable of. No interviews. If people offered you said, 'Yes', and that was the climate.

A sense of social need – the inadequacy of existing provision

We will see in subsequent sections of this book how the hospice movement grew up alongside the UK's NHS. Many hospices were separate from the NHS but worked alongside it. Others were part of developing NHS provision for the dying. The freedom to be separate from the NHS was important for some people. Marjory Cockburn and Derek Doyle had both worked in Africa and when they returned to the UK they found hospice care more convivial and consistent with the work they had done there. For example, Marjory Cockburn had experienced considerable autonomy working as a nurse in Africa:

In my mind I know that if I didn't work on the mission field until I either dropped dead or retired I would come home and do hospice work. One thing became abundantly clear to me over the years in [Africa], was that I would never fit into the NHS because out there you have a tremendous amount of responsibility, we didn't even always have a doctor in the hospital, we might have a month or two with no doctor, so we did carry an enormous load of responsibility and we had to do procedures that, you know, I would have been sacked if I'd have even contemplated under the NHS.

Likewise Derek Doyle, on returning from Africa, welcomed hospice work as an alternative to the NHS and to private medicine:

I was becoming quite disillusioned with the way medicine had gone in Britain whilst I had been away [in Africa] and not seen it first hand.

He was able to get:

… out of the health service, thank God not into private medicine, but into hospice medicine.

Sometimes the opportunity to work in hospice care *and* in the NHS was a positive attraction. Robert Twycross is clear about his beliefs in, and support for, socialised medicine:

It was certainly appealing to me because I've grown up with the NHS. OK I was born pre-NHS but from early years I've been an NHS patient and I heartily approve of the NHS. I believe in socialised medicine and I think being within an NHS unit would have a natural appeal to me.

Using the phrase that has become the title of this book (see above, page 11), Richard Hillier saw the NHS offering a context within which a wide-ranging impact could be made, broader than the walls of one institution.

For me being in the rough and tumble of what I call the real world … we were actually trying to offer a service to an area, rather than offering a bit of heaven for the few.

We will return in subsequent sections to the idea that the hospice approach can be a catalyst to change in attitudes and practices in the wider health care community.

For some individuals, perception of a social need coincided with what felt right personally. A Catholic priest and later Bishop working in the deprived community of the Bogside in Derry from the early 1960s, Edward Daly encountered a doctor working in the same geographic area:

We both had similar experiences of administering to people who were ill and particularly to people who were dying. And Dr McGinley I think in his experience felt that more could be done for the people who were terminally ill and he talked about it with me but I didn't really, I hadn't the experience to know any other way of dealing with them other than the way that they were being dealt with in a hospital, I suppose hospitals largely for people who are getting better. People who are terminally ill simply don't fit in to a hospital. There's no real place for them except very much as a, as a bit on the back burner as it were. And Dr McGinley felt for a long time that something more should be done. I don't know where he came in contact with the hospice movement. I think he just read about it in medical journals and so forth, the work of Cicely Saunders and [St Joseph's] in Hackney in London. And he decided early in the 1980s to begin a movement to establish a hospice here in this city and the area generally … [Foyle Hospice, Derry] came into being in 1991 I think. And it has been there since.

An involvement in the organisation then became more central personally to Edward Daly:

I suffered a stroke in 1993 and as a result I had to retire as Bishop, so I decided to offer my services here as a chaplain and I think it was the best decision I ever made. I feel more fulfilled in my work as a minister of religion, as a priest, than I've ever been. I think it's the most challenging, at the same time the most fulfilling work I've, I've ever carried out, part of your pastoral ministry and I feel very privileged to be part of what I call the hospice family here.

Thinking about what might be done

We have been looking so far at how certain individuals appear pushed towards something different because of bad experiences and how others seem pulled towards hospice care because of how meaningful it felt for them.

Patricia Gilbert had worked on a surgical ward in a hospital before moving to St Gemma's, Leeds in 1978. Looking to the future she shares a hope that the hospice will

… still retain the personal contact that we have with patients and relatives because that is very important. They, when they're involved with hospitals, they just feel as if they're on a bandwagon, that they're just going through the system, and then when we become involved they feel that they are at least being cared for in a very personal way, that nothing's too much trouble, that you know we'll bend over backwards to try and give them the best we can. And I just hope we don't lose that, that we don't become too clinical.

We have already heard from Jean Radley about a ward culture that did not see talking to patients as legitimate work. Here she is reflecting on the challenges raised when listening does take place. For listening carries with it a recognition that patients near to death will want to ask difficult things and these things, in turn, will have an impact on the caregiver. Patients would ask:

'Why is this happening to me?' you know, the need for hope, the need for forgiveness, the need to know the reason why and what lies ahead – all the sorts of things that people ask when they know that days are numbered. After all I mean we're all going to die, but these days it's pushed to one side, isn't it? People tend to die much older these days and so nobody really thinks about it until they get close to it. But when somebody's had a life-threatening diagnosis when they're not old, all these spiritual questions come to the fore really. Being prepared to talk about it, being prepared to listen to it and not to fob it off, and being prepared to explore issues, which actually can be quite threatening to the nurse her- or himself as well, you know, because when you begin to explore issues such as death you have to accept your own mortality to be able to do that. So they can be quite threatening issues.

This book is about hospice care for adults. There is a separate story that can be told for children's hospices for there are major differences in approach arising out of the different circumstances of life-threatening illness in children. But there are points in common and in the quotations that follow we present a picture of motivation for change that is resonant of many of the experiences of those caring for adults. Sister Frances Dominica is a nurse, Mother Superior of an Anglican religious community and founder of the world's first children's hospice, Helen House, in Oxford. In the late 1970s she had been contacted by Jacquie, the mother of a two-and-a-half-year-old girl, Helen, who was being treated in an Oxford hospital for a cerebral tumour. Both Sister Frances and others at her convent offered support for the family and in so doing sought to help them in their wish to care for Helen at home:

Six months postoperatively her parents were told that nothing further could be done to help her recover and so they were absolutely determined that the place she belonged was her own home with her own family, with Lizzie the cat sitting on her tummy and lovely music and … just the place where she belongs, with the people who love her most. And, I think the people in hospital just couldn't believe that this was possible but they proved that it was possible – at tremendous cost to themselves. It's hard for any of us to imagine I think how it is to have a critically ill child at home, who's not in all probability going to get any better, but whose condition has levelled out: long nights of sometimes no sleep at all, days and nights of terrible anxiety, not being sure when to call somebody, you know, was this … was she going to die now or, you know, was this just another episode? Was she in pain when she screamed?

Sister Frances Dominica: founder of the first hospice for children.

As the weeks and months passed Sister Frances became increasingly concerned about the exhaustion Helen's parents were experiencing:

So one day I plucked up courage and asked them if they would trust me enough to lend her to me sometimes just for a night or two to give them, you know, an unbroken night's sleep perhaps, and the chance maybe to go out somewhere lovely or have even a brief weekend away. Or, as Jacquie once put it, the luxury of an occasional bout of flu …

The family agreed and Helen began to stay for short periods:

In February 1980, I was, I actually had Helen on my knee and I was giving her a drink and I began to think: are there other people out there, other families with children with life-limiting or life-threatening illnesses who either are caring for their children at home or would like to be caring for their children at home but maybe can't because they haven't been given an offer of appropriate support?

From this, Helen House began as a short-term alternative to home or to inappropriate hospital placements.[25]

The very first little girl who came to stay with us was 11 – her parents brought her all the way from RAF Valley in Anglesey … she had Batten's disease … she was blind and she had epilepsy, but she was a lovely, bubbly person, gorgeous child. And the only alternative respite care that her parents had been offered for her was a bed in a psychogeriatric ward.

In this chapter we have gained an insight into the personal motivations of some of those who got involved in the development of hospice care in the UK in the 1960s and 1970s. Their stories remind us of the power of human agency, even in a world heavily determined by structural forces that lie beyond the individual. Some of the accounts we have presented here come from leading national and international figures in the hospice movement; they reveal a sense of synergy that was born out of a shared vision of how the care of dying people might be improved – even transformed. We have also had a chance to explore the stories of some whose contribution to hospice care has been more at the local level and for whom daily care of patients and families has been the main preoccupation. Held in common by all of them is a sense of the vocational aspects of hospice care and its potential to draw in individuals from a variety of backgrounds and experiences. We did warn at the outset that our approach might create a series of artificial distinctions and that, for many respondents, some of the 'themes' we have separated out here were in fact occurring simultaneously. Partly to underline this point, we began the chapter with a sustained and multilayered narrative from Cicely Saunders. We conclude with some further words from Sister Frances Dominica who recounts the support she received from Professor David Baum,[26] President of the Royal College of Paediatrics and Child Health up to his death in 1999:

He told me about two men walking along the beach on a very hot day, midday sun, and there were hundreds of thousands of starfish washed up on the beach, dying in the heat. And every now and again the young man would bend down and throw one back into the sea, and eventually the old man said 'What possible difference can you make? Look, there are hundreds of thousands of these starfish dying.' And the young man looked at the one in his hand and as he threw it back into the ocean he said, 'It'll make a difference to this one.'[27] And that really was David's philosophy, you can't, you can't make the whole world better, but you can do your own small best if you're the right person in the right place at the right time.

It is a story that offers a positive response to the criticism implied in the title of this book and gives a powerful insight into some of the motivations for becoming involved in hospice care.

Notes

1. See, for example, C. Saunders, 'A window in your home' in *The Light of Experience* (London: BBC, 1977); 'Dame Cicely Saunders: an Omega interview', *Omega* 27 (4): 263–69, 1993.
2. For a detailed account of these discussions, see D. Clark, 'Religion, medicine and community in the early origins of St Christopher's Hospice', *Journal of Palliative Medicine* 4 (3): 353–60, 2001.
3. Cicely Saunders, here aged 84, was speaking in May 2003.
4. For more on Mrs G, see C. Saunders, 'A patient …', *Nursing Times*, 31 March: 394–97, 1961.
5. Broadcast on BBC Radio in February 1964.
6. We see here an example of a contemporary phrase (from an interview in May 2003) being visited upon a much earlier period. *A voice for the voiceless* is the subtitle of *Patient Participation in Palliative Care* (Oxford: Oxford University Press, 2003) edited by Barbara Monroe and David Oliviere, two senior staff at St Christopher's. The phrase is used as Cicely Saunders' title for her introduction to the book, pages 3–8.
7. The popular stereotype of a hospital consultant as aloof and autocratic was epitomised by the film actor James Robertson Justice in the 'Doctor' films of the 1950s.
8. In a 1964 paper, the phrase '*all of me is wrong*' was used by Cicely Saunders to introduce the concept of 'total pain' as comprising four elements: physical symptoms, mental distress, social problems and emotional problems (C. Saunders, 'The symptomatic treatment of incurable malignant disease', *Prescribers' Journal* 4 (4), October: 68–73, 1964). For more on the evolution of the concept of 'total pain' see D. Clark, '"Total pain", disciplinary power and the body in the work of Cicely Saunders 1958–67', *Social Science and Medicine* 49 (6): 727–36, 1999. We further explore the problem of pain in Chapter 6, below.
9. Tony Crowther was speaking in December 1996.
10. In addition to Tom West, others we interviewed for this book who had worked as missionaries were Marjory Cockburn and Derek Doyle.
11. Six articles by Cicely Saunders were published in *Nursing Times* during October and November 1959. They were reprinted in pamphlet form in 1960 and were widely read. See D. Clark, 'Someone to watch over me: Cicely Saunders and St Christopher's Hospice', *Nursing Times*, 26 August: 50–51, 1997.
12. Sheila Cassidy writes about this part of her life in the book *Audacity to Believe* (London: Collins, 1977).
13. Robert Twycross first met Cicely Saunders in 1963 and in 1971 went to work as a Clinical Research Fellow at St Christopher's. He then went on to Sir Michael Sobell House, Oxford, working there for 25 years before his retirement in 2001.
14. Cruse – as an organisation for widows, and subsequently more generally for the bereaved – will be discussed in Chapter 7.
15. This article was in fact one of a series of three in the *British Journal of Hospital Medicine*. The series was titled 'The Management of Terminal Illness' and was published in 1966 and early 1967. See D. Clark, 'An annotated bibliography of the publications of Cicely Saunders – 1: 1958–67', *Palliative Medicine* 12 (3): 181–93, 1998.
16. An interesting example of the word 'palliative' used in a pejorative sense in everyday language, even by an expert in the field.
17. *No Second Chance* was the title of a report Eric Wilkes later presented to the Trent Regional Health Authority, in 1988, and which advocated a regional strategy for the development of 'terminal care services'. The report also proved to be the catalyst for the establishment of what became the Trent Palliative Care Centre, Sheffield – the original 'home' of the Hospice History Project.
18. She is referring to A. Gilmore, 'The care and management of the dying in general practice', *Practitioner* 213: 833–42, 1974.
19. Elisabeth Kübler-Ross, the American psychiatrist and best-selling author of *On Death and Dying*, first published in the USA in 1969 and in the UK in 1970.
20. Clifford Hoyle, the chest physician, at King's College Hospital, London, and one of those attributed with the development of the 'Brompton Cocktail' – see Chapter 6, below.
21. John Bowlby, from the Tavistock Clinic in London, was the leading proponent of attachment theory, which he studied in relation to the links between children and parents and also in the context of the impact of separation and loss. He was the author of many

books and reports including a World Health Organisation study on the fate of homeless children in postwar Europe titled *Maternal Care and Mental Health* (1951) and the three books that made up his *Attachment and Loss* series, published in 1969, 1973 and 1980. He died in 1990.

22. See, for example, S. Stoddard, *The Hospice Movement: A better way to care for the dying* (London: Jonathan Cape, 1979); R. Lamerton, *Care of the Dying* (Harmondsworth: Penguin, 1980). For a summary see N. Small, 'Spirituality and hospice care' in M. Cobb and V. Robertshaw (eds.), *The Spiritual Challenge of Health Care* (Edinburgh: Churchill Livingstone, 1998). The particular experience of Cicely Saunders is analysed in D. Clark, 'Religion, medicine and community in the early history of St Christopher's Hospice', *Journal of Palliative Medicine* 4 (3): 353–60, 2001 and D. Clark, 'Originating a movement: Cicely Saunders and the development of St Christopher's Hospice, 1957–67', *Mortality* 3 (1): 43–63, 1998.

23. Robert Twycross was being interviewed in January 1996.

24. He is referring to Dr Ron Welldon, who died in November 1970.

25. For more information on Helen House, see J. Worswick, *A House Called Helen*, 2nd edn (Oxford: Oxford University Press, 2000) and www.helen-house.org.uk.

26. Professor David Baum was a central figure in the work which led to the establishment of the Royal College of Paediatrics and Child Health and became its President shortly after its foundation. He died on 5 September 1999 while taking part in a sponsored bicycle ride to raise money for child health services in Kosovo and Gaza. An international foundation, established in his name, works towards better child health throughout the world.

27. This story reappears in many parts of the world. For example in South Africa the starfish is a motif associated with Cotlands Baby Sanctuary. The Sanctuary was founded by Dorothy Reece in 1936 as a home for children in need of care. It opened a hospice in 1996 that went on to include a 20-bed in-patient unit and a home care programme serving approximately 120 families; in 2003, Cotlands opened a second paediatric AIDS hospice, this time in the Western Cape. The hospice website posted the starfish story and stated: 'We don't know where this story originated but it is so appropriate to South African society today … our founder, Matron Dorothy Reece, can be compared to the starfish rescuer' (www.cotlands.org).

2 Hospice growth and spread

'Wherever I went ... I said as I walked in through the door,
"Ah, this is a hospice"' **Richard Lamerton**

ndividual motivations make up one part of the history of hospice development, but over time personal commitments and ideals were to coalesce into visible strategies for action and practical activities to achieve change. From the outset, a combination of approaches championed by St Christopher's after 1967 was applied and adapted in other settings – in an emphasis on creating local independent charities to deliver caring services, in the involvement of volunteers and fund-raising, but also in developing working relationships with the NHS and the professions, and in the exploration of new models of care. Within a decade it was accepted that the principles of hospice care could be practised in many locations: not only in specialist in-patient units, but also in home care and day care services. Likewise hospital units and support teams were established that brought the new thinking about dying into the very heartlands of acute medicine, and across the country attention was turning to the matter of how a hospice workforce could be recruited and sustained. The decade of the 1980s was a period of unprecedented growth, with about 10 new hospices coming into operation each year. Now a process of maturation was in evidence. Independent hospices were proliferating, but these were complemented by home support services and the first hospital palliative care teams, and by more significant funding from the NHS and the major cancer care charities.

This chapter shows how the hospice ideal developed from small, fragmented and isolated beginnings to become physically established across the UK. It reveals how what came to be known as the modern hospice movement did not stand apart from other innovations of the period, but was from the outset embedded in changing communities, in health care innovation, and in new concepts of professional practice.

One of the paradoxes of the twentieth-century independent hospice movement in the UK is that it originated in the shadow of a new, inclusive system of socialised medicine and welfare which offered the promise of care, 'from the cradle to the grave'. So the modern hospices might be seen to be somewhat out of tune with the times, indeed, having more in common with the voluntary hospitals that had preceded

Lord Thurlow, St Christopher's Chairman and Cicely Saunders dig the first spit to mark the start of building on 22 March 1965.

the NHS: raised by public subscription; involving prominent local doctors; and bearing religious and philanthropic associations. However, the founding of the first modern hospice by Cicely Saunders in 1967 was itself the culmination of a postwar process in which several factors conjoined to create the conditions of possibility for hospice expansion.[1] Opening its doors to patients was a momentous occasion for the hospice but, as we have already seen in Chapter 1, it formed part of a wider and growing social preoccupation with the need for better care for dying people.

Getting started

As in Chapter 1, we commence our exploration of the oral history with Cicely Saunders and her particular vision for hospice care. We learn of her initial application for a piece of land in Sydenham, South London; an action supported by prayer and underpinned by faith.

In the summer of 1957, just before she qualified in medicine at the age of 39, Cicely Saunders was also working on her first publication. Its contents set out the entire basis for a new approach to the care of dying people. By the time of its appearance the following year in the *St Thomas's Hospital Gazette*, the foundations for her life's work were fully in place. She had trained as a nurse; studied philosophy, politics and economics at Oxford; been employed as an almoner; and was about to take up the work of a physician. In fact she would be the first modern doctor to dedicate her entire career to caring for those at the end of life. The paper was clear enough about her intentions: 'It appears to me that many patients feel deserted by their doctors at the end. Ideally the doctor should remain the centre of a

team who work together to relieve where they cannot heal, to keep the patient's own struggle within his compass and to bring hope and consolation to the end.'[2] Here then was an ambition of singular proportions which would require a monumental transformation in professional knowledge, attitudes and behaviour for its realisation. By 1959, the vision had transformed into a 'scheme' which encompassed a name – 'St Christopher's Hospice' – and a detailed description of in-patient provision and organisation. Yet essential to the realisation of the scheme was also a building; and in order to build there was a need for land. So the first tangible step came with a grant from the King's Fund[3] to purchase a building plot. In the following extract Cicely Saunders recalls how the land was obtained, the part played by David Tasma's £500 and the involvement of the 'founding patients', of whom we have already heard in Chapter 1:

What happened was I was talking to a group of students on a round and they said 'Where are you going to start?' And I said, 'Well I'm going to have to start with having some land and getting going with it.' And that afternoon, my brother, a chartered surveyor, rang me to say, 'We've found a site down in Sydenham which might do for you.' And I went round this site at the weekend and it was really ideal. And so that was when I came back to the King's Fund, who I'd put in an appeal for money for the site, and rang up Mr Peers who was the Secretary then, and who I'd seen once or twice, and I said we'd found a site. He said, 'Well you'd better put a bid in for it. How much is it?' And I said, '£27,000. It, it's got planning permission for 27 flats.' So he said, 'Well you'd better go ahead.' So with the £500 from David in the bank, I, we bid (we were by that time a small steering committee), we bid that, and the town planners were meeting on the same day as the major part of the King's Fund were meeting to consider my bid for the £27,000.

When I got up that morning I was reading this little book, *Daily Light*, which I mentioned. And I turned over the page and *Daily Light* had, its top text for the day was, 'Thou shalt bless the Lord thy God for the good land which he hath given thee' and by then, I had several of my patients – Louie and Alice and Mr Pettit, and other people – were all praying like beavers. And the Secretary rang me up at about five o'clock to say, 'It, it's alright Dr Saunders – up to £30,000 to pay for the cost of purchase.' And the first person I told was Mr Pettit because he was quite near the new wing, and then I went over to the old wing and told Alice and the others. And Alice, and particularly Louie, said 'We knew we'd get it.' And it was theirs.

The issue of land has been fundamental in the evolution of many hospice projects[4] and proved to be crucial in Northern Ireland. In the following extract, Tom McGinley, Medical Director of Foyle Hospice, Derry reflects on the importance of finding a neutrally located piece of land on which to build in order for the hospice to provide a cross-border service in the Republic of Ireland's Donegal:

It was always my intention that we would start a hospice locally; it was really a matter of deciding when to take the plunge, and that happened about – in the summer of '83. About 1985 we appointed our first two home care sisters, and then the difficult task of looking for a site, which had to be neutral, in other words it had to be in a neutral position because of all the troubles at the time, and we were very lucky that we bought this site here from the Orange Lodge, from the Grand Orange Lodge of Ireland, because it has been described as therapeutically ideal, geographically ideal.[5] One of the things that I was very much aware of was for it to be a success financially and in every other way, that the service had to extend across into Donegal, which at that time was not accepted by many, many people that we should extend our service into another country; but – and that has been proven right since that that decision was right – because a lot

Foyle Hospice, Northern Ireland

The concept of a hospice for the North West of Ireland was triggered by a local GP's visit to an 18-year-old youth dying of cancer. Tom McGinley felt not only his own inadequacy to care for the young man but also the shortcomings of the health care system in general at that time. The resulting challenge was to shape the vision of a hospice for the area. A small Steering Committee was established in early 1984 and intense fund raising began in earnest. The Committee was aware from an early stage that, to be successful, the site for the in-patient unit had to bridge the gap between the two major religious communities of the area. The peaceful site eventually chosen achieved this goal. Phase One of the project was completed in 1985 with the creation of a home care team. With acceptance from local District Nurses and GPs, a high degree of immediate success was ensured. From day one excellent cooperation was gained on both sides of the border. This close cross-border cooperation continued to evolve with the addition of a third Home Care Sister based in Donegal, in the Irish Republic, from January 1989. Phase Two of the

project was completed in 1991, with the opening of a 12-bedded in-patient unit for a catchment area of approximately 250,000 people. In 1999 the Committee agreed to a proposal to upgrade day care by establishing a new and improved day hospice.

of our money does come from Donegal and there is a natural hinter-land here of Inishowen and it would have been stupid to have – to have arranged it otherwise. It was – it became then obvious that our two home care nurses were really very busy, providing a service to many parts of Donegal, and I think about 1987 we provided sort of – again, which was a unique thing – 'Hands Across the Border', where the health board in Donegal and the Minister of Health in Dublin, and ourselves had a major launch, and we appointed another home care sister, employed by the Foyle Hospice, but based in Letterkenny, and basically then it was a question – once we'd bought the land from the Orange Order, really planning – and in June, 20th June 1991, this unit was opened on a glorious Thursday afternoon, and really we've gone on from there. That's – that's basically the background to it.

In many locations, as the hospice ideal began to gain ground, groups of people sought opportunities to lobby for a local development. Individuals with religious affiliations were frequently prominent among those who took the initiative, so a pattern began to emerge as outlined here by Sheila Cassidy, who was Medical Director of St Luke's Hospice, Plymouth, from 1982 to 1997:

The actual St Luke's Hospice in Plymouth had been got together by a group of pious people who had, in fact, gone – one of them had gone to a lecture in London where somebody or other had been talking about care of the dying, and the chap then who – oh I can't remember his name, John – clergyman, can't remember for the moment – anyway, this clergyman who was the vicar of St Andrew's Church, had decided that Plymouth should have its own hospice, and had got a group of people around him and they'd had a big public meeting and they had decided to fund-raise. So this group of people had got together, they'd bought this house, they'd got all their friends, and they'd done the whole thing up. And I think this is a very typical story of hospices of my generation; of a group of Chris-

tian people deciding on a hospice, fund-raising, and putting every heart and soul that they had into it.

In some instances established religious groups, in reflecting upon their aims and purpose in a changing social context, decided on hospice care as a direction for new devel-opments. In Leeds, Sister Cecily Mary Case explains how the Sisters of the Cross and Passion responded to the call from Pope John XXIII for a wider reconsideration of mission; a call which resulted in the founding of St Gemma's Hospice:[6]

We had a second Vatican Council 1963 to '65 and the Pope – who is John XXIII at that time – asked all the religious orders to look at what they were doing and to see if this is what they really should be doing for the good of the country and for the good of people. And what we decided was that, because the education in England and Ireland at that time was quite good and it was free, that we would finish all our, all our private schools where they were paid because those children could go to free schools and that would leave us this place empty. So that was the first decision, that we would close the private school and the second decision was that we would try to find out what would be most needed in Leeds. And Sister Olivia and I were given the task by Sister Seraphine to go out and find out, you know, to do something about it. And so the first thing we did was we went to the Council and asked them what did they consider to be a, a great need and I, I think as far as I can remember they did mention a nursing home but I think we decided that there were enough nursing homes anyway. And we weren't looking for some-thing which was a paying proposition; we were looking for some-thing that was needed. And eventually Sister Olivia heard a radio report on hospices. Hospice was a word that has been used for a long, long time in religion. A hospice is a place where you would get food and shelter for the needy but that was, that was it and we could see how it fulfilled those things because it was a free service and so it was just like carrying on. We, we thought that was very good that it did carry on the religious thing in the first place. So I actually made the first appeal, part of it, in the Town Hall here [in Leeds] and we were very pleased to get £10,000 from the Bishop and it was quite good.

By the close of the 1970s hospice philosophy had captured the imagination of people in many parts of the UK. Fifty-eight hospices were founded between 1981 and 1984 compared with 36 during the previous decade. As a wave of enthusiasm swept the country, there was important work to be done convincing those who already cared for the dying in other capacities that a new form of provision was required. The story of the Northern Ireland Hospice in Belfast is emblematic of this period. Prompted by a group of clergy and health professionals, a public meeting was held in 1979 which encouraged a collaborative approach. An appeal was launched, funds were raised and premises were purchased in 1982. A home care service – staffed by two Macmillan nurses[7] – began the following year and an in-patient unit opened in 1985.[8] Yet it took time for the hospice ideal to be embraced by all sections of the community. In the following extract, Betty Irwin – the first Administrative Director of the hospice – recalls the importance of good relationships, and the positive effect of a long series of 'information meetings':

Well, that was a battle to some extent which the home care nurses, Nursing Director and Medical Director really had to take on. I was not involved very much in that. The home care nurses, I think bore the brunt of it originally, because they were the people who had to talk to GPs, to district nurses about their role and to, to combat the idea, 'Who are these hospice people; we've been looking after dying people for years, what do they know that they are muscling in on our territory?' And there were some – it took a long time in some

areas to persuade some of the GPs, some of the practices to accept it – but once there were patients who were receiving the treatment, and once it became obvious that the home care nurses at any rate were there to assist, to work with, to cooperate and to offer help – their worth was recognised and was accepted and the word spread – and we did – to this extent I had a hand in it – we did have a great many what we called 'information meetings' specifically for doctors and nurses and for ministers of religion in the areas that we invited them by personal invitation to come and to hear and to ask questions and to become aware of what was on offer – to the extent that I think maybe, maybe it took a year in some cases, but certainly once patients were being treated and the word spread that it was a useful service, it was a professional service, it did help – then that became, gathered its own momentum then.

When Richard Hillier arrived at Countess Mountbatten House in Southampton in 1977, he put great store on positive relationships with other professionals and here describes how he sought the cooperation of local consultants and GPs:

In the very early days, because I'd done a huge selling job, I'd gone out and seen all the GPs and seen the hospital consultants, I'd been out and talked to the district nurses and explained what we did and tried very hard not to be too proselytising – it got busy fairly quickly really. And very soon we had more work than we could really cope with, and so we had to start reducing the number of referrals that were coming in. So in order to do that, the next big step we took was that I would go out and see – this was quite unique really – all the patients who were referred. And in the first year doing that we reduced the admissions by over 30 per cent – these were specific requests for terminal care – and 30 per cent of those patients never came in because we actually found that we could handle them at home. And so that was a great move forward. We felt – this is slightly tidied up in retrospect – but I felt that for the first five years what we needed to do was establish the service, if there was a service to be established, because I saw in 20 years we'd be out of work, you know, because everybody, it was pretty easy to do and everybody'd know how to do it, and we wouldn't need to be there. So the first year was to get the service established, and everybody using us in the right way and developing relationships, which I absolutely believe takes a long time. I mean we can work on a very superficial thing with GPs very quickly – but I enjoy GPs when we are hurt, when we are struggling, when they need help and we need to be honest and supportive. I think that's when we're probably at our greatest strength. So that was the first five years, and also, getting us all working together and so forth.

In Scotland, the idea for a hospice in Inverness was prompted by a desire on the part of two nurses to provide more support for patients' families. Lyn Forbes, General Manager of what became Highland Hospice explains:

The founders, shall we say, were two nurses who'd been working in the local hospital.[9] And I understand, and I think this is a true story, that they'd had a particularly harrowing morning with a couple of patients dying and when they took their late cup of coffee they were really talking about how they felt that, perhaps, they'd coped with the death of the patient, and they'd been able to manage that reasonably well, but where they felt that they had not really given sufficient support was to the families. At that time, of course, St Columba's [Edinburgh] and Strathcarron[10] were already established in Scotland along with other hospices, and so they were aware of the hospice movement. And I think, over their mid-morning cup of coffee, this led them to start talking about the possibility of a hospice where the sort of issues that they felt they hadn't been able to address that morning would be a priority. And they spoke to, I think, a consultant in the area, a Dr Finlay Kerr, who worked at Raigmore Hospital; a GP, Dr Sam Marshall; a lawyer, Mr Douglas Graham. And they gathered round them a group of people who were interested in the concept of starting a hospice in the Highlands.

For Malcolm McIllmurray, an oncologist arriving in Lancaster in 1978, a top priority was to provide suitable accommodation for dying patients. When his plans were disclosed locally, he discovered that a hospice committee had already been established and there was widespread interest. The project was launched in 1981 and St John's Hospice opened in 1985:

I do remember that fairly soon after coming here I was very well aware that, in order to set up an effective and comprehensive cancer service, that you did need some facility for patients who were going to die from cancer. There is no point in me setting up something which helps with diagnosis and management and intervention at that end of the spectrum, if at the same time I didn't have some suitable accommodation for people who were going to die from the disease. Now I was very uncertain about how to go about this, but I was aware of the hospice movement. I say 'aware' because I didn't know much more about it than that … So I think it must have been within the first couple of weeks of my arriving in Lancaster, I went to see, Mrs Parker, Lucy Parker was her name. And we sat in her office, she opened the cabinet and pulled out a bottle of gin, and we had a drink together. And the reason I think she was so enthused by our discussion was that she told me that some two years before I'd arrived she had set up a committee which had been to look at establishing a hospice in Lancaster. After we met, of course, she very quickly was on the phone to a number of other people that had been party to these discussions and we, we got together and had some informal meetings about it. But she said to me, 'There's one person that you must meet, because, if we're going to make any progress, then she's going to be crucial to this.' And she took me up to meet a nun, Sister Aine, as she was called – clearly I'd not met her before

– but as soon as we met there was, was something, something had clicked, if I can put it like that. I mean, we developed a very close relationship over the years that we worked on the hospice project, and we were very like-minded. We got on very well as a team, and we always have been very fond of each other, and it's, you know, it's one of those enduring friendships that just happen from time to time.

Raising funds

The importance of fund-raising to the success of hospice projects is difficult to overestimate. As the early hospice movement operated largely outside of the NHS, the issue of fund-raising was a crucial factor in the establishment and maintenance of hospice services. St Christopher's had set a lead, obtaining support from a wide range of grant-giving bodies. The venture was somewhat precarious, however, as considerable sums were required and the financial climate of the early 1960s was rather unstable.[11] Nevertheless, enthusiasm outweighed reticence and the scene was set for the next generation of hospices to follow a similar course.

St Luke's, Sheffield, was one of two regional hospices founded in 1971, the other being St Ann's Hospice, Cheadle. Eric Wilkes, at that time a local GP, recalls how he became involved in the project and how a strategy for establishing the hospice gradually unfolded:

I had joined rather unwillingly the ranks of political agitators, because I'd seen Cicely Saunders' work, I'd surveyed it and found the unmet need locally beyond any argument. I was busy, complacent, quite happy to be a country GP, but I could not rest easily without having a go at Sheffield. And my colleagues were very kind, I mean my consultant colleagues were very kind, as well as GP colleagues. I had as a patient [Sue Osborn] the wife of the Conservative MP, John Osborn, and she became my secretary. Now, being the Conservative MP's wife, she knew all the industrialists very well indeed. She knew the wealthy social life of Sheffield intimately … and she was absolutely invaluable to me, absolutely marvellous. We had the doctors, and we began to have meetings to raise funds and to 'network' in the modern jargon. British Steel at that time was over the hill and was losing a million pounds a day. It could therefore not give us any money but it did offer us one-and-a-half acres, which is where St Luke's is today, as a gift, so long as we built a non-profit-making charitable hospice on that site within five years, and we did it in about two and a half.

I remember we had meetings of my colleagues where Sue Osborn would produce the lists of the very wealthy and influential to these doctors – that was the sort of 'networking' that went on. There were a few influential members of the Regional Health Authority who I tried to contact and was successful. I remember when we began to fund-raise, the Master Cutler that year had been at Cambridge with me and had been a member of the amateur dramatic club with me in my '37 to '39 Cambridge experience and he put on a dinner party to raise funds for St Luke's with some of the most wealthy people. I couldn't get Cicely Saunders to come, she was doing something different, but we got her deputy, Dame Albertine Winner,[12] and Dame Albertine was the civil servant in charge of all the NHS hospitals in the UK, so she was pretty senior stuff. And by that time we'd got a little cardboard plan of St Luke's, we'd chosen the site, and we'd got the Duchess of Devonshire to be its patron and to come to this dinner. And Dame Albertine spoke after the dinner and we showed them the plans, and the whole hospice in its original form cost us £120,000 to build. And after that dinner we had raised £30,000, which isn't bad for one dinner party held by the Master Cutler with a rather sort of uncouth country doctor coming in to tell them what to do.

The fund-raising and administrative role played by Sue Osborn (later Sue Duffing) was crucial at this time. She describes how she became involved:

Eric Wilkes was our GP, and he'd been doing some research in hospitals in Sheffield and finding a very depressing picture of the patients who had cancer and had nowhere to go. And this is what prompted him to start at least trying to raise money for a hospice. He didn't like calling it a 'hospice', he preferred to call it a 'nursing home' … But … he came to my husband one day who had access to charitable trust funds in Sheffield, and asked John if he thought he could ask these charitable trusts for funds. I was listening to this conversation, and I said to Eric, 'Is there anything I can do to help?' And – 'Oh.' He said '… yes, you can be my secretary.' And that was how I got involved. And we had, then, to form a Management Committee, and raise the money, and that was done in a very basic way.

We got together a marvellous Management Committee. It was very broadly based, and they were marvellous, very helpful people, all of them. We literally thought of all the people in the industry that

Eric Wilkes, hospice founder in Sheffield: 'I'd surveyed it and found the unmet need locally beyond any argument.'

we knew, then we added to it by going through the telephone book, and picking out all the industries, the names of firms that we knew of, and obviously some that we'd never even heard of in Sheffield. I had been brought up in Sheffield and I knew quite a lot of people in the industrial side of the city. And we literally wrote letters to everybody. In addition we were given a book of all the charities, and we went through that with a toothcomb. And we had to decide which ones we thought would support a medical project. When we wrote to them, each letter had to be slightly different to each charity according to what we thought they might be able to do to help us.

Local benefactors have played important roles in the founding of hospices. In the following extract, Peter Griffiths tells how, after a period attending a course at St Christopher's in 1977, he became involved in raising funds for a hospice in his home town of Swansea, and how grateful he was for the support of one particular local person. As a result, matched funding was secured from the National Society for Cancer Relief[13] – and the hospice, Ty Olwen, opened in 1981:

I came back to Swansea and I wrote to the National Society for Cancer Relief; a very naive letter, as I see it now, saying, 'How do you set up a hospice?' And they sent a most surprising reply back: 'Strange you should ask,' they said, 'we have approached West Glamorgan Health Authority with the offer of funding a hospice, and have had a reply to say that nobody down there is interested.' Well I immediately got in touch with the Health Authority and they dusted off the files and they said, 'Well, we didn't think anybody was.' And from there, until I went away in September to work at St Christopher's, I got involved with setting up an Appeals Committee and a Fund-raising Committee, and talking to the population of West Glamorgan, showing them a film about hospice care, and telling them what it was all about, and asking them to go out to their various areas where they lived and start raising funds. And another thing that I did before I went, was I

Peter Griffiths: 'I came back to Swansea and I wrote to the NSCR … saying "How do you set up a hospice?"'

approached a lady who was well known as a fund-raiser locally for good causes, Mrs J.T. Morgan, Mrs Olwen Morgan. And I remember being entertained to tea, in her very genteel way, and being given a flat refusal. She had become involved in so many things that she didn't want to take anything else on board, 'But do come in and have some tea anyway. Do stay and have some tea.' And over tea she asked me, 'What is this hospice thing about?' And I tried to explain to her, and at the end of it she said, 'Well this is just one more thing that I've got to take on.' And she agreed to chair the Appeals Committee.

And this carried on after I went up to London, and during the time that I was up [at St Christopher's] I frequently travelled back for fund-raising events or to speak to audiences in Swansea for the purpose of fund-raising. And by 1980, early 1980, the fund had raised £250,000. Now, initially what the National Society for Cancer Relief had said – in those days they used to match pound for pound on condition that the Health Authority took over the running of the unit once it was built – initially they said they wanted £200,000, and this was raised fairly quickly. But they came back to us and said, 'It

doesn't look as if we can help because we're going to need more than that. We're going to need £250,000.' And I'll never forget Mrs J.T. Morgan, in a meeting in Mount Pleasant Chapel, said, 'We've got £250,000, and if you up the stakes, we've got £300,000.' So they matched our £250,000 pound for pound to build a 25-bedded hospice. The Health Authority provided the land, and we were very lucky in that it was put down in what was then a mature garden, and the footings and the main services … it was to cover a population of half a million. And by late 1980, the building was underway.

Hundreds of miles to the north, but also concerned with raising funds, for a hospice in Glasgow, Ann Gilmore describes how a significant donation for what became the Prince and Princess of Wales Hospice appeared from an unexpected source:

I went to a party, at Christmas, and was talking to a man at the party about death, dying, grief and bereavement. What else do you talk about at parties? And saying that what we needed for Glasgow was a hospice, and he said, 'Well, why don't you come and speak to our workers' – he worked in Black & White Whisky, big plant that's now defunct, actually – 'because our ladies in the bottling plant are very charitable, they might give you some money.' So, he was quite persistent as well, because he'd had a loss in his family. And the thing was that the things that I was saying were reverberating in people. And I went along to speak to these ladies in the bottling plant. And what they did was they kind of put the tops on the bottles – it was hand done – and they had a swear box and they had coffee evenings and bingo nights and all that. And they would take any of the monies and put it into a box, and at the end of the year they would maybe give it to a charity, two or three charities and so on. So I went along and I spoke to about half a dozen of them between shifts, told them what I felt. And once again, they'd all had experience. If you live long enough, you lose people and you know what [grief] is, and you

Ann Gilmore and the Prince and Princess of Wales Hospice, Glasgow

Founded by a group of clergy seeking to establish a hospice in the Glasgow area in the early 1980s, and working with Ann Gilmore, a local GP, this hospice was gifted by the city of Glasgow to Prince Charles and Lady Diana Spencer on the occasion of their marriage in 1981. A home care service began in the autumn of 1985. On 15 May 1989 a day care and eight-bed residential facility was opened at Carlton Place on the south bank of the River Clyde and in the summer of 1999 a new day care centre was completed. See www.ppwh.org.uk.

maybe see mismanagement of your nearest and dearest and your relatives and yourself. And at the end of the meeting they all went into a wee huddle in the corner and then turned round and said, 'We've decided to give you all of our money.' And I was expecting something like £40 and it was £4,000. So that was – I mean that was a lot of money in '79. So I felt kind of duty-bound that I had to do something about it then. I was terrified, you know, when they wrote out the cheque and more or less gave it to me like that, 'cause I wasn't sure what I was doing, you know.

Graham Perolls, who established the Ellenor Foundation Home Care Service, Dartford in 1984, also discovered an unexpected source of funding at an early stage in the process. New to the hospice world, he attended a conference in Manchester where a chance meeting with a fellow delegate became a defining moment for the Foundation:

We were fortunate to start with a sum of £50,000 from a family trust to actually put something into motion, because the Health Authority wasn't interested at the beginning when I went to them, they weren't giving any money towards it. I think they were very sceptical that I could get anything off the ground. So I went with the director of nursing for the community up to London to see Macmillan because I'd done a little bit of research and found that most of the services seemed to start with a Macmillan grant but, having spoken to the chap in charge at that time – that was a Major Garnett[14] – I felt it wasn't the way that we wanted to go. I felt that, even though it was tempting to take the money for a grant for one or two Macmillan nurses, I felt that it might hamper us in the future if we wanted to develop in our own way. So we reluctantly turned down the offer of that money and decided to set up a service that responded to the need locally and the resources we were able to find.

We started fund-raising from day one – I did that. And people were very generous. I had absolutely no experience. I don't think I'd ever asked anybody for a penny in my life. I came from a fairly comfortable background so I'd had no need to ask for money, so it was a completely new experience for me to actually write letters asking for money. But I had one really big breakthrough in the early days which I'm really eternally grateful for and that was, I went to – I felt in the early days that I should try and learn as much as I possibly could about hospice care – and so I enrolled on various conferences just so that I could feel that I could know what I was talking about really. And the first conference I went on was the Hospice Administrators' Conference which was held up in Manchester. And after one of the sessions I decided to go for a walk – I'd never actually been to Manchester before – and there was a revolving door in the hotel and I managed to somehow to push round the wrong way and bumped into another gentleman who was also exiting, and he had been at the conference, I didn't know who he was, and we walked along the road together and started talking, and he asked some very pertinent questions and I told him my personal story which was very fresh in my mind then. And I then asked who he was and he told me that he was a director of a large grant-making trust and that I should write to him. And when I got back, which I did, and it was an absolutely incredible experience, you know, when I opened the letter and the reply was that they would like to fund two nurses for three years, and that was just, you know, an incredible feeling to know that we had secure money for two of our nurses. That was the Tudor Trust, I'm sure they won't mind my saying that.[15] And in those days they were funding a lot of hospice care. I mean I'd never heard of them, I didn't know such Trusts even existed. And they've helped us over the years in quite an incredible way.

Being Tom McGinley's son, hospice fund-raising has been part and parcel of Ciaran McGinley's life experiences from an early age. In the following extract, he explains how he organised a wide variety of fund-raising activities to support Foyle Hospice in Northern Ireland, which opened in 1985:

Well because my father's the chairperson and the leading person from the hospice, it's really been all of my life I've been involved with the hospice movement. My main input probably began in fund-raising about maybe 15, 16 years ago[16] and that would have just been taking part in flag days and collections and door-to-door collections, you know, things like that. My first major fund-raising event that I organised was in 1990 when I took part in the London Marathon, along with my father and two other people. And then in 1994 I organised a group of 20 people to go to New York to run the New York Marathon. So that would have been my first major fund-raising initiative in relation to, you know, the fund-raising for the hospice and since then you know we've done many fund-raising events and taken part in many fund-raising activities. We did the Boston Marathon; we've had a trip to Nepal; we've had different car

draws and a lot of different types of draws. 1985 was the first, I think, major fund-raising of the venture, it was the Foyle Female Five which we're running again this year. And then obviously in the year 1991 we had our official opening of this building and we're celebrating our 10 years next year, our tenth anniversary. So I've really grown up with the whole philosophy of the hospice and I've listened to it right through school and you know into my professional life.

Several respondents observed how raising funds is an ever-present task in the hospice context, with the service itself ultimately dependent upon it. Ann Cooney, administrator at the Northern Ireland Southern Area Hospice Services (formerly Newry Hospice, which itself evolved out of a small hospital run by nuns), speaks here of the importance of fund-raising and the inevitable worry associated with it:

Fund-raising was a whole new area for us 'cause we never, ever had anything, we had our own money and that was a big change for us, so getting a fund-raising committee off the ground, working with them, trying to get money from the community. Publicity, again in the past we wouldn't have had to do a lot of publicity, we had a sort of a history, and it was word of mouth and consultants referred patients, now we had to sort of publicise the aims of the hospice to raise the money and also to, to ensure patients came in. So I think not too dissimilar to today, so when it comes to capital improvements we don't have any money, so we've made some lottery applications and we've had success from one and we're waiting another one, but it means that the building is a 30-year-old building and there's lots of work could be done. The hospice itself when it was, we started it in 1989, it was refurbished then but since then it's just getting sort of a coat of paint here and something else there. Even equipment, I mean the nurses would look for additional, you know, special beds and we're trying to do them sort of one at a time but it will be nice now to have a sort of an injection of capital funds that we could sort of upgrade the unit. I think it would be also nice to have maybe more government funding, not necessarily 50:50, but maybe even 40:60, 'cause you would have something to start your year on, where it is, we're down to about 20:80, so that's, I mean, it's very considerable and it's always a worry.[17]

New service, new care

In this section we trace the growth of innovative work as hospice services got under way and began actively to deliver services. As hospices became established a particular feature of their work was the concern to produce a welcoming atmosphere; a special ambience that reminded patients of home. Margaret Carradice, Matron at St Luke's, Sheffield, speaks of the kind of atmosphere that they sought to create there:

It was very much like home – no rules and regulations. We were very small. We just had 25 beds, no day unit or anything else. And it was because there was a proportion of patients who were up and about and just in for symptom control, then it was a very homely atmosphere, in no way depressing, because you had got this proportion of patients. I mean when the 'Georgian' houses were built opposite, we used to take patients down to look at the show house. We used to take patients in the woods. It was a very relaxed, well some would call it, hotel.

Alongside this new atmosphere was a different approach to care. Patients received information about their condition and were consulted about their preferences. Families were included in a way which was previously unknown. It was this innovative approach towards patients and their families which impressed Jo Hockley on her arrival at St Christopher's.

The contrast with other institutions was remarkable. From a point of exclusion outside of the hospice, the family had almost become a unit of care within it:

I would say that my father's death hadn't really influenced me: if anything it had been, you know, my conversations with my brother, and then just going along and seeing it for myself, and very much having the opportunity to care for people in a way that I'd always wanted to care for people, having the time to give them and, you know, the supportive, multidisciplinary team, us all working together for the sake of the patient and the family and that was quite unique for St Christopher's because, when I did my training in the '70s, we still had visiting, you know, seven to eight in the evenings and two to three on a Wednesday. It was almost as though the hospital 'owned' patients in that time. So the family were quite excluded until somebody was imminently dying and then they would be allowed in, but there was no real getting to know the family as people – you'd give information across – whereas it was almost as though the family were the unit of care at St Christopher's, and that was very impressive.

A feature of this new approach was the development of the multidisciplinary team,[18] and an appreciation of the contribution which could be made by others. In the following extract, Richard Lamerton explains how his experience of the development of the multidisciplinary team brought him new insights into working practices:

I suddenly realised that I never would, ever again, want to practise medicine without having a healer at my side in the team. And the more I watched, the more I learnt. Acupuncture: I humbly went along to the acupuncturist with a tennis elbow that I'd got from pushing slides together when I was doing all my American lecturing, pressing the slides together, and I got this dreadful tennis elbow ... And she cured it in two stabs. Well, I mean, that was ridiculous. And I stopped being cynical, and I decided that what doctors have to do really, is grow up and stop feeling so threatened by everything and everybody, and go out there and be humble and listen to the patients, and listen to other people who have things to say. And this whole concept of the palliative care team, that we have here,[19] grew up. And we've grown into a family. The same team has been working together now for nearly 10 years. There've been additions but the core team is still the same people, and we know each other profoundly well, and patients are amazingly served by this approach.

Very quickly after the establishment of St Christopher's in 1967 there was a realisation that, if the hospice were to achieve its maximum effect, some patients would need to be cared for at home. Mary Baines, a former GP, tells how she established the first home care service with Barbara McNulty, who had been a district nurse:

I joined St Christopher's in April '68, and Cicely of course, from the beginning, knew that we needed a home care service, but I don't think really – and she wouldn't mind me saying this – had any perception about people being very ill and dying at home, because she'd never worked in the community. And so she looked around St Christopher's – there weren't a lot of people to choose from. And I'd been a GP then for 10 years when I came here, so that's the span from qualifying to coming here. And then of course there was Barbara McNulty, who'd been a district nurse and was a ward sister on Alexandra Ward. And so she approached the two of us as to whether we would be the start of the first home care service. And that would have started in 1969. Now looking back at it, I think this was, again, a revolutionary thing to do. Because it was very difficult in the home: you either said to GPs and district nurses that you thought they were all doing the job brilliantly, in which case there was no point having a home care service; or you said that they were not doing very well, which of course puts everybody's back up. So

it was a very difficult thing to start in the community. And I think it was helped by the fact that I was a GP, really, rootedly, and she was a district nurse. And I'm sure she's told you this, but the very wise thing about it was that instead of just starting the service and saying this is it, that she mostly, and to a lesser extent myself, went round district nurses and GPs in this whole community, and said, 'You'll be familiar with the work at St Christopher's. There's a suggestion that we do launch out and do something in the community. What sort of service would you like?'

Soon after the establishment of home care at St Christopher's, similar initiatives were underway at St Joseph's in Hackney – the working class area of East London. Yet a home care service required transport, and the hospice had to scrutinise its staff to find a nurse who could drive. Eventually, Sister Mary Antonia agreed to join the home care team and Richard Lamerton here comments wryly on his experience of London traffic, seen from the inside of Sister Mary Antonia's car:[20]

Home care began with discharging half a dozen patients from the hospice; they went home and we followed them up with a GP's consent, and we found that they needed a lot of follow-up because the district nurses hadn't a clue how to look after them, neither had the GPs, and most of them were only too glad when I made a suggestion about what to do to stop the pain, or whatever it was. Then one of the GPs said to me; she had some more patients who were dying at home, would we be prepared to visit them even though they'd never been in the hospice? And so I said yes. And that's when I went to the Reverend Mother and said, 'I need a nurse to help me,' and Sister Antonia was taken off one of the wards. Cicely Saunders always spoke of Antonia with reverence. She was a damn good ward sister, and very, very perceptive, very wise old bird, very clever, though she drove a car like a fiend. And on the dashboard she had this little statue of Mary which had sharp edges on it, it was quite dangerous, and of course we didn't have safety belts in those days. And I said to her, 'Sister, if ever you stop suddenly, that Virgin Mary could put your eye out.' 'Well, of all the things to suggest, now. As if the holy statue of the Virgin … Did you know that came from Rome? As if that could do any harm.' And then she splashed holy water around the car before setting off. And I said, 'What's that for?' you see, because all this was so new to me. I said, 'What on earth are you doing with that?' And this was to ensure that we had a safe journey. So I said, 'Sister, if you just drive 20 miles an hour slower … we'd, you know, God'd be even more sympathetic.' And that made her really angry, and her nostrils flared and she set her teeth and put her foot down. And ooooh! We went up Cambridge Heath Road. Aaaah! Dodging in and out of cars and generally putting the fear of God – which was the whole idea, of course; why was she else a nun? – into the whole of the traffic. Well, Sister Antonia was just amazing.

Sister Mary Antonia, in her own interview, tacitly acknowledges the character of the journeys:

In the early days, when I worked with Dr Lamerton, I was doing a bit of everything. So I did the best I could … I had lots of energy and a bit of a car, sometimes places looked so different at night from what they did in the day, you know; I used to wonder was I in the right road or not? [laughter][21]

In addition to hospice care in the home, the possibility of a hospice approach in the hospital setting – what by the late 1970s was starting to be called 'palliative care' – was not lost on innovative clinicians, and Thelma Bates explains how she came to set up the first palliative care support team at St Thomas's Hospital, London. After taking up an appointment at St Thomas's in 1968, she came to realise that end of life care was not as good as it could be. Consequently she developed a mutually beneficial relationship with St Christopher's,

and eventually conceived the idea of a hospital support team based on a similar innovation at St Luke's Hospital, New York; a plan which came to fruition in 1977.[22]

I became a consultant at St Thomas's in 1968. And I think, from fairly early on, it was apparent that we were good at treating cancer but not particularly good at looking after patients at the end of their life. And I think I was aware of that before I met Cicely Saunders. I met Cicely Saunders soon after the opening of St Christopher's Hospice, because she, of course, too, came via social work and via medicine from St Thomas's Hospital. So within a few days of St Christopher's being opened, I went to St Christopher's, met Cicely, saw the hospice and I think that in 1974 or '75, Cicely suggested that Dr Mary Baines, who was on her staff, would spend a week with me at St Thomas's and see how a radiotherapy department worked. And Mary Baines came and spent this week which was absolutely pivotal in everything that happened next, because she was amazed at what radiotherapy could do for patients with advanced cancer in relation to controlling pain and various other symptoms with radiotherapy and chemotherapy. She had no idea what radiotherapy and chemotherapy could do. So she invited me back to spend a little time, the odd day, at St Christopher's. And from that came the suggestion that I would go to St Christopher's and start a regular round there. And I went round the patients at St Christopher's about every three months, spent a whole day there and would offer treatment with radiotherapy and chemotherapy at St Thomas's for patients for whom treatment was appropriate, short treatment, a single dose of radiotherapy or simple chemotherapy. As a result of that it seemed to me that so much that they had to offer I could import into St Thomas's, whereas what I had, they were importing from me.

I learnt, from Cicely, about St Luke's Hospital[23] in New York, who wanted a hospice, couldn't afford the beds, so started an in-acute hospital team. And the St Luke's team was my model. And I went over to New York, saw what they did and then devised a plan.

I started planning in 1976. And I had about a year of consultation, getting approval, and then doing the detailed planning of finding an office and deciding what sort of staff and getting approval. The plan was to have a team that would supplement existing care without taking over. We did not want beds. I just wanted skills. And we would be a roving team within, what was then an 800–900-bedded acute hospital. It was not going to be part of the department of radiotherapy and oncology. I was going to give my time as the leader without charge, as a volunteer. And the original plan was to have two nursing sisters who had experience of hospice work, i.e. somebody who worked at St Christopher's. And I knew that there was at least one that would like to come to St Thomas's and do that work. Her name was Barbara Saunders. I knew that I didn't have all of the skills, although I'd been to St Christopher's I didn't have all of their skills, so I wanted to have a junior doctor working with me who I would teach radiotherapy and oncology, who had worked at St Christopher's. And that doctor was Dr Andrew Hoy who subsequently trained and qualified as a radiotherapist and oncologist and then, many years later, went back into pure hospice work and is now Medical Director of Princess Alice Hospice in Esher.

So the original plan was: two part-time nurses; half-time social worker; me; my junior trainee doctor with experience in palliative medicine; and the hospital Chaplain. We didn't have a secretary, so the budget was two nurses and half a social worker. I got approval, in fact, for one nurse, not two. And I wrote a simple proposal on one side of a piece of paper, I wrote a simple financial summary, other side of the piece of paper, which if my memory serves me right, was something like £12,500 per year in those days. I managed to get some joint funding with the Borough for the social worker, so I managed to cut down on that side. And the Chaplain was very supportive. And so that was the plan. I had of course to sell the idea to the hospital, and that meant consulting with ward sisters, with doctor colleagues, with head of social work and social work

department, indeed with everybody to get approval. I did it individually. I did not do it by calling everybody together, because I knew there were territorial problems, and if I got a lot of doctors together they would think of a thousand reasons why they did not want me to be interfering with the care of their patients.

We actually began in September 1977 with: Barbara Saunders; Andrew Hoy; part-time social worker, Mike Stevens; the Chaplain; and me. And we began in one room, with one telephone, and no secretary. We began on four friendly wards. By 'friendly wards' – each ward was about 20 beds, had a sister who was happy to work with us and the medical consultants staffing those wards were happy to have us. There were two surgical and two gynaecological wards. They all had cancer patients on the wards. I should say that at St Thomas's we didn't, until very recently, have dedicated cancer wards; if they were gynaecological, they were on the gynae wards; if they were surgical, they were on the surgical wards. So we began on those four wards. And because of Andrew Hoy's skills and Barbara Saunders' skills, which they brought from St Christopher's, we were able to control symptoms that these patients' own doctors had not been able to control. And so we had early success in terms of having patients who had their symptoms controlled, who had a good deal more support than they had otherwise in terms of social/psychological/spiritual type support.[24]

Day care has come to be regarded as a common feature of hospice provision but it was some time before the first service came into being in the UK. Marjory Cockburn, who began her work as administrative sister at St Luke's, Sheffield in 1974, here describes how the first hospice day care unit came to be established:

Though I didn't realise it before I came here, once I was here it was made clear that part of my role was to plan for, and open, the Day Unit. St Luke's was the first hospice to open a Day Unit, so nobody really knew very much about it. During this time also we knew that we had to employ someone who would be available to go out and assess the situation at home, invite people to come to the Day Unit, and be the community link person. And that person was Sheila Bellamy. She was already well known and so that was a tremendous help. So she and I worked a lot together before the Day Unit ever opened. Many people, as you can imagine, were very critical of this move for day care because – and this was professionals, who said, 'Well, if you're dying, how come you can come to day care?' But we had an answer, really, which was based on our practice in St Luke's, because we were finding that patients were coming in, largely in need of symptom control – because we have to remember that the years I'm talking about, symptom control was hardly known. So of course many of our patients came in to have their symptoms controlled, improved dramatically, and were able to go home again. Now because, out in the community, so little was known, doctors didn't know how to continue what we'd started, they didn't know how to increase medication. It was a very scary area, understandably. And so, before long, these same patients would be coming back in again, back into problems, needing to be sorted out, going home again. And so that we were saying, 'Oh, it'll be marvellous to have day care, because we can bring them back for a day a week and advise on symptom control to the practices. In this way the GPs will be helped, they will gradually learn more from what we're doing, and it'll be much better for the patients than coming in and out like yo-yos.' So, because we had those arguments, which were very valid ones, we had our answer to give and so we were able to proceed.

Before we opened the Day Unit, we did have tremendous arguments about whether we should open five days a week or whether we should only start three days a week. And I was absolutely adamant that I preferred to start five days a week with, perhaps, three patients a day, rather than six patients three times a week. And we started with three patients a day and I think people got

tired of asking me, as the opening date got nearer; 'Well, how are you going to do it?' And all I would say was, 'Well, we'll have to wait and see.' I would not agree that from such-and-such a time we'd have an hour's occupational therapy, and from such-and-such a time we'd have an hour's physiotherapy, 'cause I knew it wouldn't work out like that, particularly when my colleagues of the different professions were responsible for 25 patients in the ward as well, as indeed was I. And so we worked it out together, just slowly, deciding what was best. Again it depended on the type of patients we had. And so we got going.

We had our official opening by the Duchess of Kent on the 4th of December, which was a red-letter day, it was the first time that a Royal had come. We all learned a lot about that too, but it was very, very exciting and gave the Unit a really good start. Christmas came, we decided we'd have to have a Christmas party, so we had our first Day Unit Christmas party. Gathered up all our patients from the five days, I think by then we were up, mostly, to five a day. And it was, it was a wonderful party because a lot of them were people living alone. We decorated the room, it looked really super, and we were absolutely overcome because so many of them came in the door, stopped, and were so overcome themselves to see all that had been done to make it look nice, and were saying things like; 'This is the only party I'll have this Christmas,' or, 'This is going to be my last Christmas and you've given us this party.' So the whole thing went off superbly, really, and Tony Crowther – who's now the Medical Director – dressed up as Father Christmas and did the honours.

In the corridor of the Day Unit, we had a board on which we put the names of the patients who were coming and the day on which they were coming. And in these early weeks and months, Eric [Wilkes] would saunter down the corridor to look at the board and would say things like, 'Well, why have you only got five patients instead of nine?' or something like that, you know, so Sheila and I developed a habit of standing in front of the board when we saw him coming with all our necessary armour of reasons why today we only had five instead of whatever. The other thing was, of course, these were dying patients and some of them wouldn't come for many weeks but it still gave them a different quality of life for the last weeks, and it certainly gave their families, if they had any, a break. And our philosophy was, 'A day off for the carers, a day out for the patient.' Well, after a while, I mean, he stopped doing that because … he had to realise opening the Day Unit was quite a gamble in a way. I don't like that word very much, but I think it's the only word to use to describe it.[25]

The development of day units was not confined to hospices, however, and Thelma Bates tells how the UK's first hospice-style, but hospital-based day unit came into being at St Thomas's Hospital, London:

We established a day care centre in a piece of unused ground floor accommodation at the very far end of St Thomas's, which allowed us to have larger office space and a day care centre which we functioned on three days a week. We raised the money for the day care centre through the Richard Dimbleby Cancer Fund.[26] I had helped my then boss look after Richard Dimbleby when he was ill, and eventually died with his malignancy in the 1960s. So they funded the day care centre. And we gradually expanded until we reached the situation where we had four community nurses, three hospital nurses, three doctors including Andrew Hoy and myself and the research fellow.

And we gradually moved into better premises. I was walking around the hospital one day trying to get some copies of my slides. And I went to the photographic department because they hadn't sent them down to the department, and while I was hanging around in the dingy, dark place, with the black blinds down, and lots of filing cabinets, I happened to pull a black blind aside and there was this vision of the Houses of Parliament and the Thames. And it seemed

Thelma Bates: 'St Thomas's Hospital had never seen anything so beautiful as this day care centre.'

to me that this was ridiculous, that we would have a photographic department in a prime site on the first floor of St Thomas's right adjacent to beautiful lifts. So, after a bit of battle, we managed to persuade the authorities to move the St Thomas's photographic department into a Portakabin in the grounds, and we moved into this very large space on the first floor of the brand new wing of St Thomas's.

There was glass running all the way round two sides, and a fleet of offices beyond, and we turned that into a really most beautiful day care centre, with a separate community office, separate hospital nurses' office, good secretariat, computer-equipped, and we had beautiful equipment. The Richard Dimbleby Trust funded the complete refurbishment of this space. I mean it was beautiful, with beautiful painted furniture, and beautiful chairs, and wonderful interlined curtains – like St Thomas's Hospital had never seen anything so beautiful as this day care centre. I mean, not anything like any other part of the hospital; beautiful interior. I mean a top, top interior designer did the interior. And that was our base. It even had a little kitchen where patients could learn to – re-learn to scramble an egg and get confidence. Out-patients came in, and in-patients came into the day care centre as does all the day care centres today. But I think it was fairly new in those days.

As we saw in Chapter 1, the world's first children's hospice was founded by Sister Frances Dominica, at that time the Superior General of the Anglican Society of All Saints Sisters of the Poor, based in Oxford. The hospice idea grew out of her relationship with a little girl called Helen, who developed a brain tumour when she was two years old. The tumour was successfully removed but Helen's brain suffered severe, irreversible damage. As she provided respite care for Helen, Sister Frances Dominica considered founding a home-from-home that would assist other children in similar circumstances. Land was available in the gardens of All Saints Convent and planning permission was eventually granted. The hospice accepted its first two children in 1982 and grad-ually pieced together the form of care which Sister Frances Dominica, and Helen's family, considered most appropriate:

During the spring and the summer of 1980, Helen's parents and I would spend hours on the floor of their sitting-room working out what would be acceptable, what would be the best, what would Helen like, what would they find appropriate for Helen really? And we decided it must be small; we wouldn't go into double figures so that's why we've got eight, rooms for eight sick children at a time maximum; and we decided that home must be the model both in architecture and in the kind of care that we would offer; that the care would be family-driven – they would tell us how they care for their child at home and how they would like us to care for their child

here; we would learn skills that they had learnt, so in every way we would try to be a short-term alternative to home.

Because, there was no existing children's hospice anywhere in the world, I turned quite naturally to people who were working in the adult hospice world, and the first person I wrote to was Dame Cicely Saunders, who wrote me back a brief but fairly definitive letter saying, 'Don't do it.' And in fact we did a double presentation on a platform recently and I reminded her in front of the audience … And when it was her turn to speak at this conference she said, 'Probably what I said to Sister was what I would say to somebody coming to me telling me they wanted to get married: "Don't do it unless you absolutely have to!"' Of course that brought the house down. But she has become a friend and has been very supportive actually in recent years.[27]

Alongside these developments in Oxford, Ann Goldman was taking an interest in paediatric palliative care at Great Ormond Street Hospital for Children in London. After her experiences in a laboratory-based research post, she realised that her interests really lay in paediatric psycho-oncology. Consequently, she set about establishing a hospital-based palliative care team which would become involved with children in Great Ormond Street's 'shared care' hospitals from the time of diagnosis; provide families with a home-based palliative care service; and give more psychosocial support:

It became clear to me that, although I was interested in paediatric oncology, it was not the lab-based end of it I liked, it was the psycho-social end, and all the way through paediatrics that I'd done so far, it had always been much more of the interaction between the medical and the psychosocial that had been of interest to me. So … I began to think about what would I really like to be doing. And there were lots of people who had very specific interests in different tumour types … but nobody was focusing on the psychosocial aspects so much, and particularly not the palliative care aspects. And I knew about the work of Cicely Saunders and St Christopher's and the adult hospice movement, which was at that time very cancer-based, and there was just the beginning in the paediatric cancer centres – there were about 20 round the country – of a recognition that, perhaps we should be having some particular people with an interest in the psychosocial aspects, and the palliative care aspects, and the pain management, symptom management.

And there was one of the ward sisters, on our ward here, who was very interested in that. And we developed an idea of establishing a symptom care team within the unit. We wanted our team to be able to offer palliative care realistically to families at home, if that's what they wanted, and we were aware that there were families who would have liked to have taken their child home but couldn't, or didn't feel they had enough support to do so, and that was one of the areas we wanted to change. But we also wanted to be involved with families from the time of diagnosis to help with the shared care, which we do a lot of, with the liaison and communication between Great Ormond Street and its shared care hospitals, and to have the ability to go out and see the children across and link that much more. And we also wanted to be able to offer more to the families in the way of psychosocial support throughout the disease. So those were the three prongs, in a way, that we developed the team on.

I developed the idea for the team, and the proposal, and I took it to the consultants here, who were very positive and interested at the time but said there was no money for it, and they said if I could find the money they would be very glad to have me. So in the meanwhile I went away and I was a locum general paediatric consultant at the Central Middlesex [Hospital] for a year while I tried to find a charity or a fund that would sponsor the team. And eventually I did find someone who had established some nursing posts in other cities, which was called the Rupert Fund,[28] and they agreed to fund me and two nurses in the first instance to set up the team, which

we started in 1986. And I did that actually as a senior registrar, not as a consultant, I think because it was such a new idea and the consultants here wanted to feel that they still had the charge of their patients and they weren't sure what I'd shape up like. So I came back from being a locum consultant to being a senior registrar and set the team up here.

I think the children's hospice, or palliative care movement, really began in the mid-1980s, and there were several different branches developing. So it's a bit like a jigsaw puzzle where you get scattered pieces and you don't know what the whole picture's going to be at first … And clearly Helen House was just setting up in the mid-1980s and the whole children's hospice area was one aspect of that. And then the other aspect was the children's cancer model, which was what I was part of, and eventually over the late '80s and early '90s all the children's cancer centres developed teams where there were nurses, or in our case nurses and doctor, involved in being able to offer home care and palliative care and develop palliative

Ann Goldman: 'It's children with all life-threatening diseases that need palliative care.'

care expertise for the children with cancer. So that the children who had life-threatening illnesses that were cancer related got quite a lot more sophisticated support right from the mid-1980s.

And I think one of the really big differences between adult and paediatric palliative care is that in paediatrics we've tried to be aware right from the start, initially slightly separately with the hospices and the cancer model, but very quickly trying to put together that it's children with all life-threatening diseases that need palliative care. And adult palliative care came to this very much later.

Hospices from the outset have made extensive use of volunteers. Some of them staff the reception area, arrange visits or raise funds; others provide a transport service or bring a pet for a patient to handle. Marilyn Relf recalls how a new concept for volunteers – supporting the bereaved on a person-to-person level – was introduced at Sir Michael Sobell House, Oxford:

When we started to plan the Service, I went on a training day with the Volunteer Centre and met Yvonne Cannon who was a trainer for the Volunteer Centre, and was also involved in helping projects get set up. And I immediately recognised in her a great skill, and asked her if she would meet up and help us look at the training that would be needed. And in fact she ran our first two training courses, or the bulk of our first two training courses, for us. She turned out to be a very, very skilled trainer, but also with a background in psychotherapy and extensive experience of working with volunteers. So in fact she brought together a lot of the things that we needed, and she became our external consultant to the project, and still is. So she's been with us from the drawing-board right the way through, and has just been a terrific source of, well, ideas; someone to turn to when the going gets rough; and to, and to help us keep – she's also somebody who has got a background in management training and acts as a consultant to various other bodies; so she's helped us

to look at the management implications of what we're doing as the Service has grown, too, so we've been extremely fortunate with her.

We had looked at what Cruse were doing, and we turned to St Christopher's for the model of how to, to move forward. We very much based ourselves on their model. At that time Elisabeth Earnshaw-Smith and Paddy Yorkstone were running the St Christopher's Bereavement Service. And we had, they were just terrific in sharing things with us and talking things through. And we went on to do quite a lot of joint training together … at various conferences in the mid- to late 1980s. And … Susan Le Poidevin[29] was using and extending Colin Murray Parkes's work, and to an extent William Worden's, in that she was saying, 'These are good frameworks, but they don't actually help you when you're actually faced with a bereaved person.' And we set out feeling that … we wanted to learn from bereaved people what they needed. We wanted to try out this project and see if it fitted, and if it didn't we'd change it and we'd try something else, but we didn't want to start off with any preconceived ideas about how much support people would need, and what level of support they would need. We didn't see the volunteers as counsellors, we saw them as offering help 'human being-to-human being'. We felt that for most people that would be sufficient. And that people who would need more, would need counselling or therapy, would be very much in the minority, and we were basing that on Colin's work, really.

We used 'risk assessment', again talking to Colin Murray Parkes about it, taking what he said was the 'St Christopher's best' model, and then adapting it with him to take into account more recent research. So our 'vulnerability questionnaire': we started to use that in 1986. I think, I think we did have some preconceived ideas, even though we thought we hadn't. I think we did expect people to grieve, to work through grief. And we were a bit, we felt, I think of the ideas that were around then, were very much that if people didn't grieve openly then that would probably lead to problems later on. So there was a whole idea around the field – and the field was very small – that people needed to 'get it off their chest'. So I think the only preconceived idea we had was that the volunteers should help people to talk about their grief. One of the other things that I did before we set the project up, was to write to all the hospices that were up and going then – and there were only 40 – and ask them how they were work – this is in 1982 – how they were working with bereaved people. And I've still actually got all the responses.

Recruiting staff

As hospices developed and their services expanded, recruiting personnel who embraced the hospice ideal became an important issue. In a new service, past experience was limited – so finding staff with the right attitudes was crucial. Personal motivation was a key issue, and we have already explored some of that in Chapter 1. In the final section of this chapter, we look at the context of recruitment, the circumstances within which people were appointed to posts and how those appointments progressed. In this following extract, Mary Baines tells of the particular and individual circumstances in which she came to work at St Christopher's:

It was in 1964 and I was just at home, I think it was a Sunday evening, Ted was out, and just, as it appeared, by chance, I turned on the radio, and there was my old friend Cicely Saunders, whom I'd lost touch with since medical student days because of the way my life had turned out. And she was giving 'This Week's Good Cause' appeal on behalf of the hospice she was going to found. And I sent her, I'll never forget this, I sent her £3, which was a lot of money then, and especially for an impecunious clergy wife. And became a Friend of St

Christopher's from 1964 when the appeal for St Christopher's was launched. And I was continuing, then, in part-time general practice. All through my time since I was married I was in part-time general practice, with obvious gaps for having the children, and the moves that I made. And then a really extraordinary thing happened really, in that Ted was invited to become a vicar in Beckenham, which is three miles from here[30] … I then came to the opening of St Christopher's in July '67, when, you know, it was opened. And at that time met up with Cicely again after many, well I hadn't been in touch with her since we qualified at the same time. And she sent me a letter which I've got a copy of, saying, and it was a very clever letter, and I've laughed about it with her many times, saying that as I was a local GP, and would be sending patients to St Christopher's, would I like to come round one afternoon and have a private look round with her. And of course it was a great big hook. And I fell for this.

So I guess it would have been somewhere, August/September, that sort of time, that I came, and she then asked me whether I would like to join her at St Christopher's. And Ted and I thought this over at quite some length, and I decided that I did not want to go to St Christopher's; that I enjoyed general practice, I was very happy there – it fitted in. It was only part-time, but still it was four mornings and an evening surgery. Our youngest child was then just three, so they went: three, five and seven. And I didn't think I wanted to work with the dying, and all sorts of very good reasons, because it was a very unusual thing. And I sent this letter to her, and even suggested the name of a friend of mine who might be interested in the job, as I patently wasn't! But then we thought it over, and prayed it over, and talked it over, and it did seem the right thing to do. But I was still faced with the general practice that I had given my word to. So in fact, having said in September '67 that I would come, I actually gave them six months' notice in the practice, although I'd only been there for six months, so I did work with them for a year. And joined here in April '68. So that's how it happened.

Barbara McNulty, at that time a district nurse in Glouces-tershire, also explains how St Christopher's became irresist-ible to her:

I was trained originally at St Thomas's Hospital, and Cicely and I share that, but in the early '60s, late '50s and early '60s, I was doing district nursing from a religious community in which I belonged, and it was a, something I absolutely loved and enjoyed enormously in the Cotswold hills and driving round in villages and things. It was a wonderful experience. But one of the things I was meeting was people dying at home with inadequate care, not very good drugs, support and so forth, and family support; very little indeed.

And Cicely was writing articles at that time in the *Nursing Times*, and I read one of these which was about her interest in terminal care. And so I wrote to her and said how much I'd been interested in this and how I enjoyed it, and she wrote back and then we had, I should think, a year of heated, hot correspondence. And I wrote things that I was interested and concerned with and she wrote and told me what she was doing, and then she invited me up on the planning committee of St Christopher's, when they were still sitting round a table and looking at the plans. And I remember one particular, the first particular day I went, we were talking about floor coverings and curtains, you know, little details that everybody was concerned with.

Later, on the opening, she suggested I come up to the opening, which I did. I'm not sure I was there at the 'topping out' ceremony, I think not, I think it wasn't until the opening of the first, of the place itself. And I went up and was enormously impressed, and just as I was leaving she and Matron, whose name I forget at the moment ... how could I? Anyway, I have. They both asked me if I'd like to come and work there. And my first response in my mind was, 'How can I, I belong in this community, I've got children ...' although they were grown up, or growing up '... and I have a job which I love?' And in the train going back I thought to myself, 'Oh, that's exactly what I want to do.' And by the time I had reached Gloucester I had decided, and within about, oh I suppose a month, I put everything into hock, or sold, or let go, or got rid of.

In Plymouth, Carolyn Brodribb found that her commit-ment to St Luke's led to an unexpected telephone call and the offer of a job – albeit one somewhat different from the one she had previously fulfilled:

Well I'd sort of done sort of things like, dotty things like selling hot dogs on The Hoe, you know, to raise money for it, over the years. And I'd also, when the builders vacated the building that was going to be the hospice, it was considered too filthy and too grotty to actually, for the cleaners to come in. And so a couple of us actually went in when the builders left. So I could say I was intimately acquainted with every U-bend in that building because I was the one whose hand was down it, trying to get it to a point where actually paid cleaners would come in and not walk out immediately. So that takes us up to the January '82, when it was opening. It was opening on Monday, the 20th of January, I think, and on the Friday night Sheila Cassidy phoned me up and said, 'Look, I've just been going through this list of people who, who are volunteers, who have offered their services, and I see your name here and you're a qualified social worker,' you know, 'Tell me, what do you think about work with the terminally ill and the bereaved?' And I'd cut out every single article about terminal illness and bereavement over the years; up and down the country people knew that that was my great interest and sent me stuff. So I knew it, exactly what I was going to say, and I said to her. And she said, 'Fine, we open on Monday, can you be there?' And I said, 'Just hang on a moment ...' and my youngest was five at that time, there was a sense I'd marked time because I didn't want to rush back into work because I knew what my long-term dream was, and I wanted to work according to that dream. I said to John, 'You'll never believe it, but Sheila Cassidy is on the phone ...' who

I'd met previously '… suggesting this. What do you think?' And he said, 'Well, what answer is there?' So I was there on the Monday for the opening, and that was brilliant.

From a different perspective, Tim Lovel reflects upon his palliative care experience in the North-East of England and tells how palliative medicine appointments increased from less than one whole-time equivalent to six full-time posts within a 12-year period:

So those are the two hospices in Newcastle, and then another one was in South Shields, where St Clare's Hospice had been running, I think about two years before I came here, as giving home care and day care, and I was elected onto their Council, they had a very democratic set-up, where all the Council members were elected annually by the members, and I was elected, and for many years sat on their Council and gave medical advice, and general advice too, if asked, sometimes even if I wasn't asked, I would give it, and then about five years ago[31] they managed to get enough money together to build a brand new in-patient unit in partnership with the NHS, so the new building went up, the old one was sold, and the new building was built around four sides of a square, with a garden in the middle, about one-third was the hospice, one-third was the NHS for long-stay geriatrics and one-third was services common to both, and this was a very good method, and I think possibly unique partnership between a charity and the NHS, and I became their Medical Director because, now they had in-patients, they needed somebody to give medical cover for the patients.

So I resigned as a trustee of the charity, because you can't be a trustee if you have financial benefit from, so I resigned as a trustee, became their Medical Director. Now this meant I had four hospices on a 30-mile front, and so with great regret, I had to make myself resign from the Stockton and the Hartlepool hospices,[32] so I could concentrate on the Sunderland and South Tyneside ones,[33] and

cut down a lot of my travelling, because an awful lot of time was spent going up and down the A19, in fact it was said by one wit, 'If you saw a dirty white car going down the A19 with the driver fast asleep, it was probably Tim Lovel.' So I resigned from those two, with adequate warning, and they eventually appointed a consultant each, to replace me, so from being half of one consultant to only one hospice, we'd now got four hospices with two consultants down there, and me, the third one, doing the Shields and South Tyneside. And then to bring the story up to date, it was agreed that there was more work in Sunderland than we could cope with, and so two years ago a second consultant, actually my then registrar, Anne Murphy, was appointed to a second consultant post, and so that meant there were four of us, and now I've retired they want to appoint another one for South Tyneside, which will make five, and they want to have both a replacement for me and a professor of palliative medicine, which would make six. So if I can come here 12 years ago as half of one, and leave with six full-time ones, I can maybe feel I haven't done too bad a job in getting palliative medicine established in the North of England.

In the next extract, Marilyn Relf describes how she came to join the staff of Sir Michael Sobell House, Oxford – and recalls that in the early days of hospice development, what a person had to offer was rather more important than professional background:

I arrived in Oxford wanting to develop a career. Thought about personnel quite, quite carefully, but as things happen in my life I just sort of followed my nose really. And I never really sort of set out to do anything in particular. I was quite interested in going back to working with volunteers. I was very interested for working with Oxfam and … just missed a job with them. And I was also, also saw, a job was advertised for the Churchill Hospital as a Volunteer Coordinator, and I thought that it would be very interesting to get some experience of actually running a project rather than supporting a project, and working in a project rather than working for a national organisation, looking, moving, very aware of voluntary sector issues, to actually sort of get stuck in at the coalface. When I came to meet the then Personnel Officer, I was told that it was in a hospice, that it was Sobell House, and began to read a little bit about Sobell House. I realised that one of the, of course I read the, Zorzas' book,[34] which was one of the few books around at the time, and realised that I'd been an exact contemporary of Jane [Zorza] at Sussex. And although I didn't know her, I must have known her, because we were both doing sociology, we were both in the same year, and she had a room in the hall of residence opposite mine. So that, of course, I, sort of stimulated me as well, I suppose. I was offered the job here and had one of those feelings of, 'Do I really want to get into this?' Didn't think I'd actually be here for very long. It was very badly paid, and I was thinking in terms, then, of going back into the national voluntary organisations at some point. I was very quickly impressed with Sobell House. And I suppose it was the quality of the people who were working here, and the sense of pioneering. I really, really, enjoy developing things. And at that point the hospice world was very fluid, and it was who you were and what you had to offer, rather than what particular professional background or training that you were bringing with you. And I thrived on that.

Finally, Liz Atkinson – the first ward sister to be appointed to the Northern Ireland Hospice, in Belfast – explains how she became involved in staff recruitment and saw the hospice grow from small beginnings into a comprehensive, multifaceted service, staffed by qualified personnel:

I was involved before the hospice opened in terms of fund-raising in one of the local support groups. Then when I got the ward sister's appointment – I was the first member of staff appointed after the Nursing Director for the in-patient unit – so I was involved in helping

to commission in terms of choosing beds and furnishings, and appointing, which was all very new for me because I really came with very little management experience, but had a lot in terms of oncology and community. So I learnt a lot of management from the Nursing Director,[35] and together we sort of pulled ourselves through those early years. But it was an exciting time, a very exciting time seeing something grow from embryo, and I don't think any of us involved in the Northern Ireland Hospice ever expected it to become the size of organisation it is. Because we opened, we opened six beds initially and then we opened the remainder of the beds. But at that time there were two home care sisters. And we now have 21 beds.[36] We have 26 home care sisters – well we now call them community specialist palliative care nurses. We have hospice at home. We have a bereavement programme. We have day hospice both here and in Ballymena, with dyspnoea clinics, lymphoedema clinics. We've medical out-patient clinics, a very extensive education programme. None of us expected it to grow the way it did.

These extracts capture some of the complexities and the challenges of hospice development at the local level; a feeling of liberation from the old and anticipation of the new. They incorporate the sense of expectancy as a new wave of hospice and palliative care services was founded. Throughout the country hospice pioneers faced several challenges: acquiring land, raising funds, developing care and recruiting staff. Although similar in character, these challenges were locally addressed – with vision and imagination, commitment and a sense of ownership. In essence, these extracts bear witness to the determination of those groups and individuals who nurtured a deep-seated desire to improve the care of the dying, and were prepared to go to remarkable

Cicely Saunders on site with the Sisters from St Joseph's, Hackney, 22 March 1965; Sister Mary Antonia is facing the camera, third from left and Lord Thurlow is on the far right.

lengths to bring about patient and family oriented changes in clinical practice and service organisation.

The overwhelming concern of hospices during these years was care of the dying in 'homely' environments in small units which offered detailed attention to personal comfort and care. Indeed, to this extent the hospices emerged at a time when there was no strategic or operational guidance within the NHS on terminal care, or systematic commitment to the subject as a clinical issue. Enthusiastic and charismatic pioneers of the hospice movement, like Cicely Saunders and Eric Wilkes, were able to begin to fill this gap by mobilising support for hospice development in local communities across the country. Very quickly they learned to lobby NHS administrators for financial support and were, more often than not, successful in this. Eric Wilkes, writing in 1981, captures the spirit of setting up a hospice in Sheffield some 15 years earlier:

> The regional hospital board agreed that such a unit was needed but said that they could not possibly afford to build it. They did agree, however, that if we raised the money to build it from private sources they would help generously with the running costs. Of course they would not promise this now. Even then, I suspect, they agreed because they thought we would never raise the money ...[37]

In this way, the establishment of hospices gathered pace across the country, with health care planners making commitments to local projects without any clear idea of what their commitments would really entail and how the projects would unfold. What was clear, and difficult for the planners to resist, was the strength of 'grass roots' public enthusiasm for these new initiatives. By 1979 hospices were growing rapidly, but in an essentially unplanned manner. As it was observed at the time:

> There was no monitoring of the growth of these services. Attempts to plan or to coordinate services were made difficult by the lack of any systematic information on what services existed, on what scale and with what to offer. Information was also lacking on the scale of provision which might be required to meet the needs of any given population.[38]

Hospices thus found themselves having to liaise with an NHS that was becoming more managerialist, better coordinated and more strategic. Support now had to be canvassed from the health authorities and hospices were, for the first time, factored into the calculations of which services were required for local needs. A new era of cooperation between hospices and other in-patient and community services thus emerged. A landmark of policy recognition for the hospices came in 1980, with the publication of the report of the Working Group on Terminal Care produced by the Standing Subcommittee on Cancer of the Standing Medical Advisory Committee, and chaired by Eric Wilkes.[39] It was with evidence of the change in NHS concerns that this committee was called upon to consider the direction that should be taken with regard to the rapidly proliferating hospices. Concerns about the further uncoordinated growth of hospices, the costs of this growth and the spectre of a lack of suitable staff, resulted in Wilkes and his colleagues reporting that they did 'not consider that there would be any advantage in promoting a large increase in the number of hospices at present'. Instead they recommended that the government should 'encourage the dissemination of the principles of terminal care throughout the health service and to develop an integrated system of care with emphasis on coordination between the primary care sector, the hospital sector and the hospice movement'. Despite its warnings of unsustainable proliferation of hospice, the report led to a huge upturn in interest: in the decade after publication there was a three-fold increase in the number of in-patient hospice units. This period also saw a growth of home care teams and hospital support teams. While some of these initiatives were directly funded by the NHS, many were funded through the efforts of a powerful cancer charity, The National Society for Cancer Relief (later Macmillan Cancer Relief). Efforts to stimulate and coordinate the growth of hospices, while at the same time lobbying government to increase its funding, became more concerted.

The first tangible evidence of the possibility of long-term and sustainable state funding for palliative care came in 1987, when the government published its first official circular on terminal care. This gave guidance to District Health Authorities,[40] which were then required to identify a long-term funding mechanism for the voluntary hospices. This 1987 circular made a number of key points: 1) District Health Authorities should take the lead in planning and coordinating a comprehensive and integrated range of services for termi-nally ill people; 2) District Health Authorities should ensure, in consultation with the voluntary sector, family practitioner committees and local authorities, that mechanisms exist to assess the needs and preferences of clients, and to identify deficiencies in services and staff training; 3) Clear strategies, with monitoring arrangements, should be produced.

Thus, within 20 years of the first modern hospice opening its doors in the UK, there was a marked shift in recognition. From a relative neglect by government of terminal and palliative care, and a locally driven, patchy diver-sity in hospice provision, a position was established in which government started to make strategic plans for the provision and long-term funding of palliative care. Within this, the idea of planning appropriately and sensibly for local needs was central. At the same time voluntary hospices, which were born less from a dispassionate assessment of local needs and more from fervent local enthusiasm for the *cause célèbre* of terminal care, were able to call for support in ways that were much more likely to command the attention of politicians and policy makers.

Notes

1. D. Clark, 'Cradled to the grave? Pre-conditions for the hospice movement in the UK, 1948–67', *Mortality* 4 (3): 225–47, 1999; and see Introduction, above.
2. C. Saunders, 'Dying of cancer', *St Thomas's Hospital Gazette* 56 (2): 37–47, 1958.
3. Cicely Saunders found the King's Fund to be very supportive. Encouraging Eric Wilkes with his plans for St Luke's, Sheffield, she wrote (7 October 1963), 'The King's Fund are being extremely helpful and having their imprimatur is a tremendous advantage to us'; see D. Clark, *Cicely Saunders – founder of the hospice movement. Selected Letters 1959–1999* (Oxford: Oxford University Press, 2002: 59).
4. See D. Clark, *Partners in Care? Hospices and health authorities* (Aldershot: Ashgate, 1993) for a detailed case study in Notting-hamshire.
5. Geographically ideal perhaps, but a former property of one distinct group within Northern Ireland's divided culture nonetheless.
6. St Gemma's opened in 1978 as a nine-bed in-patient unit. By January 1979 a decision had been taken to add a purpose-built, 47-bed extension at a cost of £1 million. Under the headline 'Go ahead for new hospice' St Gemma's first newsletter states: 'The unit has been designed by Messrs Stewart Hendry and Smith, acknowledged experts in hospice design – they already have to their credit St Luke's, Sheffield, and London's St Christopher's and St Joseph's' (*Newsletter* St Gemma's 1 (1): 1, 1979).
7. We discuss the origins of the 'Macmillan nurses' in Chapter 4, below.

8. A member of the group wrote shortly afterwards: 'In 1985, Somerton House opened and the full hospice service we had worked for was a reality. On 22 April, our first day, staff and council members were invited to a short communion service in the Hospice chapel, a very moving and fitting way to begin our work. On 20 May, friends of the Hospice from all over Northern Ireland attended a service in St Anne's Cathedral to give thanks for the past and to rededicate ourselves for hospice service in the future' (B. Irwin, *Hospice Care* 1 (4): 1986, no page number).

9. They were Flora Rhind and Cecilia Bottomley.

10. Strathcarron Hospice, Denny near Stirling, was founded in 1981.

11. Elsewhere one of us has noted of St Christopher's: 'Between 1961 and 1964 over £330,000 was raised from groups such as King Edward's Hospital Fund; the City Parochial Foundation; the Drapers' Company; the Nuffield Foundation; the Sembal Trust; the Max Rayne Foundation; the Kleinwort Benson Charitable Foundation and Settlement; and the Goldsmiths' Company. An appeal had been broadcast on BBC Radio and some substantial anonymous donations were received, including one of $30,000 from the United States. By 1966, however, with building at St Christopher's well underway and the estimated project budget now in excess of £400,000, there was still a considerable shortfall and the national financial climate was not favourable' (D. Clark, 'Originating a movement: Cicely Saunders and the development of St Christopher's Hospice, 1957–67', *Mortality* 3 (1): 43–63, 1998).

12. Dame Albertine Winner (1907–88) had been England's Deputy Chief Medical Officer before moving to St Christopher's as Deputy Medical Director.

13. For more on the National Society for Cancer Relief, see Chapter 4, below.

14. For more on Major Henry Garnett, see Chapter 4, below.

15. The Tudor Trust is an independent grant-making charitable trust, which exists to enhance people's quality of life. Established in 1955 by Sir Godfrey Mitchell with a gift of shares in the building company George Wimpey, it became known as the Tudor Trust in 1979. See www.tudortrust.org.uk.

16. Ciaran McGinley was interviewed in August 2000.

17. There is a complex background to this statement here about 'partnership' funding between independent hospices and the government. In 1990 the UK government announced its intention for 'health authorities to work towards a full partnership which matches the voluntary giving towards hospice services' (Department of Health Press release, 15 March; London: Department of Health, 1990: 1). With the new monies attached to this statement, government support for hospice funds stood at an estimated £20 million. By 1993, this figure doubled. However, significant problems began to emerge. First, unplanned growth that had been a matter of policy concern in earlier years appeared to be encouraged by this pattern of funding. Second, there was growing recognition that an upper funding limit was necessary. Stating that charitable funding would be matched pound for pound risked being a 'blank cheque' that government could ill afford. Third, and most importantly, the scheme was divisive. The new funds applied only to the voluntary sector and the government was thus seen to be discriminating against palliative care services planned and delivered within the NHS. Competition for resources became strong, and the allocations of funds were highly contested, causing 'a good deal of controversy within the hospice world: local competition for available funds, lack of clarity about criteria for eligibility, allegations of underspending by regions' (D. Clark, 'Whither the hospices?' in D. Clark (ed.), *The Future for Palliative Care* (Buckingham: Open University Press, 1993: 170).

18. We explore the development of the multidisciplinary team in more depth in Chapter 3, below.

19. Richard Lamerton is referring here to the Hospice of the Marches (later Hospice of the Valleys, Tredegar), where he was interviewed in January 1997, but his earlier experience was at St Joseph's Hospice, Hackney.

20. For further accounts of these experiences see R. Lamerton, *East End Doc* (Cambridge: Lutterworth Press, 1986).

21. Born in 1915, Sister Mary Antonia died in her native Ireland in 2001; she was speaking here in November 1995.

22. The following year the idea was given ringing endorsement in Cicely Saunders' first textbook: 'A few hospices will be needed for patients with intractable problems and for research and teaching in terminal care, but most patients will continue to die in general hospitals, cancer or geriatric centres or in their own homes; the staff they will find there should be learning how to meet their needs' (C. Saunders, 'The philosophy of terminal care' in C. Saunders (ed.), *The Management of Terminal Malignant Disease* (London: Edward Arnold, 1978: 195)).

23. Chaired by the Reverend Carleton Sweetser, this programme at St Luke's Hospital in New York was formed in 1973 and launched as a pilot project in 1974 – the second in the United States after Connecticut. Carleton Sweetser (1921–96) had met Cicely Saunders on her first visit to the United States in 1963 and they became good friends. See D. Clark, *Cicely Saunders – founder of the hospice movement. Selected letters 1959–1999* (Oxford: Oxford University Press, 2002). The hospice team at St Luke's was the first to be incorporated into an existing medical centre and

sought to augment the care given to terminally ill patients by focusing on pain control and symptom management. In 1986 the hospice changed its name to the St Luke's Palliative Care Program, to reflect the wide variety of services provided and to comply with changing state regulations. The programme was forced to close in 1990 due to funding difficulties.

24. For more on the work of Thelma Bates, see T. Bates, A.M. Hoy, D.G. Clark and P.P. Laird, 'The St Thomas's Hospital terminal care support team – A new concept of hospice care', *The Lancet* 1: 1201–03, 1981; and on her professional life at St Thomas's, her work with St Christopher's and the Princess Alice Hospice, Esher: T. Bates, 'A life of adventure', *Illness, Crisis and Loss* 9 (1): 31–34, 2001.

25. For more on the early plans for the hospice day unit at Sheffield see M. Cockburn and J. Twine, 'A different kind of day unit', *Nursing Times,* 18 August: 1410–11, 1982.

26. A charity set up in memory of the broadcaster Richard Dimbleby following his death from cancer in 1965. The Fund supports research laboratories and a cancer care and information service at St Thomas's Hospital in London. See www.richarddimbleby.orq.

27. The letter was written by Cicely Saunders on 13 November 1979 and contained the sentence 'On the whole I do not believe in Hospices for children but I may be wrong and there may really be a need in Oxford'. See D. Clark, *Cicely Saunders – founder of the hospice movement. Selected letters 1959–1999* (Oxford: Oxford University Press, 2002: 192).

28. The Rupert Fund dates back to 1975 when two Royal Ulster Constabulary officers liaised with the City of London Police Federation to arrange a visit to London for a group of RUC widows and their children. The name was suggested by Branch Secretary Mike Simms who recalled the time when he was a London schoolboy evacuated away from his family and home during the Second World War. During those years his father cut the Rupert Bear comic strip from the *Daily Express* each day and sent it to him with his weekly letter and sweet ration. The Bear thus became an important link with home and parents and brought hm comfort. The Rupert Fund achieved charitable status in 1994.

29. Susan Le Poidevin died in 1989, before her work was published. A summary can be found in C.M. Parkes, M. Relf and A. Couldrick, *Counselling in Terminal Care and Bereavement* (Leicester: British Psychological Society, 1996).

30. Mary Baines was being interviewed at St Christopher's in July 1996.

31. Tim Lovel was interviewed in September 2000.

32. Butterwick Hospice, Stockton-on-Tees and Hartlepool and District Hospice, Alice House, Hartlepool.

33. St Benedict's Hospice, Sunderland and St Clare's Hospice, Jarrow.

34. Victor and Rosemary Zorza, after the death of their daughter Jane Zorza in June 1977, wrote extensively about her experience and the hospice care she had received at the end of her life. See R. Zorza and V. Zorza, *A Way to Die* (London: Sphere Books, 1981) and also M. Wright *Victor Zorza. A life amid loss* (Lancaster: Observatory Publications, in press).

35. She is referring here to Rita Beattie, from whose interview (in November 1998) we also quote in this book.

36. Liz Atkinson was speaking in July 2000.

37. E. Wilkes, 'General practitioner in a hospice', *British Medical Journal* 282: 1591, 1981.

38. B. Lunt, 'Terminal cancer care services: recent changes in regional inequalities in Great Britain', *Social Science and Medicine* 20: 754, 1985.

39. Working Group on Terminal Care [The Wilkes Report], *Report of the Working Group on Terminal Care* (London: DHSS, 1980).

40. Department of Health, *HC (87)4(2)* (London: Department of Health, 1987).

3 Hospice teamwork: towards an integrated community

'… although it's awfully important to learn how to work together, it's very important not to lose the sharpness of one's own professional expertise' **Elisabeth Earnshaw-Smith**

We have seen that the vision, energy and ability of pioneers to influence others was a visible, tangible and high-profile aspect of hospice development in the UK in the latter part of the twentieth century. But along-side and behind those leaders can also be discerned varieties of working together with others from different backgrounds and professions. It was this *teamwork* that also had a major influence on the success and growth of the whole enter-prise. In our interviews, we heard about teamwork at many levels, from negotiation with health authorities, to caring for patients in the hospice; from expanding palliative care services into hospitals and communities, to the provision of education for a growing palliative care workforce.

The writings of Cicely Saunders provide a rich source for those interested in the notion of teamwork in hospice care. In a paper from the early 1970s,[1] she describes St Christopher's as 'a medical foundation whose research reaches out widely in writing and teaching' and as 'a community in which the patients are the central members'. It is a place which has set out to understand the needs associated with progressive and mortal illness and also chronic pain. Moreover the team employed there has gradually enlarged as physicians and nurses have been joined by physiotherapists, occupational therapists and others. Particular emphasis is placed upon collaboration within a multidisciplinary group, so that the 'most important and uniting moments of the life of St Christopher's come when the group tries to understand and meet the needs of one patient at the deepest level'. Indeed, her ground-breaking concept of the 'total pain'[2] experienced by some patients was further expanded at one stage to include 'staff pain' and she notes in another paper from the early 1980s '… the closer staff are to the weaknesses of the patients and the grief of the families the more they too will suffer the pangs of bereavement. Many will find they are suffering the process of numbness and exhaustion, protest anger and depression and will need to share this if they are to find their way through.'[3] This was to recognise that the shared concerns and values of teamwork were not only vital in delivering care to patients and families but also crucial to the well-being of the staff group and the organisation as a whole. So in this chapter we take a broad view of teamwork and its characteristics in the hospice context, exploring the different types of team and some of the varieties of teamwork that have occurred in the development of hospice care.

A team has been defined as 'a set of persons working or playing in combination' and teamwork as 'work done by organised division of labour: cooperation, pulling together, regard to success of the whole rather than personal exploits'.[4] In his book on teamwork among caregivers,[5] Malcolm Payne summarises 15 definitions of teams and teamwork taken from writings published between 1975 and 1997 – years very much associated with the developments described in this book. Ideas of shared purpose and responsibility, of bringing to the team different but complementary skills, of being able to achieve more by collective than by individual effort, appear in many of these definitions. There has also been reflection in the hospice and palliative care literature on the particular working of the *multidisciplinary team* – a notion that has become so central to the hospice approach, but still seems rather poorly understood at a more conceptual level.[6]

Many types of teams are described in our interviews. They include: those involved in setting up a hospice; management teams (sometimes referred to as the 'triumvirate' of Matron, Medical Director and Hospice Administrator); hospice staff from a range of professional disciplines; volunteers and fund-raisers; different teams within the hospice (in-patient teams, day care, home care); specialist nurse teams; community palliative care teams; hospital palliative care teams; primary care teams. The list seems endless! Patients and families are also included as part of the team in the thinking of some of those to whom we talked.

From this it appears that teamwork takes place at several levels or layers. First, there are patient-focused groupings among professionals and volunteers within a single hospice or team; here we see collaborative relationships between professionals and patients and the teamwork of those within the hospice supported by behind-the-scenes activity; for example, steering groups, fund-raising groups, prayer groups. Second, teamwork is reported at an organisational level, in relation to health authorities and charitable funding organisations, as well as between hospices. Third, individuals within the hospice movement were instrumental in establishing and contributing to the work of new professional associations and networks – for example, the Association of Palliative Medicine, the Palliative Care Research Forum, the Association of Hospice Social Workers and the National Association of Hospice Volunteer Coordinators – and in collaborating with important existing organisations like the World Health Organisation.[7]

The character of hospice teamwork is described as being somehow different from other (mainly hospital) teamwork. It is said to be more egalitarian in structure and democratic in process, with a strong sense of camaraderie and mutual support which brought relief from stress. Teamwork between two individuals is often reported as having been particularly creative and significant. At the same time, elements of conflict are reported both at a strategic or organisational level, around new ways of working and learning together and around the issue of who was in charge. We identified several key themes about teams and teamwork: teamwork at an organisational level; teamwork in providing hospice care; teamwork in hospice education; team structures and processes; elements of tension and conflict.

Teamwork at the organisational level

The majority of hospices in the UK have been established as independent foundations, largely funded by local communities and with some funding from the state. Nevertheless, the relationship between an individual hospice and the NHS, usually in the form of a local or regional health authority (RHA), has always been important. In the late 1960s Gillian Ford worked as a doctor at St Christopher's and, at the same time, held a post at the Department of Health. She talks here about a collaborative approach with the NHS which bore substantial fruits for the hospice:

I think that it was important for St Christopher's and for other hospices to feel that they weren't seen as being competitive with the NHS; that there was space for such a thing to happen in the voluntary sector. And we're looking at several governments of different political persuasions, but all being able to give this developing movement a fair wind. And it must have helped to have people in the Department who knew what it was and were practically supporting it in various ways, but it also, I think, owes a lot to the fact that Cicely used to invite people to visit and didn't present what was being done in an ... antagonistic or aggressive way: 'you ought to be', and, 'this ought to be happening throughout the NHS', was not her theme. And after all, the NHS, in various shapes or forms was supporting it, not just Department of Health's research money, but also the South East Thames RHA – as it then was, Health Board probably, they weren't called RHA to begin with ... but that gave her a contract for the care of patients, and later substantially funded the education at St Christopher's. I mean *really* generously funded education.

The importance of a relationship with the NHS has been sustained throughout four decades of hospice development.

Malcolm Rapson, Administrator at St Luke's Hospice, Sheffield in the 1990s, also talks about a productive relationship with the Health Authority, brought about by teamwork between the hospice managers (Administrator, Medical Director and Matron) supported by the whole staff:

We have been encouraged ... very, very well by the Health Authority. So our business has developed with their support, both financially and in other helpful ways, into what we have at the moment. I feel that the only way that that expansion could have taken place was really having three full-time managers, each left to their own business. So we've had a Medical Director who was able to concentrate on his core business, which is looking after patients. And in fact handling the element of development that was a change in our services by having a Matron who could pay very much attention to what was happening in the outside world, as far as in nursing circles and medical circles. And by having an Administrator who was able really to look at the budget, develop the budgets, and manipulate the ... financial side of it, and to enable the development to take place without losing any cash. I think it would be fair to say that we have only once recorded a year where it looked as though we were likely to be in the red at the end of that year, and that was to the amount of about £35,000, and we were able to retrieve that situation by asking for more money from the Health Authority ... and receiving it. So I think we've managed very capably, but the reason that we've managed capably is not entirely the managers, it's the value of the teamwork, although that seems rather stupid to say teamwork, but it's all our employees pulling together to create goodwill. And it's that creation of goodwill that I would volunteer is the reason for St Luke's being financially stable. If we started to lose goodwill at any one time, then I would be terribly worried for our financial foundation.

Another feature of organisational collaboration and

teamwork in the early years of hospice growth was the coop-eration between hospices. Prue Clench describes this in some detail from her experiences in the late 1970s:

There was enormous goodwill between hospices. We sank our differ-ences in those days, and people helped the next ones along the line. Whatever you discovered, whatever your experience, you shared it with the next people that were coming along, and there was a wonderful, wonderful spirit of support. Whatever form somebody else had developed, they were willing to let you have the whole set and send it. And when you consider in those days hardly anybody had a secretary or anything like that, so if they promised you, you knew they did it when they went home last thing at night, and it came with a handwritten note and plenty of cartoons, and always with a very light touch. But we actually all helped each other. And I suppose I was especially conscious of that because most of the people, if you go back to that era, were actually very senior, usually this was the end of a very eminent career, and I was a very jumped-up, you know, part-time staff nurse as I started. I never had much in the way of qualifications to go towards this, and it's very remark-able to me that people were so willing to teach me everything that they thought I might need. They made you feel that yours was the only hospice that was being planned, and really entered into your enthusiasm and what you were planning to do. And I think it's a very remarkable feature of those early days that there was this tremen-dous comradeship.

As hospice organisations became more mature, collab-oration between them was also formalised by the establish-ment of professional associations, which could form powerful lobbies on behalf of hospice interests. Peter Laidlaw, then Secretary of Marie Curie Cancer Care Scotland, described the creation and impact of the Scottish Partnership Agency for Palliative and Cancer Care (SPAPCC) in the late 1980s:

St Luke's Hospice, Sheffield

Opened in October 1971, St Luke's originated in a small investigation conducted with assistance from the Regional Health Board which revealed that 12 per cent of cancer patients in Sheffield were dying in need of better care than they were getting at home. This identi-fication of the unmet needs of terminal and pre-terminal patients gave rise to two years of fund raising to meet the capital costs neces-sary for the unit to become a reality. Having met the financial targets earlier than anticipated, the hospice was designed using the same architect responsible for St Christopher's – Peter Smith. The opera-tional model also followed that of St Christopher's, especially with a heavy use of volunteers from the outset. Known for its pioneering implementation of a Day Hospice which began in 1975, St Luke's had introduced a home care service two years earlier in 1973. Heavily promoted by Eric Wilkes, the success of the Day Hospice strongly influenced the arguments behind the Wilkes Report of 1980.

It was a major step forward and amongst other things, provided for the administrative teams and individuals representing all 13 Scottish hospices to visit each other's establishments regularly. I was a very enthusiastic supporter of the Agency from day one. All the hospices were providing palliative care in their areas – 90 per cent of their problems were similar, if not identical, and all experienced different interpretations and emphasis from their Health Boards. These visits were a wonderfully cohesive part of the whole palliative outreach in Scotland, and extremely helpful for fast-track decision making. I think it worked particularly well because although the things we were discussing were not a secret in any sense … they would have been considered classified about the ways that we would deal with the Health Board for instance. When the Health Boards discovered, in fact, that they were speaking not to rivals when they were talking to these 13 different hospice managers, but colleagues, it made a big difference to their attitude to us. I would imagine that's totally unquantifiable in monetary terms. After 1989, when the Hospices Initiative became government policy,[8] each individual Health Board was given complete autonomy as to the way it interpreted that initiative and some of them didn't interpret it in a particularly generous way. After the advent of the SPAPCC, under Margaret Stevenson, unity was established, which benefited the hospice movement in Scotland. Not only did the Agency unify the whole of palliative care outreach, it gave a point of contact for any official body interested in hospices for whatever reason.

Teamwork in providing hospice care

As we have already begun to see, a fundamental aspect of teamwork in hospices relates to the particular view of patient care they have sought to develop. Patricia Scott describes the team and the organisation of care at Sir Michael Sobell House, Oxford as it was when she first worked there as a nurse in 1983:

The ward team comprised two ward sisters, and an equal division, roughly, of staff nurses and untrained auxiliary nurses. And the nursing, at that stage, was in … allocation per shift. And one would have an early shift: one trained nurse/one auxiliary nurse would deal with, probably a bay of patients and a side room, something like that. So you'd have four or five patients to each *pair* of nurses, for the … morning shift and afternoon and evening shifts, there was a similar pattern. On an evening shift one would have four nurses on: two trained and two untrained. And I guess there were very clear definitions, then, of what the trained nurses did and what the auxiliaries did, on that particular shift, although there was, there was never a feeling of the 'trained nurses only …' did something. We were all expected, quite rightly, to clear up after ourselves and to do what was necessary to be done for the patients. Obviously there were limits on what the auxiliaries could do … dressings and drugs and all that sort of thing were not for them …

Having described the nursing team on the ward, Patricia Scott expands her account by talking about the multidisciplinary team, the hospice day centre and the home care team:

The unit, at that stage, had a part-time physiotherapist, a part-time occupational therapist, a part-time social worker and a chaplain who was part of the hospital. They represented the multidisciplinary team. There was the weekly ward review where doctors and nurses and the multidisciplinary team got together and would talk about all the patients, with the particular view of sort of psychosocial care, and discharge, and where the next week's admissions would perhaps be *planned*, in as far as one could …

The little day centre that we had at that stage had three part-time nurses. They were all staff nurses. And there was a GP, Donald Richards, who used to come in every day for the day centre. He was in practice in Headington, and he'd come in every morning to be the medical presence, and see everybody that was needed by the day centre. He was actually a founding member of the House as well. And the day centre brought enormous life to the ward. And at the weekends, when the day centre wasn't here, one was very conscious … of the silence, really, because they'd bring noise with them, and life, which was great.

And in the home care team: that, at that stage, I think, was two nurses … working out in the community, and really developing their role of Macmillan nurses, which has changed and altered *a lot* in the intervening years, but in those days was very much establishing the role, out there with GPs and the district nurses. And I think there was quite a lot of reserve and anxiety about what these

Patricia Scott: 'There was the weekly ward review where the multidisciplinary team got together and would talk about all the patients.'

nurses were doing, and a lot of fear amongst district nurses that they would cream off the nice jobs and leave them to handle all the other … so there was a lot of education going on in an attempt to be able to share more … more clearly … with them.

There has also developed a range of teams that contribute to the palliative care of patients and that are not attached to hospices, but work in community settings and in hospitals. Mary Holland, for example, describes working as a clinical nurse specialist in palliative care in the English Lake District from 1995:

I work as a clinical nurse specialist so I'm very conscious that we're *not* the primary carers; that we work in an advisory and consultative role. I work with a team of one hospital Macmillan nurse and one other community Macmillan nurse in the actual area which I work in, but in the whole of the Health Authority there are other Macmillan nurses and we meet on a reasonably regular basis for support and sort of clinical input and things like that. We see patients possibly from the time of diagnosis, but that would mainly be so they've got a contact number and we can let them know what's available for them in the community, such as Cancer Care[9] with its complementary therapies; if they need financial help or support; or we can actually access avenues which they might need at that particular time – for example social services, or physiotherapy or occupational therapy. We do try and work as clinical nurse specialists, in specialist palliative care, so we really would aim only to keep patients with specialist care needs on and work with them. The area is really quite enormous, it's 300 square miles that we cover, so there is a lot of travelling and, although it is a beautiful area, it's quite difficult to actually get round it. I mean, for example, if I had to go from Kendal to Grasmere, that might take me an hour each way. So we have to work in conjunction with the primary health care team and district nurses, and really be accessible when there are problems, you know, taking on the most complex issues.

A common theme in the interviews relating to teamwork and patient care is the idea of the multidisciplinary or multi-professional team. There is continuing debate in health care about which name best fits the collection of workers collaborating together to provide the best possible care in the most effective way. Malcolm Payne[10] suggests that 'multiprofessional' implies several different groups working together but not 'that they adapt aspects of their professional role, their skill or knowledge base … to fit in with the roles, knowledge and skills of other groups'. On the other hand, 'interprofessional' or 'interdisciplinary' groups do make adaptations to take account of and interact with the roles of others, adjusting their knowledge and skills and varying their responsibilities accordingly. Beyond this, as Payne points out, the concept of 'transdisciplinary work'[11] has been used to indicate the transfer of information, knowledge and skills across disciplinary boundaries, so that, ultimately, professionals take on roles usually associated with another occupational group. We found echoes of these themes in several interviews and show here how our informants are able to describe these issues within the development of teamwork in the hospice context.

Tom West joined St Christopher's in 1973 on returning from a period with the Church Missionary Society in West Africa. He recalls that the evolution of collaborative work between different professional groups at the hospice followed a predominantly multidisciplinary (rather than an interdisciplinary or transdisciplinary) orientation:

And I now, as we're talking,[12] realise that there's a third aspect of hospice that I think has changed enormously in 20 years, and that is

Tom West:
'The multidisciplinary approach … had to evolve.'

the multidisciplinary, or as some people would like (but have failed) to get it called, the interdisciplinary approach. As I say, when I first joined St Christopher's the whole institution was very much, in my view, doctor-led. And the ward rounds, for example, were a doctor's progress, with or without attending staff, very often done alone. And certainly my colleagues on the whole felt that the doctor should go round the ward alone, so it was a one-to-one relationship with the patient.

I acknowledge that as being of great importance, but I personally found it equally useful to go round with a ward nurse and a junior doctor. And I found myself, then, that it was more like, we might call it, a mixed doubles: the nurse and the patient supported each other, and the junior doctor supported me. And this was no bad thing, it, I think, helped the patient to say things. The nurse helped the patient to say things that needed to be said, and certainly the junior doctor was able to observe whether what I was saying was being taken on board properly, by both the patient and, indeed, by the ward staff.

And so there were two ways of doing rounds there; originally it was a doctor's round, and then I saw it modified into being more of a multidisciplinary round. The multidisciplinary approach, I think, had to evolve because the care of patients with terminal cancer – and of course now many other diseases – became more and more compli-cated, and even doctors were finally forced to acknowledge that they couldn't be experts in nursing and occupational therapy and social work and everything else, and it was therefore imperative that the different disciplines were represented and did in fact have input.

Social worker Miriam Warren talks about the creative overlapping between the contributions of different profes-sionals in successful multidisciplinary working at St Gemma's, Leeds. She describes 'interaction' and 'overlap' between members of the team which, again, shares features of multi-disciplinary working rather than an inter- or transdisciplinary approach. This is an example of a *coordinated*[13] or *coordi-nated professional*[14] team in which separate professionals, each with their own roles and accountable to their own professional hierarchies, refer work to each other and are influenced by each other's ideas.[15] Miriam Warren explains:

I think social work comes from a different perspective. I think the Hospice is very good at multidisciplinary working but I think that, you know, people with a medical background see things from a medical viewpoint, nursing see it from a nursing viewpoint so the social worker can see it from a different perspective – being more aware maybe of the social issues. It's a different slant really. I wouldn't like to say a broader slant 'cause that sounds like it's a criticism, it's not, it's just that we're from different disciplines [but] … there's a lot of interaction. There's a lot of overlap, for example, with the community nurses. If we get a referral from the community nurses for emotional support and they're already putting some of that support in, but it may be that it needs more intensive work, then they would refer to us. On the wards there's a bit of overlap, a lot of the nurses have counselling skills and so they're able to respond to patients' needs at particular times. But there may be issues that are unresolved for people and so they would refer to us so that we could have kind of a structured input over a period of time in order to address these issues. And with spiritual care there's an overlap as well because people will talk about their feelings and it will encompass spiritual distress and I'm sure for Sister Brigid [the Spiritual Director at St Gemma's] working with spiritual distress it'll encompass social distress … So there is a lot of overlap and it is a very good example of teamworking here. I must say from my experience of visiting other places, and even from comments from social work students, that the multidisciplinary working is as good as it can be really.

Volunteers and other hospice staff were also seen as essential team members in the hospice context. Bill Rourke, a volunteer for 15 years at the Northern Ireland Hospice, Belfast, talks about the changes in the way volunteers' services were used during his time at the hospice between 1985 and 2000:

But I mean I can remember – I mean we used to go round putting up shelves and putting in cupboards and, as I say, all sorts of things like that, which certainly that has changed. And people are now – now I'm not saying that one person only does one job but, you know, there can be – there are some who do help in the unit, they also at times are available for the tea bar, they do various things. Other people, when they're happy to work in the Hospice, don't want any great direct contact with people who are ill if you like, which is fair enough, but I mean they come in and out, they count collec-tion boxes, they deal with covenants, they help out in Finance Office, various things, they look after – I mean when there's special appeals they help to send out either the appeals or the receipts or whatever, that sort of thing.

And there was maybe more, I wouldn't say emergencies – people would have been called on maybe more at short notice, earlier on to do things – now it's more, I wouldn't say organised, that sounds like it wasn't – it was organised but now, with the numbers we have, people are allocated their duties and – someone does tea bar every Monday or either the afternoon or the morning or whatever – they know precisely what their duties are. We then have a number of people who are down in emergencies when they're needed to fill in for holidays or sickness or something like that, but those would be the exception. The vast majority have a fixed time and there is not a great deal of turnover and the majority are very committed. I mean it'll take a lot for them to cry off – it has to be a very legitimate reason for them not coming in at their allotted time, really.

Lyn Forbes, a hospice manager, attributed the success of the Highland Hospice, Inverness and her longevity in post (between 1986 and the date of her interview with us in 1996) to effective teamworking between all the staff in the Hospice, including volunteers:

Well, from my point of view I think it's been the move from the separate teams (even within the clinical teams, you know; the nurses were nurses, the doctors were doctors, the OTs were OTs[16]), to one whole team. And I have to be honest with you and say that I put a lot of that down to [a] real, structured way of working at it. I mean we're the first hospice in Britain recently to get the 'Investor in People' Award[17] and that award is all about everybody in the team, even the cleaners – and I don't mean that in a condescending way – being aware of what our objectives are, our development plans, our future. And we're told by the 'Investor in People', the award people, that it was the first place they'd ever come into, and when they'd asked any member of staff – and out of a staff of 56 they

interviewed 24 of them plus 12 volunteers – you know, 'What are you working towards? What are the aims? What's the mission statement?' They all could tell them right down to the last letter about what we were doing and I think it's been the real joy of watching the team develop.

We've gone through a lot of change and in that change it's just brought the team closer and closer together. I mean our nurses will rota themselves off if we're not busy, to save money. They are aware of our financial position and the point of income against expenditure, they know what services we're looking to develop and so it's all very much one big team, and, yeah, I think that's been the biggest thing for me; that I believe that you wouldn't go into a hospice where they don't say that they provide multidisciplinary teamwork but I think there are a lot of ways of actually describing what that is, and I think here we have come closest that I've ever seen to a team that values each other. I think one of my sadnesses within hospice is that, for instance the fund-raising side, or the administration side, might be marginalised from where people believe the real work goes on at the clinical level, and I think that we've managed to develop a team here where everybody is supportive of everybody else and appreciates what everybody else does, and that feels really good. And it's probably why I'm still here, 10 years on.

As the number of hospice volunteers grew, so did the need for their activities to be coordinated or managed. This gave rise to the role of the volunteer coordinator. Marilyn Relf worked as a volunteer coordinator, among other things, at Sir Michael Sobell House, Oxford. Here she talks about the importance of getting volunteers and nurses to work together in developing a bereavement service in the early 1980s:

One of the first things we did was to start doing training of the nursing staff as well, so that they didn't feel left out and left behind by the volunteers. And I was very aware from my previous experience that we needed to build links between the Bereavement Service and the volunteers, and the nursing teams, otherwise we could very much get into a sort of 'them and us' situation, with the nurses potentially feeling quite jealous of the volunteers, and also volunteers are always in awe of the nurses. So that's why we decided that … volunteers … being recruited from outside the hospice, needed to work in the House.

Ros Beetham, Volunteer Coordinator at St Luke's, Sheffield for 24 years from 1971, discovered at the outset the importance of helping nurses learn how best to work with the volunteers:

On day one of volunteering everybody froze with horror, because the volunteers came in, in fear and trembling, onto the wards, the nurses stood there thinking, [gasps] 'What do they do? We daren't ask them,' because nurses are not used to telling other nurses what

Ros Beetham: 'On day one of volunteering everybody froze with horror.'

to do: Sister is, but amongst their peers they're not. And they were frozen with horror at daring to ask anybody to do anything, sort of terribly tentatively, 'Do you think you could …?' 'Absolutely …' [laughter]. And so it was total disaster, and ever so funny. And I watched this going on, and I decided that the first thing after this we needed was some induction for nurses on how to deal with volunteers. So we had to start giving them a little sort of lecture on, 'If you don't tell them what to do, then that means: do anything.' [laughter] 'Oh well, they might not like to do it …' you know, all this sort of … and I was surprised because, having been on this course together and getting on so well, these were not unknown people, but it was just typical of people feeling fearful of what they're doing, and how threatened you are in a new job, really.

Training has been important for the volunteers as well as for the nurses, and has enabled volunteers to use their skills effectively in the hospice. Marilyn Relf recalls the enjoyment of helping volunteers to develop:

It's been great working with the volunteers, and I can't remember how many volunteers we've had now, but I mean something like, I think we've trained something like 50 or 60 people, and the training is always very exciting. You start off with a group of very nervous individuals who usually very quickly gel into being a solid group, and by the end of the first part of the training … will begin to say things like, 'I'm not used to having relationships like this with other people. I can say things to people in this group that I don't normally talk about.' And … it's always really exciting to see how people develop their skills, develop their confidence, in what they can do, and learn to use their everyday skills with a lot, with much greater awareness and intention.

The sense of working together to provide care has been enhanced by the complex nature of the work undertaken by the volunteers. Marilyn Relf continues:

And the other way in which the project [the Bereavement Service] has developed is to really to try and … develop how we're supporting the volunteers as the people they're working with have become more complex, and they do work with some very difficult situations. I mean, I think people assume, because they're volunteers, they'll be doing work that is not as, that is qualitatively different from the professionals, and I don't think it is, actually. And I think one of the things I'd like to do whilst I'm still part of palliative care[18] is to try and paint a picture on a wider canvas of what it's like to be a volunteer doing this work.

In the early days of hospice development, when funding was scarce, all kinds of voluntary services and activity would be sought from the local community, so the community became, in effect, part of the team. Sheila Hanna recalled the flurry of activity in her role as Volunteer Coordinator as St Christopher's was about to open, in 1967:

Well my first request, of course, was to help to get people in to get the building ready for the grand opening because Princess Alexandra was coming along and I had to get the local fire brigade in to hang curtains, great big curtains. We had to get Boy Scouts in to put dusters under their feet and go up and down the corridors because there was just … we had no other staff. We had no means otherwise, so it was a case of pulling everybody in that we could. And I remember I had to find people to help on the opening to be there, and from that moment onwards – the first ward was opened, Alexandra Ward – and I had to begin to note where the help was going to be needed, both on the ward and in the main building of course.

Mary Box, a community pharmacist associated with St Christopher's, talks about ways in which the Hospice created a reciprocal relationship with the community it served:

It really all worked very well because everybody was committed to the idea, the whole idea of palliative care, and dying with dignity,

and talking about cancer, saying, 'Yes, it's there, it's in the community, we'll serve it.' That fired everybody's imagination and everybody really was ready to put all their efforts into making the whole thing work. And they very soon developed interest in the community, great support from the community – they have terrific support work in the community, everybody understands what they're doing and they in turn are very good in talking to people, in giving lectures, and brought the whole dread of cancer into the daylight and made it an acceptable thing to talk about, that there was such a thing as cancer of which people died, sometimes quite quickly, sometimes in great pain but their mission in life was to make it as acceptable and easy as possible. And this really fired people's imagination and they did a lot to educate people about it and to be able to talk about it.

This sense of the hospice belonging to the community has persisted, as John Easun, Acting Administrator of the Pilgrim's Hospice, in Ashford, Kent (opened in 2001) recounts:

So generally we are part of the community. And of course we're still very conscious of the fact – and the community's conscious – that it is a community project, it's the community hospice, it was built with local money if you like, and everybody has an interest in it – it's *their* hospice. OK, so it's controlled from Canterbury via a Board of Trustees etc, but it is still the community's hospice.

Teamwork in hospice education

Education, as well as clinical care, has been a focus for multidisciplinary working in hospice care from the earliest days. But it has not always been easily achieved because of professional differences (in learning needs and styles as well as in professional status) principally between doctors and others. Gillian Ford highlights the tension inherent in these differences and shows how multiprofessional education at St Christopher's grew from being something that was initially 'hidden' to something that was open and welcomed, despite the persistence of some tension:

We now think, we take for granted that multiprofessional working and multiprofessional education is a good thing, *must* be in the interests of patients. But, in the early days at St Christopher's, we were running courses where we combined nurses with doctors. And we actually concealed this fact in that we published a programme which said 'Doctors' Week'. Now, if you look carefully at it, you would see that coincided with … I think it was a nurses' two-week course, but we felt that if we had said that we were actually combining these, that doctors would not wish to be learning with nurses. And so there was that kind of tension, and perhaps there still is to some extent.

And one by one we added more of the professions to these multiprofessional weeks, and they were popular. We found that … instead of having to hide the fact, we could actually promote it as a multiprofessional educational experience. This developed nicely. Then we also put into place conferences which were in a sense small courses in that there would be four separate conferences but increasingly advanced as you went on … And those attracted multiprofessional audiences, so it did become more and more multiprofessional.

Dorothy Summers, a nurse educator working at St Christopher's at the same time as Gillian Ford, gives an additional perspective on multidisciplinary education at the Hospice:

We realised that there was a need for a longer period of experience for a multidisciplinary group, and this was where the sort of coordination idea came in. And so we had one month multidisciplinary courses, and, of that month, one week was orientation – like the trained nurses – and the three weeks were work experience under the supervision of qualified nurse tutors who, in fact, planned the courses. And from these grew the next phase which we'll come to in a moment. But the idea of multidisciplinary courses, I think, was very, very important. The nurses took to it like ducks to water. The medical students complained that they didn't get enough contact with the doctors, and the doctors were under great pressure for teaching and, I think, felt that if people were there for a month they got an awful lot out of ward reports and the nursing staff, and really ought not to be demanding on doctors. But that was a complaint, they weren't too happy about that. And a little bit further on, again when there were more medical staff, then it became possible to give them more time. And the social work students had their own time with the social worker, and theological students had time with the Chaplain during their experience. So that was a good, big step forward.

Others we interviewed suggested that the reality of multiprofessional working did not always match the rhetoric which spoke of its value. Richard Hillier describes how he functioned in the environment of having to build a multidisciplinary team at Countess Mountbatten House, one of the first NHS hospices, in Southampton:

… actually we've got some good people here and we're actually trying to look at these team issues. We're very much into multiprofessional working and learning, and the first thing we've had to do is actually acknowledge that it is very difficult indeed. And that is very, very hard, I think. And when we've looked around the country at what's going on, there is an awful lot of rhetoric about how people are working in teams, and how they're doing multiprofessional things, and when I actually go and talk to them, I find that they're finding it also very, very difficult and tend to abandon it, the multiprofessional education side, 'cause it's just so difficult to get it to happen.

Talking in 1996 about his vision for a proposed Oxford

Countess Mountbatten House, Southampton

This NHS Palliative Care Unit opened in 1977 with 25 in-patient beds and a home care team for patients with advanced cancer in three health districts: Southampton, Portsmouth and Winchester. A day care service began in 1982. Teaching became an integral and important part of the Unit's work. In 1983, as part of a national initiative to support the development of education in palliative care, the National Society for Cancer Relief funded an extension to Countess Mountbatten House and a number of education staff appointments. The Arthur Rank Education Centre was opened in 1984 and officially began operation on 1 May 1986. The NSCR funding ran out in April 1991; initially this was a cause of great concern but a benefactor was found in the Friends of Countess Mountbatten House, the Charity associated with the Unit, who donated £400,000 over a five-year period starting in 1993 to revive the Educational Programme. See www.cmh.org.uk.

International Centre for Palliative Care, Robert Twycross echoes the view that there are still some tensions about multidisciplinary education and expresses his hope for a truly multiprofessional approach in the provision of university palliative care education:

I want a multiprofessional department representing multiprofessional palliative care. So it's the Oxford International Centre for Palliative Care, not palliative medicine. It will have a suite of rooms for palliative medicine, palliative nursing and the ragbag called psychosocial studies. It will have the Study Centre administrative offices. It will have an international department. But within these separate suites there will be the commitment to an integrated community. So we hope that we will be the trendsetters for the next century, so that when we've set up our truly multiprofessional building and begin to move towards our truly multiprofessional centre, then we won't see, so much, the developments of departments of palliative medicine, but multiprofessional departments of palliative care. And that's my vision, because it's a tragedy: you go into a department

of medicine – where are the nurse lecturers? They're not. You go into gerontology – where are the nurse lecturers? Where are the social work lecturers? They're not. And we talk more and more about teamwork in health care …

But certainly we want to help in the process of moving from the twentieth-century uniprofessional department to the twenty-first-century multiprofessional department, which I hope will be replicated deliberately in other universities, and will not only be in palliative care but will spread to other areas, certainly other areas of chronic medical care.

Team structures and processes

Successful teamwork was often attributed to the particular character of hospice teams. They were seen as more egalitarian in structure, and more democratic in their processes than hospital teams. Patricia Scott recalls a period when she worked on a placement at Sir Michael Sobell House, Oxford in the early 1980s, while she was still a ward sister at Stoke Mandeville Hospital:

Certainly … in the hospital there was much more clear distinction between the professionals. The consultant, there was no doubt, led the team. Well OK, the consultant leads the team here. There was no doubt about that. I, as the ward sister, would have always been very conscious of the fact that I was the leader of the nursing team. One never felt the same … one cared for one's team, of course, but it wasn't in the same way, the same feeling of … equality, really, as here, where we're all humans in this *together*, supporting each other, very needful of it. And certainly, although we worked with, very closely, with physios … in the general hospital field, the working with them … in the hospice setting has … much more overlap, much more intertwining, less edges that are sharp, more blurred edges, which is not always easy, is it? It takes work. And I began to be very conscious of how strong this concept was, and how positive it was for the sake of the patients and the families and … these were very early impressions. I remember … realising just how enormous it was, and how difficult it would be to bring all this back to a general ward and make any impression.

Tim Lovel describes the democratic approach to multidisciplinary working which evolved at St Benedict's, an NHS Hospice in Sunderland, when he took over as Medical Director in 1988:

Roland Ramsey was very much the Director of the Hospice, and what he said went … but he had a lot of time for all the nurses. They had excellent social workers, gradually we were able to bring in physiotherapists, pharmacists, occupational therapists, and develop a truly multidisciplinary team, who met regularly, discussed the patients, put forward their viewpoints. And certainly in my time I encouraged them to do that, and if I was outvoted about what we should or should not do for a patient, I didn't ever feel that I then had to say 'Well, I'm Director and that's what we're going to do.' Some hospices did run in a more autocratic way than that, rather like President Lincoln, who put a proposal to his cabinet and took a vote on something he wanted to do, and he said, 'Right, this is a result of the vote, gentlemen, the ayes 1, the noes 12, the ayes have it!' Well some hospices did, for a time, continue to run like that, where the Medical Director in the last analysis had the casting vote, but not now, I think, and there's no real reason why, just because somebody is the senior doctor, he should or she should be able to dictate all policy and, particularly, all care for a patient.

Maddy Gerrish, an American nurse with a background in psychiatric nursing and family therapy, was instrumental in the development of hospice in the USA. She visited St Luke's, Sheffield in the 1970s at the invitation of Eric Wilkes, to teach the staff there about family systems approaches to care. In her interview she talks about the importance not just of multidisciplinary teamwork, in which the distinctive contributions of team members are pooled together to create more effective working, but of multidisciplinary roles. This is the only clear example in the interviews of an aspiration to transdisciplinary teamwork, as described above, in which boundaries between disciplines blur to the extent of team members taking on each others' roles. Interestingly, Payne[19] notes that this approach originated among nurses in the USA. Maddy Gerrish recalls:

And one of the things … that I wanted to really emphasise to you that I think I did when I came to St Luke's: I believe that from my early nursing and the way that I had worked in terms of understanding the holistic model and the systems model which I'd had very early; it had to be multidisciplinary. I don't know about what was happening in the UK but in the United States the disciplines were very much territorial and there was a slotted role: physicians did this, nursing did this, and social worker did this. Psychologists were not very involved in the '60s in any kind of physical health care. My belief was that you had to integrate, and I continue to believe that. And that if we could have multidisciplinary roles, and that the team could be developed, we were going to provide a better kind of care, and quality for staff as well as for family and patients.

Elements of tension and conflict

As already indicated in some of these extracts, teamwork has not always been easily achieved. Interprofessional conflicts, strongly held differences of opinion about policy and strategy, the tensions inherent in driving change forward have all played a part in the hospice story. Prue Clench encapsulates many of these problems in the following extract:

How do teams operate? How do people get job satisfaction out of what they're doing? A lot of empty talk about, 'We're just one big family,' but in fact families have divorces and problems. And I see the whole evolution of hospice care as being rather like going through childhood to teenage years to young adult, and the problems that go with the different eras. And we were very much at a sort of young adult stage, with people with very strong views not all that well tried out. And to be in the first generation of hospice people you needed to be somebody who was willing to stand alone, to be rather idealistic. And usually people came from a very clinical base so they didn't have management experience. You can also look at who led care through each of the sort of stages. Well primarily in the beginning, doctors led care, even in the earliest Macmillan teams it was perceived that they needed to have a doctor linked to the team. And that resulted in some quite crazy situations where sort of retired pathologists were sort of tame enough to agree to be in on the meetings now and again, and were sort of nominated as the palliative care consultant for that team, and gradually that was abandoned.

So management began with sort of Medical Director, then you had your nurse responsible for nine-tenths of the staff who were nurses. And often there was a conflict because doctors don't usually have management skills, they're notoriously bad at getting any money out of Health Authorities because they operated from the simple logic that, if we're looking after the patient in the hospice,

you don't have to look after them in the hospital so therefore there must be some money free, and couldn't actually understand that another patient filled up that bed so it didn't actually save the Health Authority money. And the very fact that often doctors were trying to negotiate things where nurses were holding the power and authority didn't go down too well. Nurses didn't like being told things by doctors. So there were all sorts of those conflicts.

Well then, nurses, I think, became perhaps a bit more recognised and more seen, as the post of Matron became a bit more influential than it was initially. And usually the doctor and the nurse got on all right, but by this time you might have a Chairman and Trustees who felt they'd worked all these years to get this thing up and going, and weren't consulted about anything. You know, the medical people seemed to think they were the only ones that had an opinion or mattered. So conflicts occurred at that point.

Later on it's gone on, and we've developed the Administrator who's now become the Chief Executive. And a lot of Dr Desmond Graves'[20] discussion at management conferences was about, you know: who is the team? And how, who should be the leader of the team? And can three people ... for several years everybody tried to have three people equal – the Administrator, the Matron and the doctor, which doesn't work very well either, you know. And these things had to be explored, but they needed the language and they needed the experiential learning of management techniques to try and find a way through. And I think, happily, that actually isn't today's problem.

Finally, social worker Julia Franklin talks openly about a less tangible area of conflict which she calls the 'dark side' of working in the hospice environment. She describes some of the effects which can contradict and undermine the collaborative ethic of teamwork, and how she managed these elements within herself:

I ask myself: what happens to us when we're working forever with death and dying and we're giving out such a lot, and we are so good, and people say it's so wonderful in your establishment … what happens to the dark side? And sometimes I feel that it comes out in all sorts of extremely competitive and ruthless ways. I don't know exactly what we do with it. I know what I try and do sometimes, myself, and then I feel very disloyal to the organisation I work for; I actually try and dispel the myth that we're all so good. And I think I'm inclined, personally, within our organisation, to get a bit over the top, and to swear, and to sort of … well, be like an ordinary person, and not be precious. But I think the dark side comes out in, quite often, backstabbing each other, or projecting our anger and our grief onto, either people or the Council, that is the Trustees, or individuals within organisations; we scapegoat.

And I'm not actually criticising exactly, 'cause I think it's got to go somewhere, but for me personally I've had to stick to my … I've had to have my supervision and my support and my own personal growth workshops that I've chosen to go on, where I can feel that I'm getting rid of, or dealing with, you know, some of my own dark side. But I think it's very hard to talk that language to other professions sometimes. You know, I don't think that that concept that you gain through, or that I've gained through, my training in various things, and my … I'm interested in Gestalt and all sorts of things … that I sort of feel like I can talk that language, and I can begin to understand it a bit, and think about how I am myself. But it's very difficult to talk that language to others, perhaps, who aren't at the same stage.

The extracts in this chapter reveal the important contribution of teamworking to the successful development of the hospice movement. More than this they show the unique character of teamwork in hospices, which have captured the powerful motivations of a wide range of individuals and blended them into a force for communal growth. We have seen that patients have been regarded as central members of the hospice community from the earliest days and that many different types of teams have been forged among individuals and organisations to further the ideals of providing care for the terminally ill. The synergy of partnership working going on simultaneously among committed individuals 'on the ground' and at a strategic level between organisations created a powerful fuel to sustain the development of the movement.

The notion of the multidisciplinary team grew to be an important feature of teamwork within hospices. This wider team was conceptualised not only to include doctors, nurses and other health and social care professionals but also hospice administrators, volunteers of all kinds and, importantly, even the wider community in which an individual hospice is located.

We learned in our interviews that teamwork has permeated all aspects of hospice development and each stage of growth. From the driving forward of initial ideas in the late 1960s, through an explosion of development in the 1980s and 1990s to a vision for the twenty-first century, the ability to work together in a variety of ways for a common purpose – despite some elements of tension and conflict – has been a central theme in the success of the hospice movement.

Notes

1. C. Saunders, 'A place to die', *Crux* 11 (3): 24–27, 1973–74.
2. The concept of 'total pain' is discussed in more detail in Chapter 6, below.
3. C. Saunders, 'Current views on pain relief and terminal care' in M. Swerdlow (ed.), *The Therapy of Pain* (Lancaster: MTP Press, 1981: 215–41).
4. *Chambers Twentieth-Century Dictionary*.
5. M. Payne, *Teamwork in Multiprofessional Care* (London: Macmillan, 2000).
6. J. Corner, 'The multidisciplinary team – fact or fiction', plenary lecture given at Eighth Congress of European Association for Palliative Care, The Hague, The Netherlands, 2–5 April 2003.
7. See Chapter 4, below, for more details on some of these organisations.
8. Peter Laidlaw is referring here to the 'partnership' funding arrangement between government and the independent hospices, discussed in Chapter 2, above.
9. Cancer Care is a Lancaster-based charity that provides complementary care to patients at earlier stages of their disease and works closely with local hospice and palliative care services.
10. M. Payne, *Teamwork in Multiprofessional Care* (London: Macmillan, 2000: 9).
11. H. Garner and F.P. Orelove, *Teamwork in Human Services: Models and applications across the life span* (Newton, MA: Butterworth-Heinemann, 1994).
12. Tom West was speaking in January 1997.
13. J.J. Horwitz, *Team Practice and the Specialist* (Springfield, IL: Charles C. Thomas, 1970).
14. J. Øvretveit, 'How to describe interprofessional working' in J. Øvretveit, P. Mathias and T. Thompson (eds.), *Interprofessional Working for Health and Social Care* (London: Macmillan, 1997: 9–33).
15. M. Payne, *Teamwork in Multiprofessional Care* (London: Macmillan, 2000).
16. Occupational Therapists.
17. Investors in People is a national quality standard which sets a level of good practice for improving an organisation's performance through its people. It is monitored by Investors in People UK. See www.iipuk.co.uk.
18. Marilyn Relf was talking in November 1997.
19. M. Payne, *Teamwork in Multiprofessional Care* (London: Macmillan, 2000).
20. Desmond Graves, an adviser on hospice management issues during the mid-1980s.

4 Diversification: the rise of hospice organisations and professional associations

'Leaders do the right things, managers do things right ...'
Michael Murphy

As the hospice movement in the UK spread at the local level, it was quickly accompanied by what became a proliferation of associations and organisations that took on representative roles nationally. The period from the mid-1980s was one of challenge and growth as new hospices on the ground brought emerging issues about their representation in policy and in professional practice. The hospice movement began to enjoy a level of public recognition that it had been seeking from the outset and significantly, various professional groups began to show a serious interest in specialising in this field of endeavour. With this came greater policy recognition and opportunities to influence the strategic development of hospice and palliative care. In particular, there were concerns about how the growing number of voluntary, independent hospices would relate to the structures and methods of the NHS. Quite quickly a diverse range of organisations was formed – and it might well be asked just what purpose was served by such a patchwork of overlapping interests.

This chapter therefore focuses on the charitable foundations, multidisciplinary partnerships and professional associations which have come to support the disparate groups within hospice and palliative care. We can see in Table 1 the range of such organisations and we have grouped them here into four broad categories: service providers, umbrella organisations, single profession associations and single role associations. As the chapter unfolds we gain an insight into some of these organisations and the contexts in which they were established.

Service providers

In this first section we turn our attention to the work of two major charities that have had a significant role in shaping the development of hospice care in the UK: Macmillan Cancer Relief and Marie Curie Cancer Care.

Macmillan Cancer Relief

In the UK the earliest cancer care organisation of the twentieth century was the charity which is now Macmillan

Table 1 Hospice and palliative care associations in the UK

Service providers	Umbrella organisations	Single profession associations	Single role associations
Clinical Macmillan Cancer Relief Marie Curie Cancer Care Sue Ryder Care *Non-clinical* Council for Music in Hospitals (provides live concerts in hospices) Hospice information (Service) Jessie's Fund (supports music therapy for children) Paintings in Hospitals (provides pictures to hospices) Pets as Therapy (provides animals for patient stimulation) Rosetta Life (enables patients to explore their experiences through photography, poetry and drama)	*Multidisciplinary* Help the Hospices National Council for Hospice and Specialist Palliative Care Services Scottish Partnership for Palliative Care *Service type* Association of Children's Hospices National Forum for Hospice at Home *Special group* Independent Hospice Representative Committee National Association of Complementary Therapists in Hospice and Palliative Care National Network for the Palliative Care of People with Learning Disabilities St Columba's Fellowship (for Christians) *Single interest* Bereavement Research Forum Libraries in Hospices Palliative Care Research Society	Association of Chartered Physiotherapists in Oncology and Palliative Care Association of Hospice and Palliative Care Chaplains Association of Hospice and Specialist Palliative Care Social Workers Association for Palliative Medicine of Great Britain and Ireland HOPE – Occupational Therapists Specialist Section Hospice and Palliative Care Pharmacists' Association RCN Palliative Nurses Group The Creative Response: Art Therapy in Palliative Care, AIDS, Cancer and Loss	Association for Hospice Management Association of Palliative Day Care Leaders Forum of Chairmen of Independent Hospices InVOLve – Managing Volunteers in Palliative care National Association of Hospice Fundraisers

Cancer Relief. After witnessing the effects of cancer on the life of his father, Douglas Macmillan founded the charity[1] in 1911, and maintained a hands-on involvement for the next 53 years. He resigned as chairman in 1964, aged 80. Under Macmillan's patronage, Cancer Relief became a registered Benevolent Society in 1924 and became known as the National Society for Cancer Relief, distributing funds to patients and their families to cover cancer-related costs. Macmillan's vision included the establishment of care homes and the provision of trained nurses to enhance domiciliary care.

Although nurse visitors were appointed in 1933, it was not until 1975 that the first 'Macmillan' nurse cared for dying cancer patients[2] and the first Macmillan cancer care unit opened in Christchurch, Dorset. Both these innovations were due to the vision of Major Henry Garnett[3] who joined the charity as Deputy Chairman in 1973. Before his retirement in 1987, the Society had also developed education programmes in cancer care and advanced pain control (1980) and introduced the concept of Macmillan-funded doctors (1986).

A tall, ex-Guards' officer, Garnett presented a formidable image as the public face of the organisation, and he drew heavily on his postwar experience as Chairman of Gillette Europe. In the following extract, Richard Hillier lightheartedly recalls his rare talent for negotiation:

He was a rogue, and he thought I was a rogue, and so we got on very well … And, yes, watching him negotiate with this tough Health Authority here [in Southampton] was stunning really. I mean he was a really ace negotiator. And I must admit I think he's the most talented person, although he was a terrible sort of manipulator, and used people to get what he wanted. I think he was the flair behind Cancer Relief.

Prue Clench became a national adviser for the hospice movement, working especially with the Macmillan organisation. She travelled frequently with Henry Garnett and recalls his commitment to the Macmillan nurse:

I learned a lot travelling with Henry Garnett. I was usually the driver, he was a six-foot-eight Guards' officer – and I had little cars, so it was folding him up to get him into my car. But I often drove because we would do many meetings in one or two days, but we also used to travel quite a lot by train. So I learned an enormous amount about negotiating with Health Authorities and planning and presenting ideas and budgets and so on. He was always, always totally in tune with what the ordinary man in the street needed, wanted, enthused them. He was absolutely loyalty itself to any Macmillan nurse. He would put down his life for a Macmillan nurse.

The origin of the 'Macmillan nurse' designation and the location of the first service have become matters of debate.[4] In the following extract, Richard Lamerton of St Joseph's, Hackney recalls how he secured funding for four nurses from

Left to right: Sir Charles Davis, Chair of the National Society for Cancer Relief, Prue Clench and Major Henry Garnett.

Henry Garnett at Cancer Relief. When Lamerton rejected Garnett's suggestion that they be called 'Cancer Relief nurses', an alternative emerged: the 'Macmillan Service' – and the modern Macmillan nurse was added to the Hackney team:

Our nurses were doing more and more and it was evident that we were needing more nurses as the numbers increased. We had four Boroughs, each one giving us a nurse, and four more who we had to find the money for. And at that time I met Henry Garnett from Cancer Relief and asked him if he would be prepared to fund them. This was a brand new idea. They'd never heard of it before. And they went and discussed it and came back and said it was a very interesting idea;

would we call them Cancer Relief nurses? And we said no, because in those days quite a lot of patients didn't know they had cancer. And so they dug around and they came up with this name Macmillan, and it was entirely because I'd said no, we wouldn't call them Cancer Relief nurses. They'd dug out the name of Douglas Macmillan, the founder. They were not called the Macmillan Fund, or anything like it in those days. And so we were called the Macmillan Service, and that was how the first Macmillan nurses arose.[5]

Prue Clench remembers that Cancer Relief was a source of funding for many pioneers. She too visited the charity's head office in Dorset Square, London, a journey that led to the establishment of a 'Macmillan Service' at the Dorothy House Foundation, Bath:

In the beginning, I think, anybody who was trying to develop hospice care went to St Christopher's for inspiration, and they went to Cancer Relief, as it then was, for money. And we were no exception. So we had our interview, off to Dorset Square in London. And we had an interview with Major Garnett, and he said, you know, it was an interesting idea, but a hospice needed to have a full multidisciplinary team, and he didn't really think we had reached that stage. So we came away a bit dampened, but not too much … I'm not quite sure whether we then reapplied, or whether Major Garnett contacted me. He certainly remained very much interested in our progress. So about 18 months later he said they were prepared to give a grant. But we were already known as 'Dorothy House nurses', we didn't want to have individual members of staff funded. We wanted a grant straight to the charity, and so we had a very early grant towards our domiciliary service, as we then called it, and became a Macmillan service. But they weren't Macmillan nurses, and therefore when you go back to this wonderful competition of who got there first and did things, we are not the first Macmillan grant on their list. What Henry Garnett would say, if he were able to speak up into this, is that it was the

model of a place on which they based their subsequent Macmillan nurses. They had one or two nurses who were funded by Macmillan before Dorothy House began, like I think maybe at St Luke's [Sheffield], but certainly at Christchurch – I think Christchurch was the first unit that had home care nurses who were called Macmillan nurses, and they were funded right from the beginning.

Turning next to the Macmillan units, Prue Clench gives an insight into the practical difficulties surrounding this initiative.[6] Sited on hospital premises, the charity provided the unit's capital costs while the NHS picked up the running costs. Unfortunately, the Macmillan expansion coincided with a series of cutbacks within the NHS, a factor which led Garnett to adopt a more cautious approach to future developments:

The major problem that Macmillan faced in those days was that they had built – 10, I think it was then – in-patient units in conjunction with hospitals, on hospital premises, as Macmillan units. The simplified version was that they raised the capital and then the Health Authority continued to fund. And the first of the really big cutbacks in the NHS happened in 1975,[7] I think it was, and so many Health Authorities couldn't see their way to being able to take on that kind of an obligation. And so they had a hiatus with quite a number of projects. And St Peter's [Hospice] at Bristol was a perfect example of that, where in fact they started much the same time as Dorothy House, but they were orientated to an in-patient unit, and they couldn't get any assurance from the Health Authority that they would pay the ongoing cost. And so what to do, really? 'Cause the public gets very impatient with having raised money for two or three years and nothing to show for it. And so it was a breakthrough to say, 'We'll stage this care, start off with two nurses on the ground,' and two was really because that was the sort of money that anybody could afford at that moment, 'Put two nurses on the road, visiting in conjunction with district nurses and GPs or the radiotherapy unit.' And then as your funds continue to grow, maybe you could start day care to expand that, and when you could see your way to running, as well as building, a unit, then go for the bedded. And so it was famous for its staged approach, and that appealed very much to Major Garnett. He thought it was a sensible way of going about things; nothing too big, or lost by trying your hand at that.

Gloria Day, at that time a district nurse, was recruited by Eric Wilkes to work with another district nurse, Shelagh Bellamy, and establish a Macmillan service in Sheffield in the mid-1970s. In the following extract she recalls her experiences:

I was travelling all over the city, working every hour that God sent, and Shelagh and I at that time, because we were developing this service, we actually gave it our all. We would go out in the middle of the night; we would go out early morning; we would go out late at night; we would go out mid-evening. If people were in trouble the nurses knew that they could actually send for us; that if they were having problems that we would listen. They would ring us up, I would have something, well they should be ringing the doctor and they would end up ringing the doctor, and I would ring the doctor, but no, they just wanted to talk, and they knew we were approachable, they knew we would do anything. And because we were both well known from the district, that actually the nurses were the ones that we won the first. We had a lot of opposition at times because there were nurses that didn't know us and thought we were interfering and difficult, and that we were trying to show off and, you know, 'Why did we know all this stuff about medication when they'd been doing quite a good job?'

But eventually, I think, because of our attitude – and we had a lot of success stories, you know, a lot of good things – there were a lot of failures as well, you know, that we didn't do so well, and you felt terribly sad about those. But I don't think anything would have made a difference in those instances: you just tried your best. But generally we used the expertise of the hospice to relate to and we would go back and ask Professor Wilkes, Dr Crowther, 'What medication should we give?' 'How often should it be given?' You know, 'What's the right dosage?' And I was actually there for 16 years: I never wanted to move on to anything else. I totally destroyed any ambition I'd got, and I just became a Macmillan nurse, you know – I was offered other jobs at times and I didn't want to do them. I just wanted to do Macmillan nursing.

Patricia Gilbert was appointed to the nursing staff of St Gemma's, Leeds in 1978, caring for in-patients. Nine years later, she joined the home care team as a Macmillan nurse and discovered the two roles contrasted sharply:

It was vastly different because you're out working on your own, you know. You were based at the hospice. In the morning you'd come in and have your admission meeting with the doctors and the social workers and the rest of the community team, but then you'd got your own caseload to sort out. You're out on your own all day long visiting patients in their own home, which is a totally different environment, and you have to remember that you are a visitor in their home, and the house might be filthy dirty or it might be spick and span but you just have to try and make yourself feel comfortable, even if you've got dogs jumping all over you and television's blaring away and, you know, you've still got to try and do the best you can for the patient. So yes, I find it a big change and I find it a huge responsibility because, although there are other professionals involved in this patient's care, you felt very responsible for them and to give them the best you could, and that was emotional support, sorting out their symptoms, getting them pain controlled, symptom controlled, sorting out their finances if they were having difficulties applying to Cancer Relief Macmillan Fund for grants, getting Attendance Allowance for them, getting equipment, involving the district nurse, involving social workers – yes it was, it took a lot of learning. And you know it was very much you'd got to remember that you weren't there to do the hands-on nursing; you were there in an advisory capacity and in a supportive capacity, and you had to be careful that you didn't tread on toes with the district nurses.

In addition to pump-priming medical and nursing posts, Macmillan sponsored lectureships in social work. Carolyn Brodribb recalls her reluctance to lead the Association of Hospice Social Workers, a reticence due solely to her intended application for a Macmillan post planned for the University of Plymouth:

At that point Macmillan had decided there needed to be input into social work in terms of university-based lecturers – there was in nursing, and there was in medicine – and so they've set up three posts: Southampton, with Frances Sheldon first – Southampton, Reading and Hull and the second tranche was to be Plymouth, Cheltenham and the University of Middlesex. And I remember when I was asked if I would consider becoming Chair [of the Association of Hospice Social Workers], saying, 'But how would this fit in? Because I do want to apply for this post that's coming up in Plymouth?' And being told firmly that that would be ideal, you know – the profile of hospice social work. So I could go ahead with applying for the job and, and taking on the role of Chair of the Association of Hospice Social Workers … So I applied for the post in 1993 here: 'Macmillan Social Work Lecturer in Palliative Care', and took up post in 1994. So I was working, setting up a post here, and working as Chair of the Association, at that point. And that was quite interesting; the kind of ideas, the naive ideas I had about how, pushing forward, the post could be achieved in an academic institution. I was familiar with a hospital institution, I was familiar with hospices as a kind of entity, but, by golly, I was not prepared for what a university was like. And

that's another story, you know, sort of trying to introduce the concept of palliative care into a world that was very different.

Marie Curie Cancer Care

When during the Second World War Winston Churchill observed to his liaison officer, Squadron Leader Bernard Robinson, that casualties from cancer were higher than casualties from hostilities, he could not have imagined the effect of his remark. In 1947, as plans were being devised for the inception of the NHS, Bernard Robinson and four colleagues of the Marie Curie Hospital, Hampstead, opted to remain outside of the NHS and continue their cancer care and related activities within the voluntary sector. The terms of a trust deed were agreed in 1949 and the Inaugural Committee confirmed the three objectives of what became known as the Marie Curie Memorial Foundation: a nursing and welfare service for patients in their own homes; the provision of residential nursing homes; and the encouragement and funding of scientific learning.[8]

To determine priorities, a survey was conducted into the needs of cancer patients being nursed at home.[9] Following the recommendations of a report presented in 1952,[10] the first of 11 Marie Curie nursing homes – Hill of Tarvit – opened in Scotland at Cupar, Fife in December of that year. In addition, a new nursing service was introduced to enhance the care of those dying at home, based upon an extended role for district nurses. The Day and Night Nursing Service was established in September 1958 and the research laboratories opened in 1961.[11]

A feature of Marie Curie Cancer Care has been its focus on social and material deprivation and a special interest in the impact of cancer upon the poor. Gillian Petrie, who joined the charity as Welfare Officer in 1979, recalls how the

Welfare Grant Scheme was used to make whatever improvements were possible as people approached the end of their lives:

There was – which was in my hands and the Health Authority's hands – a thing called the Welfare Grant Scheme, which was a sticking plaster grant which the Health Authorities were empowered to give to people who were dying in their own homes, to buy them things which they needed; for example, bed linen. It was a grant which could be applied immediately, that the Foundation in a sense almost underwrote, that if they thought they needed something that would make their lives happier, or better, or whatever, in the last days, they could do this, they could apply for this grant and then we would underwrite it. And it was used for all sorts of things actually. I remember a bottle of Asti spumante, and a set of 'painting by numbers', and a little gardening set, that they could, sort of, do gardening on the windowsill with, apart from the usual things like new bed linen or whatever. And it was a very useful grant, and this was, of course, a grant designed to alleviate poverty – of the patient dying, dying at home.

After the high energy of the 1950s and 1960s, there was a sense that the charity's drive had begun to dissipate during the 1970s. As a consequence, Gillian Petrie was faced with a nursing service she considered to be in disarray. She instituted a package of reforms, making major improvements through the augmentation of community nursing to incorporate care of the dying. In the following extract, she outlines some of the challenges she faced:

The gospel was that [the community nursing service] had been working perfectly well ever since 1952, but I question that very much. Certainly in some sense, yes, it had been working, but it was impossible to say who was a Marie Curie nurse, because they were counting, I guess, people who passed in and out of the system as agency nurses – and in many Health Authorities, as I know, they had never, never implemented the Marie Curie Service ever, I mean. So it is very difficult to know. I take no pleasure in saying this, because it actually was, when I really discovered the state of the real situation, an incredibly difficult and painful situation to cope with, because I was having to tell people who believed that Marie Curie had been doing this work so wonderfully all these years, this was not, in fact, the case. Well you can imagine this didn't make me very popular.

One of the first things we had to do was to discourage the use of agency nursing, to see that Marie Curie teams were genuinely built up in Health Authorities, and to introduce in-service training, because there was absolutely no training. We were very lucky with a lot of Marie Curie nurses because they had previously been district nurses and very often had the experience of being on the district, and therefore could translate those skills. But they were – none of them had any special training in palliative nursing at all.

When Michael Carleton-Smith retired from the army in 1985, he joined Marie Curie as Director General. In 1988 his wife was diagnosed with cancer and, until she died in 1993, he cared for her at home with the help of Marie Curie nurses, district nurses and the local hospice services. As a national charity, the organisation had begun to lose direction, however, and its corporate antagonism towards hospices was becoming a hindrance. The response of Carleton-Smith was to reform the management structure, and to soften the approach by establishing working relationships with hospice partners. Within 10 years, income had increased from £9 million to £55 million; 5,000 part-time Marie Curie nurses were seeing 19,000 patients a year; the 11 centres had 300 beds, catering for some 4,000 patients per year (12 per cent of all voluntary beds in hospice/palliative care) and 70 educational courses were being organised from centres in London and Edinburgh.[12] In an interview conducted in 1995, he highlights the reforming process as follows:

I might have mentioned to you before, that charities have phases of life as, almost, humans do. They have infancy, which is the stage at which the Trustees who form it are the hands-on operators, then there's adolescence which might be quite a long period – and out of which it might never grow – when they have to bring in staff, they have to bring in management and, as with parents and adolescents, there may be conflict between the two. And then ultimately a charity gets to the point of maturity where the Trustees stand back, whilst retaining the overall legal responsibilities they have, but let management manage this now mature organisation. As an organisation Marie Curie, when I joined in 1985, was old enough, in the sense that it was founded in 1948, but was very adolescent in managerial terms. Many of the original Trustees were on the Council and the Executive Committee, and they had a very jealous hold on what went on, with a plethora of committees and no managerial structure

Michael Carleton-Smith joined Marie Curie Cancer Care in 1985.

or systems, really, at all. It was amazing, actually, that it was as effective as it was.

One of the peculiarities of life with Marie Curie was an attitude at that time, that [the Trustees] did not like the word 'hospices' and would have little to do with the hospice movement. Very early on – I mean within weeks, I suppose, of arrival – I went and met Cicely Saunders, of course, and talked with her. I met Eric Wilkes and talked with him. And I went to a conference of Help the Hospices and was generously given the platform, and so I exposed my views of the way I thought that we should mutually cooperate together.

This vision of cooperation was incorporated into a new strategy, providing a fresh impetus and energising the organisation:

I am really excited because I think we've got a fund-raising, marketing and public relations structure which is so much better than we've ever had before. And although we've gone from £9 million to £55 million I think there is a terrific potential for growth in income, although there might be turbulence in that at various stages on the way and this might indeed be a difficult year for legacies, so it's never going to be easy. But I think there's going to be a lot more income still to use. We've got a strategy which has got a lot of room for development in it … Our growth area is the nursing service, where at the moment we've got about 40 per cent of all the cancer patients who die at home, having a Marie Curie nurse, what we want is to get to at least 50 per cent. We have an average of 52 hours per patient, we want to have an average of 80 hours and, incidentally, my wife had 75 hours so I've got a feel for what is right. And of course we are expanding our excellent management system whereby we control them over a sort of regional basis which we call Nurse Link, extending – we've got it in 70 Trusts now and that will go up to circa 200 Trusts over time. All that will cost a great deal of money. On the educational side there's a great deal of work to be done, it's an expanding area. We've got Marie Curie diplomas now in 'health care' and 'palliative care'. We've got nearly all our courses accredited for university degree CAT[13] points. We could spend more money on education, and will do, but it also generates money. We also want to spend more money on training our own staff, not just in nursing and medical matters, but in managerial issues, and of course computer issues.

So there's a lot of training to be done internally and that needs expanding and will expand. And then the Research Institute, well they could always take more money. What we've strategically said is that the size of the envelope of our present building and site at Oxsted in Surrey is to be the foreseeable ceiling of it. We have got, already, a fully developed, but empty, laboratory so we've got the scope for a seventh team but not yet the money for it. So that's the foreseeable immediate future. I think that in terms of influence Marie Curie with the new team will continue to grow in influence and importance and gradually to get overseas. I think that we've already got, starting to have tentacles overseas. We're running, we're going to run the fifth congress of the Association for Palliative Medicine[14] in England next year, international conference, which is a very big event, will be attended by about 2,000 people.

Alongside these developments came the transition of Marie Curie nursing homes to specialist palliative care units. In the following extract, Tim Lovel recalls a defining moment in the founding of a new Marie Curie palliative care centre in Newcastle:

Conrad House [was] an old-fashioned Marie Curie establishment staffed by very good GPs – one practice staffed it – but it was an antiquated old building, which had really been, I think, in pre-war times a home for incurables, and I was told that people in Newcastle would cross the road before they got to it rather than pass the dreaded doors, because that's where you went in to die, and the

only way out is in a wooden box, so there was a great fear of Conrad House. And about, I suppose, six years ago,[15] the Marie Curie Foundation, which ran it, decided to build a brand new modern hospice to replace it, launched an appeal for funds and got, I don't know, half or two-thirds of what they needed. It cost them over £4 million to build it, so there was a big shortfall in the amount of money required.

And at that time I was the Northern Region representative on the National Hospice Council, and their Director General, Michael Carleton-Smith rang me up and said, 'What shall we do? Our Council and Marie Curie meets today, and we have to make a decision, should we go ahead with building this new hospice that everybody wants, or should we withdraw because we haven't got all the money?' and I said, 'You must go ahead, Michael, you've raised all this money in Newcastle, you can't possibly give it back, even if you could identify who'd given it to you' … I don't know whether that advice made any difference, but on that morning the Council did decide to build it and it's been a tremendous success, and of course it's just opposite the site of the present oncology centre, at the Newcastle General Hospital, so it's very well situated for giving immediate cover and particularly for giving a service in the hospital for palliative care when they require specialist help.

Sally Campalani, Clinical Services Manager at the Marie Curie Centre, Belfast, outlines the particular role of the Marie Curie nurse, and points to the reputation of Marie Curie in the field of education:

The Marie Curie nurses provide practical nursing care in people's homes – they actually do a full shift. You know, where a Macmillan nurse will dip in and out and give counselling work alongside the district nurse, and they'll be dipping in and out, Marie Curie nurses are providing actual one-to-one nursing in patients' own homes, usually in the last few weeks of life. And they will go in and stay all night with that patient and do any washing, or bathing, or syringe drivers that need to be done – and that's the main, main difference between them.

I'm Secretary to Northern Ireland Cancer Nursing Research Group, I was forced into taking that responsibility. I'm a bit over-stretched, but they tend to invite me along and I think it's a reflec-tion of the change in Marie Curie, whereas before it would have been very much the hospice seen as sort of, you know, the leader in the field of education and nurse development and things. I think that's balanced itself out now and we're equally invited along, and the feedback we get is that we're seen as being very progressive, and inventive, and creative. We tend to get a lot of people asking to come for updates and things with us. We've a huge throughput now of students – we get Macmillan nurses who want to come and update with us. Everybody comes to us with an induction, wherever they are. So we've got a huge workload there – the students, the educa-tion that we provide has really made a big impact on our workload because the nurses all take their mentorship very seriously and we get excellent results from our audits and things, and the feedback we get from the universities. But the placements are taken seriously and the girls really do learn a lot, and they go out of their way to mentor very carefully the students – they all write their objectives and check that they're meeting them and whatever. So – it works very well, the relationship seems OK.

Finally, Steve Kirk, interviewed in 2000 whilst working at St Gemma's, Leeds, recalls his earlier experience of working in a Marie Curie centre and indicates the support which a national organisation can provide:

I think Marie Curie [provides] national support – they've got a Head Office providing a lot of support mechanisms. They have a Director of Caring Services, personnel support, finance support that will provide both telephone advice as well as coming out to visit the hospice if necessary. You know there's always somebody at the end of the phone

for advice and support. There are ten other Marie Curie Hospices – all in a similar position to yourself and available for support. The matrons – as they were called at the time – meet twice a year at a workshop for three to five days with the medical consultants, all the senior fundraising staff where you can find support, reassurance and advice as well as hear what else is going on in the other hospices.

Umbrella organisations

From these two major national care providers, we now turn to the work of the multidisciplinary umbrella organisations which emerged to represent the broad interests of a wide range of hospice and palliative caregivers. These organisations include Help the Hospices, the National Council for Hospice and Specialist Palliative Care Services and the Scottish Partnership for Palliative Care. In contrast to these 'broad remit' organisations, other multidisciplinary associations – such as the Bereavement Research Forum, Libraries in Hospices and the Palliative Care Research Society – were also developed to focus on particular areas of interest within the hospice/palliative care field.

Help the Hospices

Help the Hospices was established in 1984 by the Duchess of Norfolk and others as a national charity with the purpose of supporting hospices by means of a variety of grant-giving and lobbying activities.[16] Its founder members included Eric Wilkes and Peter Quilliam; Cicely Saunders became its Presi-dent; and Paul Rossi was its first Chief Executive.[17] Active in its formation, Eric Wilkes reflects on the founding of Help the Hospices and, with it, the establishment of a valuable representative voice for independent hospices:

The Duchess of Norfolk had been asked … to help produce a teaching centre at St Joseph's Hospice [Hackney] for which they required the very considerable sum – 'cause we're talking of 12 or 14 years ago[18] – of a million pounds. And the Duchess was very committed: she'd visited St Joseph's, she was impressed and she got on like a house on fire with the nuns, and she raised a million pounds with almost embarrassing ease in the matter of a year or so. But the hospice work had rather got under her skin and she had taken an interest in hospices other than St Joseph's and the hospice movement generally … So she quickly got on to the fact that Marie Curie looked after its own, the Cancer Relief Macmillan Fund in those days was almost exclusively in support of NHS initiatives and was not interested in getting involved with private independent charities of doubtful reliability. And yet, most of the work was being done by private, independent, charitable hospices who had no one to represent their interests on a national scale.

When Help the Hospices came, this was a mechanism whereby the independent hospice units could, at last, achieve some kind of representative body. And at the moment, at the time we started, there was Marie Curie with multiple contracts with Health Authorities doing the nursing side, looking after their own 11 units, there was Sue Ryder[19] looking after its fewer units, there was Macmillan with its Macmillan nurses, and the independent hospices were doing most of the work and had no national voice at all. And so I thought it was proper to move over from Macmillan to Help the Hospices, a much smaller, less established charity, but I thought it had a role to play, however small. And I think I was right and I think it has had a good role to play.

Paul Rossi, subsequently employed by Macmillan Cancer Relief, recalls here how he became the first employee of Help the Hospices in 1984 and how, from small beginnings, the organisation developed a broad and influential role:

[My involvement was] not quite by accident, but I certainly didn't have a plan to work in this area. I had been working in the public sector, in politics, in public administration for a number of years and in 1983, was it three or four? – can't remember now – saw a job advertised as the Press and Parliamentary Officer for the new organisation called Help the Hospices, which had just been established by the Duchess of Norfolk and the British Medical Association [BMA]. And so I was interested in this job and I applied for it, and I got it. And then found that as well as being the Press and Parliamentary Officer, you were also secretary, chief officer, typing secretary, administrator and everything else, because it was a new organisation – and indeed, I was the first person the organisation employed. And the role of the organisation, as perceived at the time, was an organisation that would work to support and help all the voluntary hospices around the UK which lacked a national association and a national voice …

Paul Rossi: first employee of Help the Hospices.

I think the most important challenge internally was to have Help the Hospices accepted as the sort of organisation that it wanted to be, which was to support and help, and indeed to represent, the interests of the hospices around the UK. And that was a challenge for all sorts of reasons: I think there was firstly some suspicion about Help the Hospices and its link with the BMA – I think some people felt that hospice work was not just about doctoring, why should the BMA have such a prominent role in it? I think others felt that really, who was this organisation setting itself up without perhaps too much consultation to represent us on a UK wide stage? So I think we had to spend an awful long time getting the acceptance of hospices and the hospice world generally to having this sort of organisation … Most hospices, in fact all hospices, are by their nature local organisations, their fund-raising is local, their realm of activity is local, and a lot of them at the time didn't really see the need to have a national body. Indeed some of them thought it was a positively negative step to have a national body, they thought they would survive much better as local organisations making their own way, making their own contacts. There was also a degree of rivalry between some of them and that was sometimes professional rivalry and sometimes rivalry over territory; it's quite a small pond actually. So the possibilities for discord could be sometimes considerable.

Tony Crowther, Medical Director of St Luke's, Sheffield, remembers that Help the Hospices set up regional committees in order to be more in touch with local issues:

They set up regional committees that served Help the Hospices, so that Help the Hospices were, in theory, in touch with what was going on throughout the country. And I think partly because of me, partly because of Eric [Wilkes] – probably more because of Eric – the one in Trent [Region] kept going and we still, as you know, have meetings every quarter. Rather informal meetings but nice meetings, in that

there's nobody backbiting, we're all comparing notes and seeing how we're getting on.

Among the developing values and practices of the hospice movement, there was clearly a need for a new forum where hospice activists could debate emerging issues and establish inter-hospice networks and groups. That need was partially met when Help the Hospices launched its annual conference in 1984. Prue Clench reflects on the passion of the speakers and the excitement inherent in these early conferences:

I look at the Help the Hospices annual conferences, and I think they're wonderful, but I think they've lost something.[20] Aren't I lucky that I was part of those days, and the fun that we had, and people like Robert Twycross and Richard Lamerton? I mean part of the excitement of the day was the wonderfully articulate debates – if not arguments – that they had over many issues. And most of us learned to think out all aspects of problems by listening to these very soapbox opinions that were put forward by different pioneers which really helped you to choose kind of where you came into all of that. And they were very gifted people, they believed with everything they'd got, with passion, in what they were doing, and it was very inspiring. And you crept back last thing at night having had a day that kept you going for the next six months.

Along with many others, Prue Clench was originally sceptical about the Help the Hospices concept,[21] but here explains how she became convinced of its value:

I thought that it was a real red herring that Help the Hospices came in the first place, because we needed the sort of concept of the National Council then, and Macmillan, by dint of its money, had an enormous amount of clout, and Help the Hospices sort of really floated another irritating group. They went on to be very sophisticated, and much more useful in actually handling the government aspects of policy and things. Paul Rossi was quite marvellous at telling us all what was going on and priming us and getting action going, and I was sad, and I think something has been lost by handing over to the National Council.

Among Help the Hospices' initiatives was a series of Fellowships. In the following extract, Julia Franklin remembers how in 1988 one of the last Fellowships to be awarded took her to Israel the following year to study bereavement services:

There were so many things happening in the hospice movement around the time I was up in London, certainly Help the Hospices started up in a big way. And they offered these Fellowships for doctors and nurses and social workers and I applied for one, because the whole experience of Israel was pretty amazing that first time. I found it very exciting, interesting, I began to think about the Holocaust and the effects of loss and change, and one thing and another. So I decided to ask for the Fellowship to take me back to Israel to see whether some of the hospices that they were setting up – both in various parts of Israel and also some support teams – whether they'd actually started to think about bereavement, and what they were offering to bereaved relatives, 'cause the bit of me that is quite naive, I guess, thought that they must be experts in grief and bereavement because of their history, their background. So I applied to Help the Hospices and, you know, I was chosen to go. So I had a certain amount of money to spend. And I went. I went for three-and-a-half weeks on my own to the Middle East, which was an absolutely amazing personal experience; but I went to look, you know, at bereavement care and bereavement services out there. And whilst I was out there, I mean I had a lot of really good contacts, the Archbishop of Jerusalem was an old family friend, and he was very, very elderly, but he introduced me to the Mayor of Jerusalem who's an amazing character. And through him I met some very interesting social workers who were trying to set up new things. So, the experience of going back to Israel and writing my report for Help the Hospices was another sort of real [personal] turning point, in a way.

National Council for Hospice and Specialist Palliative Care Services

By the end of the 1980s, perceptions were arising in many quarters, and particularly in government, of a need for a single umbrella organisation that would have the support of palliative care workers in the NHS, Macmillan, Marie Curie, Sue Ryder Care and also across the various professions associated with hospice and palliative care. Amidst heated debate, the National Council for Hospice and Specialist Palliative Care Services was founded in 1991. It was established as a multidisciplinary, representative and coordinating body for NHS and voluntary hospice and specialist palliative care services in England, Wales and Northern Ireland. Key features of its role were: to represent the interests of its members to ministers, civil servants and the media; to provide advice to hospice organisations and palliative care services in their dealings with health authorities and other agencies; to provide a forum for the sharing of knowledge; to develop professional standards, encourage and improve education and undertake measures to improve facilities, resources and skills within palliative care.

Eric Wilkes recalls some of the factors that shaped how the National Council came into being:

Many of us in Help the Hospices, in the days of our success and our unique role, felt it was really improper for a small, informal charity to have this sort of power. We weren't equipped to handle it and therefore what we were doing in starting the idea of the National Council was, to some degree, consciously and selflessly sidelining ourselves.

It was our initiative. You see we had no representative of the NHS, well we did, we had one director who was the director of an NHS hospice, but all the pressures, all the work, all the outgoings were designed for the charities, and we felt, well, if we're going to do this, we've got to bring the NHS in, and we've got to bring the charities together, and we've got to bring in the grand charities of Macmillan and Marie Curie and, slightly smaller scale, Sue Ryder. At the same time, the administrators were slightly hostile to some of the 'Johnny-come-lately' organisations, and were very keen that we did not have, on our Board, what they called in their magazines, sardonically and sarcastically and wittily for administrators, 'The National Associa-tion of Hospice Car Park Attendants'. There was that sort of danger coming.

So we have, I think, seen what was going to happen, into the future, a little more than our other charity colleagues. We saw that there would be hard times for the hospice movement. My own personal enthusiasms for the National Council were not only the theoretical policy-making role with the Ministers, but also the fact that I was very worried that some hospices should not have been built, they should not have been built where they were built, they were perhaps not very good and if they were going to be closed at some time in the future, I thought it was very important to have the National Council to support the butchers of the NHS in this, to try and diffuse the thing and say, 'Well, you know, we have some sympathy, they have a case.' Far more comfortably, I was very keen that where fund-raising was at its most difficult, places like Paddington or Wigan or wherever, the local Health Authority should not walk away from its hospice that it had been supporting for a year, and that the National Council should use its muscle to say, 'Now, this is not right.'

Rita Beattie represented the Northern Ireland voluntary sector on the National Council and highlights the Council's role in networking and dissemination:

There was always, from the Northern Ireland Hospice particularly, and I would have to emphasise this, a keen desire to keep strong links with the mainland – initially Help the Hospices and then, when National Council was formed, with National Council. And I, in particular, because of my having worked outside the Province and worked in Scotland and in England, felt it very important that we kept those strong links; that we learned and shared where we could. So when the National Council was established, I was nominated to be the representative from Northern Ireland to go and represent the voluntary hospice units in the Province. That involved attending three Council meetings a year, and three professional committees per year. My responsibility was to feed into those respective commit-tees, feedback from Northern Ireland, current happenings, develop-ments, not only within the voluntary hospice sector, but within the wider national health scene, within the Department of Health. And to feed back from those meetings the minutes, the main focus of the meetings, items for discussion, so that we would discuss those at our quarterly Forum meetings, and hence take back feedback from Northern Ireland, so that we were keeping abreast of the develop-ment of specialist palliative care that was happening in the mainland, that we would be working in close liaison with. That brought me into contact with a huge number of people from the North of England to the South, and in Wales. And often at lunch breaks, and at coffee time, just sitting down could have offered very useful dialogue where you could share, pick up ideas, discuss new thoughts, problem areas. So it had a multifaceted role and for me personally, it helped increase my vision, and keep me in touch with central government developments; what National Council was doing about issues, and their lobbying with central government. Then I was able to bring it back here and lobby at our local government level.

For Tony Crowther, a feature of the Council's credibility has been its international stature:

I think [the National Council] does carry weight. I mean, you mentioned the euthanasia debate. It's had a lot of pressure on it, a lot of other countries are wanting Great Britain to take a lead on this. Now who do they go to? Well the answer is they go to the National Council. And so there has been a lot of work and there is still some further work going on that. And I think we probably underestimate how other countries look to the National Council for guidance on these things. And I think a lot of the working parties they've had, and the documents they've produced, are, by and large, extremely well received and are, fundamentally, fairly common sense, good basic stuff.

Gillian Ford served on the National Council as Marie Curie representative and considers that it has been instrumental in encouraging the professional development of hospice and palliative care activists:

I moved over to Marie Curie [in 1988] with a brief to provide medical direction throughout. And at the same time the whole business of specialist palliative care was gathering momentum. The National Council was set up a year or so later; I was Secretary of the Specialty Advisory Committee of the Royal College of Physicians charged with establishing training programmes, inspecting places to be training senior registrars, and consultant posts were being set up. I'm a sort of quasi-consultant in that the College uses me as a Fellow, or did until there were a few more people who were better qualified than I, in the sense that they were practising clinical medicine, to be the assessor on Advisory Appointments Committees. It was one of the things I'd insisted with St Christopher's, and even more so with Marie Curie: that all senior appointments were made as joint ones with either actual or honorary contracts with the NHS, and they were made in accordance with the statutes covering regulations, because I feel that, certainly for Marie Curie, and for other hospices: we're

bridging a gap. You know, in an ideal world it wouldn't be necessary, would it?

But the resources that have gone into non-NHS specialist palliative care and hospice care, have enabled it to keep ahead of the NHS. I mean in the sense that the knowledge base, the research base is building, and it rather potentiates this as a separate activity. Some of the Marie Curie Homes, which became Marie Curie Centres, as I say, already had consultants, but at the same time the National Council was developing things like Definitions[22] which wasn't published 'til last year, but it was in fact, I think, fuelling the professionalism of those of us who were working in hospice and specialist palliative care, which was extremely useful to Marie Curie at this time of change. We've been, you know, supporting the work of the National Council, including its setting up and its year-to-year activities. A little money has gone into it; but Michael Carleton-Smith has been a Vice-Chairman and I have been the Marie Curie representative and a member of a lot of the working groups … set up by the tireless Jean Gaffin who did so much to ensure the Council's success. And so I think that's been useful both for Marie Curie's development and perhaps, too, I think, for the National Council's.

Scottish Partnership for Palliative Care

Under its original name, the Scottish Partnership Agency for Palliative and Cancer Care was established in 1991 to bring together voluntary and statutory bodies concerned with palliative care in Scotland. Under Chairman, Tom Scott and Vice-Chairman, John Berkeley, the Agency sought to facilitate communication, liaise with government and encourage palliative care education and research.[23] John Berkeley recalls how the Partnership Agency came to be founded:

Tom [Scott] was University Chaplain at Heriot-Watt [University, Edinburgh] before he moved full-time to his Cancer Relief work.[24]

A tremendous enthusiast for palliative care, he was involved in setting up Strathcarron [Hospice, Denny] and getting it going. So I mean he wasn't simply a committee person from Macmillan Cancer Relief, but he was a practical person who had actually been responsible for setting up, developing and running a hospice ... We really needed some mechanism for pulling together all the hospice, all the palliative care work, all the hospices in Scotland. And so it was from this background – from looking at how we could actually bring together all these disparate parts of palliative care – that led to the formation of the Scottish Partnership Agency. And so we set it up, or we, I mean Tom did the major work of setting it up, and we ran almost on a trial basis for several months before we actually formulated it as a partnership agency. And Tom was Chairman, and I was Vice-Chairman for the first three years of its running. It proved very valuable because, again, as you know, we're in the fortunate position in Scotland that we're a fairly close-knit community, as opposed to England. So immediately we were set up, we were recognised by Scottish Home and Health Department, and of course Ken Calman[25] was around in

Scotland at that time, which was a major advantage. And now[26] the Partnership Agency is well recognised and well regarded in Scotland, both by the units that contribute to it, and by Scottish Office.

For Derek Doyle, working as a hospice doctor in Edinburgh and subsequently active in the 'National Council', the separation from the Agency seemed unnecessary and unhelpful:

When the National Association was formed, by then the Scottish Partnership Agency had been formed, I had been asked to be one of the office bearers of that and had turned it down. That appeared, I know, to people as: 'Me – I want a big national job, I don't want a Scottish job.' It really was not that at all, it was because I was not at all sure that I could take on any more, and at that time we still had the Forum, and of course rapidly, within the year of the Scottish Partnership Agency, the SPA, being formed (which was Tom's doing, and did great work), then suddenly we got the National Council. And a bit of a sadness to me that the SPA, which does, it's an excellent organisation, is now on its own.[27] We have cross-reference, we have cross-sitting, and reciprocity and all these things, and it's a very happy cooperation ... I feel it's a little bit of a pity, if you're asking me, that we should have Northern Ireland and Wales and England and Scotland ... have a different agency.

Bereavement Research Forum

When Marilyn Relf was appointed to the post of Volunteer Coordinator at Sir Michael Sobell House, Oxford in 1982, she began to involve volunteers in bereavement care. This activity resulted in the establishment of the Bereavement Research Forum which by the mid-1990s had around 70 members:

There was very little research going on when we started, really 1988 was the time when I was looking around for other people, and we put some adverts in the bereavement journals like *Bereavement*

Care and *Life*, the National Association of Bereavement Services' newsletter. And about nine people met, including Sheila Payne and Julie Stokes from Winston's Wish[28] which was then a glimmer of the future. We decided that we would meet three times a year, and set up an organisation to act as a focal point for people who are involved in bereavement research. And it really grew by word of mouth to begin with. It was very small for a while. And then I suppose about 1993 it started to grow quite dramatically. And we've now got something like 60 or 70 members, and we're beginning to get an international membership. But it basically started off as a 'self help' group for people doing research; to give support to each other. And we now we run three or four symposia or workshops per year, and get involved with the Palliative Care Research Forum, and recently[29] with the European Conference to help to organise the bereavement aspects of the work. And I've been Chair or Co-Chair of it since the beginning. And it's very much administered through this Service. And maybe that will change with a new Chair, when a new Chair gets appointed, maybe the administration will go, I don't know. But it's been quite interesting to sort of act as a sort of exchange house; putting other researchers in touch with each other. And of course it's been a wonderful way of learning about research for me.

Libraries in Hospices

In 1995, 40 people with an interest in hospice libraries attended a meeting at St Christopher's led by Denise Brady.[30] Contributions from Millie Hare (St Helena Hospice, Colchester), Jane Burley (St Francis Hospice, Romford), Robin Stevens (St Michael's Hospice, Basingstoke) and Jan Brooman (Princess Alice Hospice, Esher) highlighted the range of library provision found within UK hospices. Subsequently, a network was established which focused upon the role of hospice libraries and the needs of those associated with them. By 1997, a similar meeting included hospice administrators and tutors.

Topics of interest covered accessibility, copyright, website creation, classification systems and catalogue production. One of the delegates was Julia Hitchens, who had worked at St Luke's, Sheffield since 1971. In the following extract she reflects upon her appointment as a volunteer at the hospice and the nature of her library work:

I'd been interviewed by Rosalind Beetham who'd noted in my file that I was a professional librarian, and so possibly six months into my time at St Luke's, Eileen Mann [the Matron] said, would I like to start with a little bookcase of books? But from the beginning there was an emphasis on education and training, and in what was the little interview room, which is now the aromatherapy room, there were regular lectures for staff and auxiliaries and volunteers. And we started from very small beginnings ... And I worked every Tuesday and every fourth Sunday in the morning. And then, when the library got big enough, the bookcase moved down to where the volunteer rooms are on the corridor. In those days it was bedrooms, either for families, and a bit later on for students who came and did first of all the six-month 931 course.[31]

I worked as a volunteer, I was the Honorary Librarian for the first 15 years of my service. And then in 1986, 10 years ago, because we started our 285 course,[32] I was appointed librarian by Eric Wilkes. And Eric's writings were of great value for visitors. They bought people along in shoals.

But, in addition to the duties of Librarian, we started our Summer Fayre, and the person who was helping with the bookstall was a lady, Vicky Bronks who had worked in Wards, the bookshop in town. She had been, as a young woman, sent by her family to England by herself, as a young student. I think she'd been studying law in Vienna and was sent over here on her own, and went as an au pair to Anthony Thwaite, the poet. And stayed in his household and then, I think, moved to Sheffield for a job and married her husband late in life, Norman Bronks ... she had a very academic and scholastic

Frances Sheldon

Frances Sheldon was interviewed in June 2003; she died on 26 February 2004. Born and raised in North London, she took a degree at Cambridge before embarking upon a career in social work. Palliative care became a major focus of her work from the late 1970s. Her integrity, warmth and passion for improving end of life care were admired and respected by all of the authors of this book and her death coincided with the final period of its preparation.

For an obituary of Frances Sheldon, see that by Maureen Woodhall, in *The Independent*, Friday 16 April 2004.

mind and a wide knowledge of books, and she had taken on herself the setting up of the secondhand bookstall. And I'd been delving into secondhand books, working under another senior assistant in Wards bookshop. She worked in St Augustine's and they had grand book-stalls, and I did my training under her, as it were. But I helped Vicky Bronks here, and then took over. And so, as a fund-raising means, I still do two book sales a year: the Summer Fayre and the Autumn Fayre, with, this last year, five stalls and something like 18 helpers. So in a way I've created my own childhood again, because I run a library, I sell new books like Blacklock and Farries and I have a grand time with the secondhand books as well.

Palliative Care Research Society

Research came gradually to feature alongside clinical and educational dimensions of hospice and palliative care and in 1991 Robert Twycross proposed the establishment of a multidisciplinary research forum. In the following extract he explains how the idea was taken up and how the forum – later the Palliative Care Research Society, gained ground:

I was back on my multiprofessional wicket, I said, 'We need a Research Forum, but it's got to be multiprofessional, but we don't want to be seen to be declaring UDI from APM,[33] so we'll always hold it immediately before APM and there'll be some loose association.' And that has grown dramatically, as you know: half a day with 29 attending in Cardiff; to a full two days the next year and every subse-quent year, with an increasing number of abstracts, with increasing multiprofessional representation on the Committee, increasing non-medical involvement, and a total of over 260 people participating in Durham in 1995. So that clearly has been, for me, a very important development. Now, as you know, in '95 we decided to have a group of people, including yourself,[34] look at the possibility of a Palliative

Care Network. And here we are 12 months later and I am thrilled, you know, that that looks like becoming a reality.

The social worker Frances Sheldon comments on her involvement in this work, and emphasises the important role of Robert Twycross:

Robert Twycross set that up practically, you know, on his own … a powerful and dynamic person gets an idea and wants to develop it and gets a group of people around them who they think will be in tune with it to develop it. So I think it was at the meeting in Dublin [in November 1994] that he asked me if I would join that group that he'd assembled, which was mainly involved in putting on this annual meeting, drawing on the research activity that was around in the UK. And I think you went on it more or less the same time,[35] so again it was a multiprofessional, multidisciplinary in the academic sense, group which was working on this, but we weren't representative or could hardly be seen as that, though we might be hopefully people who our peers in our professional discipline respected: we weren't, we weren't their choices. So, you know, in a sense you can reflect [that] a lot of early developments in a field like this are very much about powerful people choosing groups that they feel will work well with them to get something going and over time, just as with the EAPC[36] and just as with the Palliative Care Research Forum, there has to develop a more representational structure to create legitimacy in the end, which is again what happened with the translation of the Forum into a, you know, more representational organisation under your leadership. Which is perfectly right, you know, which is the right thing to happen.

The growth of single profession and single role associations

A remarkable aspect of hospice and palliative care has been the upsurge of single profession and single role associations. Graham Thorpe remembers that at one particular time there were three chairs of professional associations at the hospice where he worked in Southampton:

Rightly or wrongly, what happened was, the disciplines developed their own associations. Now you could argue, I suppose, that more teamwork from the start would have been better, but the doctors ploughed on, and the nurses ploughed on, and got their sort of two forums, and then followed physios – at one time Countess Mountbatten House had three Chairmen of associations: there was myself, Judith Hill was one of the nurses, and Bob Gray the physio – that was an embryo association that got off the ground.

Association of Hospice and Specialist Palliative Care Social Workers

The first national professional association in the hospice field to be established in the UK was the Association of Hospice Social Workers, formed by Elisabeth Earnshaw-Smith and colleagues in 1982. At that time, she was Principal Social Worker at St Christopher's. She remembers how the Association grew from small beginnings:

Well I think it was about three years after I went to the hospice, that I got to know other hospice social workers. There weren't very many of us at that time, and all these people I got to know were working single-handed, and eventually, I think after about three years, we got together for a weekend, oh, it may have been only a day or two, at St Christopher's, to talk about what we were doing and to try and counteract this sense of isolation, and to chisel out together what social work had to offer to the hospice movement, and how we could work in multidisciplinary teams, constructively. And from this very small beginning there then grew the Association of Hospice Social Workers, and an annual 'get together'. And it became a very important meeting, this yearly weekend, when people could gain enormous support, they could be themselves, they could let their hair down, they could have fun, they could share together what they were doing and build up a real understanding together of the multifaceted job that a hospice social worker has. And we were really thrilled that from that beginning, and our enthusiasm for it, that the doctors then founded their own association, and the nurses, and the physiotherapists. Because I think, as I said at the beginning, although it's awfully important to learn how to work together, it's very important not to lose the sharpness of one's own professional expertise, and that's what enriches a team. And so the Association now, I'm not sure how large it is, but it's well over the hundred mark.

Frances Sheldon echoes a similar sense of enthusiasm about the work of the Association and what it could achieve:

… when the Hospice Social Workers' Association was set up I was Vice-Chair and actually I chaired the first meetings of the Executive Committee because Elisabeth Earnshaw-Smith was off sick at the time. So, so in a sense I was lucky enough to be, you know, in a reasonably leading role in that organisation and then became Chair myself from 1988 to 1990. And that organisation had a great feeling of buzz and energy at that time: it was very much involved in the campaign to end the 'six months' rule in relation to the Attendance Allowance,[37] which Julia Franklin and Jonathan Lloyd were leading nationally with some input from other professions, but social work was really taking a lead in that, and that was a very – those were very exciting times – we actually won that battle and got the 'six months' rule disappeared.

Association for Palliative Medicine of Great Britain and Ireland

Another catalyst for the growth of professional associations was the foundation, in 1986, of the Association for Palliative Medicine of Great Britain and Ireland.[38] Robert Twycross recalls:

We didn't have a 'palliative care association' and I guess round about 1983/84 Cancer Relief Macmillan Fund was playing a major part and was bringing together people from the NHS units in an annual weekend in November, not far from Oxford, and we'd meet and talk. And that was a very paternalistic meeting, you know, it wasn't run by the professionals, it was run by Cancer Relief, and it was good to a point, but like many meetings it's good for the people you meet rather than for the programme. And I remember talking, particularly with Richard Hillier, about, you know, should we have some national organisation. But we were also living under the shadow of Cicely Saunders and we didn't want to do anything to offend her, which I think is fair enough, and she didn't come forward and say, 'Here is the national organisation.' So I think there was a reticence. And by the time we got to '84 or thereabouts, Richard was certainly of the opinion we should set up a 'palliative care association'. I felt, however, this would be dominated by doctors, and there were one or two professional groups already knocking around, and the paradox is they're multiprofessional in delivery. But I felt we should, as doctors, get our act together, and then as a doctors' group go to the nurses, go to the social workers and say, 'Let's come together as a national organisation.' But if we set up a national organisation for all comers, it would be medically dominated, and I think this was not what I wanted. So I won the argument.

Graham Thorpe explains the important issue of training as the Association sought to establish itself, and in particular the concern to achieve the recognition of palliative medicine as a specialty, which came about in 1987:

When we were devising a training programme, we had to think, you know, what backgrounds really suited people coming into this work, given the extremely varied backgrounds like the mission field or, you know, Dame Cicely being a sort of one-person multiprofessional team in herself, did you have to have gone through all these to make a success of it? What about anaesthetics? What about radiotherapy? What about oncology? What about general practice? And of course, as things have gone on, it was established as a specialty, sub-specialty of general medicine, and now it's out of its seven-year novitiate and has become a specialty in its own right. And I think it has broken new ground, as far as the Colleges are concerned, in accepting as appropriate qualification Membership of the Royal College of General Practice, as well as the College of Physicians, and the College of Radiology, and College of Anaesthetics. So that broad-based background is very much now accepted, and that palliative medicine is rather different from a lot of other specialties.

Association for Hospice Management

Under its original name – the Association of Hospice Administrators[39] – the organisation was formally constituted in 1984 when an application was made to the Charity Commissioners for the granting of charitable status. The Association's informal activities predate this application by several years, however, and an annual conference was inaugurated in 1981. These conferences were the first of their kind, hosted and organised by individual hospices in the UK and Ireland.

Michael Murphy became the Administrator of Our Lady's Hospice, Dublin in 1972. He recounts his impressions of the first conference held for hospice administrators, and amplifies what the role of administrator came to mean for him:

When the Association of Hospice Managers was set up in the UK, I went to the first meeting, I think it was in 1981, and in some ways it was a bit embarrassing because every other person at the conference was very highly involved in fund-raising and where they were going to get resources for this, that or the other. And here was I coming from Ireland where the actual Department of Health were funding the facility; I didn't have to go looking for money, you know, to maintain the services, whereas everyone in the UK, the independent voluntary hospices, were in the situation where the manager, or the secretary, or whoever, was going out to pubs and getting involved in fund-raising. So it was a bit embarrassing for me in one way because we were so well off by comparison.

The current thinking might be that 'leaders do the right things, managers do things right', you know, that's the difference, I think. I mean the reason that administrators kind of got in the Health Service in the first instance was that the doctors were too busy to be doing the paperwork, and that's how administrators came on the scene. It's really to make things – really you're there to look after the resources so that the people at the sharp end, in the front line, can do their work. If nurses and doctors were to be involved in sending out invoices they'd have very little time for patient care. And it's a bit like the, I think Cicely Saunders said at one stage about when the administrators had their first conference; that people don't realise that it's a bit like the, you know, the Napoleonic Wars, to have one soldier in the field you needed 10, you know, behind the lines, getting the supplies, getting the ammunition, you know, keeping the fires lit. It's one of these sorts of situations. So that was the basis of it. But one of my own hobby-horses is that management is everybody's business. It's a bit like Health and Safety, you know, you say to staff, 'Look, you know, you have to work safely, you have an obligation and a duty to work safely.' And the same of management, that's the whole sort of problem nowadays, and particularly at the clinical end, doctors would say they want the best for their patient, it doesn't matter what it costs, you know, they want the best. And people say, well doctors and nurses should be more involved in deciding what – or have an idea as to what – so it's resource management you're into really. But the people themselves are resources as well.

After a career managing Arab-owned companies in the Middle East, Malcolm Rapson returned to England and became Administrator of St Luke's, Sheffield. He reflects below upon his role and the challenges associated with it:

I saw my role, as an administrator, to help steer St Luke's through the period of change by, if you like, the lateral thinking that I could introduce, and really, I suppose, to formalise a lot of the administrative management that hitherto had been handled by someone part-time.

When I took up my appointment here I spent, I think, three months really just sitting alongside the previous administrator who was still in post, and I didn't take over for that period of time. But it gave me the freedom, really, to look and see how the place was run, how it was managed. I had the opportunity of going round to any, and all, personnel and discussing with them their jobs; what they did, how they did it. And very, very quickly I was able to get a feel for the – and I don't want to be unkind but it might sound unkind – the haphazard way in which the organisation ran itself. And Eric Wilkes, I think, had been able to keep it going purely and simply by the strength of his personality, and by the fact that people liked him and were mesmerised by him. And, you know, I came under that mesmerisation myself ...

We were facing fairly traumatic changes in the way the Health Service were behaving towards us, and the way we were having to introduce management tools to St Luke's ... But of course, the older school were very resentful of administrators in any event. Why?

Because the Health Service naturally hated administrators, and for that reason I would never describe myself as 'an administrator'. In actual fact, if anyone asked me what I did I always said I was 'an administrative director', which to me sounded a little less harsh. When people ask what I am now [at] any of the lectures that I give, or courses, then I describe myself as 'the gremlin' basically because the buck stops here. If anything goes wrong in the place then it can usually be pegged back to me. And it seems to go down reasonably well. But my role, I now see, [is] as the provider of everything that the doctor and the nurse needs to run their sole, their core business, of caring.

We still had a part-time Medical Director, and that was very quickly corrected, and he became full-time. So we moved into a situation with three full-time managers. And we initiated meetings, and we implemented the changes that were necessary, and, in actual fact, probably, I think, quite successfully. When I say 'quite successfully', our business has altered – and I'm speaking from memory now – but when I arrived in 1989 our turnover at that time was £600,000, which was quite a large business. I have recently completed a budget that has been submitted but not yet agreed, for £3.5 million turnover. So in the seven to eight years that I've been here, we have increased our business from £600,000 to £3.5 million, which is quite a rapid turnover and would not normally be acceptable in any commercial business without a period of consolidation.

Wider ramifications

The last section of this chapter indicates ways in which national organisations have influenced palliative care development. In the 1970s in England the Area Health Authorities were directed by the Department of Health and Social Security to collaborate with the Marie Curie Foundation based on a new system of joint funding, as Gillian Petrie explains:

And there had been a directive from the Department of Health and Social Security dated 1975, which was really the basis of the modern Community Nursing Service, directing, as they then were, Area Health Authorities and District Health Authorities to embrace what the Foundation had to offer in the way of, and I quote, 'genuine augmentation of community nursing'. Based on that, I realised that it was the policy of the Department of Health that there should be some degree of joint funding between the Foundation and the District Health Authorities, and in some places it was 50:50, in others it was different, in Northern Ireland there was no joint funding at all, which I later put in place. I was not responsible for Scotland, to my great regret, and that was a shame, but England, Wales and Northern Ireland, there was huge diversity in how the District Health Authority viewed this potential partnership. And, of course, one really had to go and kind of stitch this up all over the country.

As the hospice movement expanded, special interest groups began to proliferate, making it impossible for a single voice to speak for the whole movement. Eric Wilkes explains how prompting from government ministers provided the motivation for a single umbrella organisation to represent the movement at the interface with government:

Coupled with a certain amount of negotiation in a very piecemeal and ineffective way with various Ministers of Health, it had been said to us quite often – there is no voice for these, or more accurately, many, many voices in the wilderness: 'Why don't you get together?' Virginia Bottomley's phrase was, 'Get your act together.'[40]

Despite the influence of the large umbrella organisations such as Help the Hospices and the National Council for Hospice and Specialist Palliative Care Services, successful lobbying has also occurred from single interest and professional organisations. One such example concerned the activities of Julia Franklin and her colleagues in the Association of Hospice Social Workers and the Bloomsbury Support Team – a group made up of associates in Camden Social Services and University College Hospital. The focus of the group's activity concerned an eligibility criterion of the Attendance Allowance: the six-month wait for benefits that discriminated against people with a short prognosis:

It was amazingly difficult. But again I had such a good sort of networking feel. Molly Meacher, who's the wife of Michael Meacher, the Labour politician, I worked with at Northwick Park [Hospital], and she was the first BASW [British Association of Social Workers] parliamentary representative, and her office was just round the corner from me, and I thought, 'Right, well I'll find out from Molly how you work parliament.' That was in 1986, and Molly Meacher helped amazingly at the beginning. She wrote a paper for BASW for a start, and she helped me understand how the regulations worked and how we might be able to get into the regulations side. And so we met various people at the Department of Social Security, and basically it's like all the things I've found to do with death and dying: once you get, you know, people who are seeing you face-to-face, and you're able to explain to them how difficult it is when you're dying, and what the needs of people are, that you sort of get to them on their sort of emotional bit as well as their academic bit and they have to listen to you somehow … I used to get so angry about the injustice of it, that we'd be writing letters, we'd be – through the Association – we'd be getting to our MPs about it. We wrote, I wrote to no end of Ministers of Health, and Mrs Thatcher, and all sorts of people, and got all these stonewalling letters back saying there was no hope.

But there was sort of various things that happened; one thing was that the *Watchdog* [consumer affairs] programme, which has now been going on television for years, it was starting up, and they hadn't

Julia Franklin with the then Prime Minister, John Major, following changes to the Attendance Allowance.

got very much that was very interesting to show that first week. And I had a client in Camden who was a politician *par excellence*, but had a brain tumour. And he was really livid that he couldn't claim his benefit. And I actually taped him on a camcorder, which Patrick Dixon[41] helped us with. Amazing! And he started to tell his story on this tape. And we had various clients who were going through a terrible death, who were very poor, and this guy from *Watchdog* saw my client's obituary in the Camden newspaper, and said, you know, was there a story there? And I said, 'Yes, please. Wow!' So in fact he came and filmed our clients, and filmed me, interviewed me and the team, and we got a – the first week of *Watchdog* programme we got a full spot about benefits for the terminally ill. And all sorts of things we did, ending up with Sir Peter Barclay on the Social Security Advisory Committee … But in fact, really, it all changed being in the committee room, up in the House of Commons, with Nicholas Scott[42] putting through some amendments to the Social Security Bill. Briefing papers had been given out, and I spoke to a man; we were lurking in the corridor and I sort of said, 'Well I don't know who you are, but we're here to try and sort of change the rules' and all this. And he was terribly interested suddenly, and said his name, and he was very high up in the Civil Service and a sort of advisor to somebody, and he said, 'Do you know, my mother's just died in the hospice, and I've got this experience,' you know. And I thought, 'Well Julia, this is your moment.' And, you know, from then on we began to get to the right people who could actually begin to understand the need.

These extracts recall some formative aspects of early hospice development. We can see how for a time the hospice movement stood outside of the NHS and developed alternative values, practices and organisations. We are also made aware of the points of linkage that began to develop between the voluntary and statutory sectors and the key roles played by professional organisations in bridging these. The picture of longer-established charities restructuring to embrace the hospice movement is also striking. So is the need for a single voice to communicate with government; a factor underscored by grass roots activists and government ministers alike. As hospice care progressed, the need for education, for research and development followed in its wake. Service provider groups and umbrella organisations, single profession and single role associations began to emerge. Such organisations promoted debate, the dissemination of information, the creation of networks, engagement with government and the development of education and corporate representation. The spectrum of multipurpose organisations that came into existence bears witness to a remarkable wave of activity taking place during a short but vibrant period in the history of the UK hospice movement.

Notes

1. Originally known as the Society for the Prevention and Relief of Cancer.
2. The 2000th Macmillan nurse was funded a quarter of a century later, in 2000.
3. Henry Garnett (1913–90) was educated at Eton and Sandhurst and commissioned in the Royal Horseguards. He served in the Second World War as leader of the Household Cavalry armoured car troop of the Royal Family's immediate protection mission. After the war, he joined Gillette Industries and worked in America and Australia before returning to the UK as Chairman of Gillette Europe. After

leading the Cancer Relief Society as Deputy Chairman and then Chief Executive (1973–87), he maintained an interest, despite failing health, until his death in 1990.

4. By 1980, the Macmillan nurses were well established if not widely known, as shown in the following letter written by Cicely Saunders to Dr Elizabeth Hall, of Colchester (30 June 1980): 'I wonder if you are in touch with the National Society for Cancer Relief because, as you no doubt know and Mrs Clench probably told you, they will sometimes fund Macmillan nurses to start work in a community area. They like the nurses to be called for Douglas Macmillan who founded the Society but do not in fact have a supply of nurses of their own.' In D. Clark, *Cicely Saunders – founder of the hospice movement. Selected letters 1959–1999* (Oxford: Oxford University Press, 2002: 203).

5. This is an interesting point about the Macmillan name; it was not until 1985, 10 years after the creation of the first Macmillan nurse post, that the charity changed its name to Cancer Relief Macmillan Fund.

6. These difficulties also related to personnel issues and were not confined solely to Macmillan, as illustrated in the following letter from Cicely Saunders to Dr Sylvia Lack (formerly a Senior House Officer at St Joseph's Hospice, Hackney) of Newhaven, USA (19 August 1976): 'As you know, Robert [Twycross] got the Oxford job and Southampton did not make an appointment. I think this is no bad thing because it will underline to the NSCR [National Society for Cancer Relief] that it is really useless to set up units and have no thought as to who are going to be the staff. I believe that they have had rather a disaster at Northampton so this is an excellent moment to get this across. I am, incidentally, having a meeting with one or two 'high-ups' from Marie Curie (not Ronnie Raven), NSCR, Gill [Ford] (as from the Department) and a couple of us. This is ostensibly to sort out "Where are we now?" geographically. From my point of view the message I want to get across is the need for proper medical backing and nursing experience. The latest *draft* of "Components of Hospice Care" is enclosed.' In D. Clark, *Cicely Saunders – founder of the hospice movement. Selected letters 1959–1999* (Oxford, Oxford University Press, 2002:168).

7. In fact the cutbacks, imposed by a Labour government, had been agreed even before the general election that took place in February 1974. Charles Webster gives a full account of this and quotes the (for this volume) interesting choice of language of the Royal College of Nursing at the time: 'radical action is required on fundamental issues; palliatives are now both totally inadequate to deal with the situation and totally unacceptable to the profession'; C. Webster, *The Health Services Since the War. Volume II, Government and Health Care, The British National Health Service 1958–79* (London: The Stationery Office, 1996: 613).

8. P. Sturgess, *The Marie Curie Memorial Foundation: A brief history 1948–1984* (London: Marie Curie Memorial Foundation, 1985).

9. This work was undertaken in 1951, when 179 of the 193 health authorities cooperated and 7,050 patients were surveyed.

10. Joint Cancer Survey Committee of the Marie Curie Foundation and the Queen's Institute of District Nursing, *Report on a National Survey Concerning Patients with Cancer Nursed at Home* (London: Marie Curie Memorial Foundation, 1952).

11. Known as the Research Institute from 1982.

12. Marie Curie briefing paper 1995.

13. Credit Accumulation and Transfer – a system to encourage the portability of credits in higher education.

14. Actually it was the Fifth Congress of the European Association for Palliative Care, held at the Barbican in London in September 1997, and the costs of which were underwritten by Marie Curie Cancer Care.

15. Tim Lovel was speaking in September 2000.

16. Help the Hospices subsequently developed a wide range of information, education and consultative activities while continuing its particular support for the independent hospices. New forms of collaboration were forged with the former Hospice Information Service at St Christopher's, to create *hospice information*, and in 2001 Help the Hospices launched an international initiative, the UK Forum for Hospice and Palliative Care Worldwide. See www.helpthehospices.org.uk.

17. After a career in politics and public administration, Paul Rossi was appointed Press and Parliamentary Officer for Help the Hospices in 1984; he was the organisation's first employee and undertook a variety of duties including those of secretary and administrator. In 1991, he helped to establish the National Council for Hospice and Specialist Palliative Care Services before moving to Macmillan Cancer Relief in 1992.

18. Eric Wilkes was speaking in November 1995.

19. Sue Ryder (Lady Ryder of Warsaw, 1923–2000), served with the Polish section of the secret Special Operations Executive during the Second World War. When peace came, she began relief work for the sick and destitute across Europe and then broadened her scope to include other parts of the world. The charity bearing her name was established in 1953, with the creation of the first Sue Ryder Nursing Home in Suffolk. Today, the organisation is known as Sue Ryder Care and specialises in caring for people with neurological and hospice care needs, but also provides nursing, elderly and adult mental health care. See www.suerydercare.org.

20. Prue Clench was speaking in December 1996.
21. The establishment of Help the Hospices was surrounded by a degree of controversy and Prue Clench was not alone in her concerns, as shown in the following letters from Cicely Saunders:

    To Major Henry Garnett, National Society for Cancer Relief (26 March 1984): 'In spite of my reservations, which we have discussed together in the past, I have now been persuaded that the time has come for some kind of general hospice organisation. I think that the initiative of the BMA has come together very well with the Duchess of Norfolk's enthusiasm for this and as you already know, Eric Wilkes and I have accepted positions with "Help the Hospices".'

    To Dr Derek Doyle, St Columba's Hospice, Edinburgh (24 May 1984): 'I was not surprised to have a long letter from you nor to have another from Richard Hillier the following day. I, too, have misgivings but was persuaded to join with Help the Hospices at the point when I felt the pro's finally outweighed the cons. The name and the terms of reference had already gone to the Charity Commissioners and there was nothing I could do to change that, although I tried. I think we can get round this by a repeated emphasis that Hospice means a team or a community, or even a small number of people doing hospice work, in the home, in hospital as well as in any kind of institution. Certainly the Americans have been saying this since 1974 and I have been doing so for quite a long time also.'

    In D. Clark, *Cicely Saunders – founder of the hospice movement. Selected letters 1959–1999* (Oxford: Oxford University Press, 2002:246–47, 249).
22. A reference to *Specialist Palliative Care: A statement of definitions* (London: National Council for Hospice and Specialist Palliative Care Services, 1995).
23. The Scottish Partnership subsequently developed a membership of over 70 statutory and voluntary organisations. Sir Kenneth Calman served as President, with Derek Doyle as Vice-President and Martin Leiper as Chairman.
24. Tom Scott's influential lecture on the nature of chaplaincy, presented at Heriot-Watt in 1979, was reprinted after his death. See T. Scott, 'Chaplaincy – a resource of Christian presence', *Scottish Journal of Healthcare Chaplaincy* 3 (1): 15–19, 2000. Sadly, arrangements were being made with Tom Scott to conduct an interview with him for the Hospice History Project, when he became ill and died in 1997.
25. At the time he was Professor of Oncology and Dean of Medicine at Glasgow; later Sir Kenneth Calman was Chief Medical Officer for England, and then Vice-Chancellor of Durham University.
26. John Berkeley was speaking in June 1997.
27. Derek Doyle was speaking in February 1996.
28. Winston's Wish is a charity set up to meet the needs of bereaved children, young people and their families. See also Chapter 7, note 17.
29. Marilyn Relf was speaking in November 1997.
30. D. Brady, *Report of meeting for those involved in libraries in hospices*, 27 November 1995.
31. The English National Board of Nursing Course (931) on 'Care of the Dying Patient and Family'.
32. The English National Board of Nursing Course (285) on 'Continuing Care of the Dying Patient and Family'.
33. The Association for Palliative Medicine.
34. Robert Twycross is referring here to David Clark who conducted the interview in October 1996.
35. The interviewer was David Clark.
36. European Association for Palliative Care.
37. See below, 'Wider ramifications', this chapter.
38. The Association for Palliative Medicine subsequently grew to around 800 members, including doctors who work abroad.
39. Changed to Association for Hospice Management in 1997.
40. Virginia Bottomley, Minister of State for Health, 1989–90; Secretary of State for Health 1992–95.
41. Dr Patrick Dixon worked at St Joseph's Hospice, Hackney and then as part of the Community Care Team at University College Hospital, London. In 1988 he launched the international AIDS agency, AIDS Care Education and Training Ltd (ACET) as a Christian response to the challenge of HIV/AIDS, which later evolved into the ACET International Alliance. Dr Dixon is also widely known for his role as Chairman of Global Change Ltd, which advises business on the implications of global trends.
42. Nicholas Scott, Minister of State for Health and Social Security, 1987–88; Secretary of State for Social Security 1988–94.

5   Spirituality and hospice care

'I know you can't save me but do you know someone who can?'
Patient to Barbara McNulty

This book is chiefly concerned with the development of hospices in the UK in the closing decades of the twentieth century. Yet it is possible to trace an earlier period of institutional provision for the care of the dying in England, in which important developments took place within the 30 years from 1885 to 1905. Indeed the hospices founded at that time, some of which were still in existence a century later, had a significant influence on the founders of the 'modern' movement. During that period at least five homes were founded in London alone with the object of providing a place of peace and comfort for the dying poor. At this time we see that the care of the dying and matters of formal religion were inextricably linked. For example, three of those early 'hospices' were run directly by religious orders and the other two had strong religious affiliations. There was also a marked denominational character to the homes (one Catholic, three Anglican, one Methodist) and this had a profound impact upon the way in which the deathbed was managed. In this context the spiritual care of the patient came above any other consideration, with a primary emphasis being placed on achieving 'Soul Cures'.[1]

This Victorian and Edwardian legacy was to have a particular influence upon Cicely Saunders as she began to develop her own ideas about the care of the dying in the 1950s. Inspired by her experiences as a volunteer in two of London's homes for the dying, we have seen how she began to forge a uniquely modern approach to terminal care, which would bring together advanced clinical practice, education and research. Key elements within this model were a rational and scientific orientation to pain and symptom management, coupled with a strong emphasis upon the importance of openness and authenticity in 'being with' dying patients and those close to them. But the model also contained two other powerful components: of community and of religion.[2] In the early 1960s Cicely Saunders was grappling to bring these multiple elements together in a single vision. Her success in doing so, and in particular her ability to somehow reconcile the separate claims of medicine and religion, appear pivotal in creating the conditions for the future development of a hospice and palliative care movement. Careful analysis of the contemporary record, and in particular Cicely Saunders' correspondence of the time, has revealed that this was part of a conscious process of decision making which had been explored in detail long before St Christopher's Hospice welcomed its first patients in the summer of 1967.

As the hospice movement then developed in the UK it seems that a broader spiritual perspective began to emerge. Whilst still acknowledging the Christian origins of many hospices, there was growing interest in the needs of those who subscribed to other faiths, or none. Clinical experience appeared to show that non-religious patients demonstrated similar needs to their religious counterparts: for love, for meaning, for forgiveness, for reconciliation and for transcendence. Accordingly, a more encompassing concept of spirituality came into being; a concept which sought to recognise both religious and non-religious perspectives of personhood.

This chapter addresses the spiritual dimension of hospice care and reflects changing perceptions of what spirituality has come to mean. It recognises how the Christian faith became a motivating force among the hospice early pioneers and how this continued in certain ways. Yet alongside this faith tradition there has developed a broader, 'religion-free' concept of spirituality which became widespread by the close of the twentieth century. While they are not mutually exclusive, balancing these diverse spiritual perceptions within an institutional milieu has presented challenges at both the organisational and personal levels of care – as demonstrated by several of the accounts presented here.[3,4]

The spiritual dimension of hospice care

Malcolm McIllmurray is an oncologist working in both the acute hospital and the hospice setting in Lancaster. In the following extract, he sets his life and work in a broad spiritual context, exemplifying the widely held view that spirituality is a universal human attribute. Portrayed as relational and personal, it is bound up in the uniqueness of each individual; grounded in beliefs;[5] shaped by the experiences of life; and comes to prominence during times of illness. Within such a scenario, life may be rediscovered as a precious gift, prompting new priorities and a sense of healing in the experiences of forgiving and being forgiven. Malcolm McIllmurray elaborates:

Clearly your own belief and spirituality, or the awareness of that spiritual dimension, is bound to have a shape on your life. I mean in that we're all made up of different bits and pieces, and, you know, as well as us having the physical components and the mind to go with it, that there is always this spiritual element to whatever we do, which we recognise to a greater or lesser extent. And so, of course, what I do, the way I am, the way I react and behave and respond, is bound to be influenced by my own view of the meaning of my life, and what life is all about and the relationship I feel I have with the people around me, and, I guess, creation in its widest sense. So, because I see that I do have a role, if you like, in that way, I also see that everyone else has a role, too. And so maybe the value that I put on people as individuals is affected by the way in which I see life myself. So I guess it is because of my own spiritual awareness that I acknowledge the uniqueness of others, and that they, like me, have the same elements to them, and that we are bonded together through that common spiritual resource that we can find in all of us. If, though, you mean that my spiritual senses make it easier for me to accept the problems that people have to encounter, and accept loss, then I would say that that isn't the case. What I think it does is that it means that I am open to the possibility that illness, like cancer, which is life-threatening, may offer an opportunity to people for transformational change in their own lives. And I think if I didn't have any kind of spiritual awareness, I probably wouldn't give it a second thought, but I have seen countless examples of this and that has reinforced my own certainty that there is something spiritual about all of this.

If you were to say: well, what do I mean by 'transformational change'? I think, at a very simple level, what life-threatening illness can do for people is that it can make them reorientate their thinking, so that those things which were important to them before no longer seem to be important. And they seem, they seem to have a different view of the world. Life can become very precious at the prospect of it being lost, and yet for the most part we lead our lives as if we're going to live forever. And it can be through the challenge of illness like cancer, which as we've said is for some people a death sentence,

Malcolm McIllmurray: 'Life can become very precious at the prospect of it being lost.'

or perceived as such, that that sudden thought that they may not be here tomorrow means that they suddenly understand what a wonderful gift life is to them, and they begin to appreciate the things that are around them, and that they no longer are so bothered by acquisitions and belongings and the sorts of things that often will take up a lot of our thinking time, like the next car and holidays and, you know, the sorts of things which are tied up with materialism, if I can put it like that. And they seem to be much more aware of the world around them, and of people, and relationships.

And I think, from what I have witnessed, what I have experienced, what I have seen of other people going through this process, this journey, as we've said, is that there seems to be a great opportunity for them to realise that they do have a value; they are important to people; that people mean a lot to one another; that love, and to be loved, is actually much more rewarding than anything else you can imagine; and that where they have carried with them – as many people do – these terrible guilts, burdens of guilt, of things which they've done or haven't done, or said or haven't said, that there's a great need to talk about that, and to feel that they can forgive something that's been done to them, or be forgiven for something which they may have done. And there's this tremendous sort of healing that can come from forgiving and being forgiven. So all those things seem to become very important to people when their life is on the line.

Robert Twycross articulates a different view: of weakness and pilgrimage, of suffering and transition that finds its origin in the biblical narrative of Gethsemane.[6] Although a Christian in belief, he found a dislocation between the nature of hospice care and a death-denying triumphalism on the part of the Church. Significantly, his theology of suffering was encapsulated in a report entitled *Mud and Stars*, which challenged the miracle-oriented approach towards healing sometimes found within the Church:[7]

Well, life is about growth, isn't it? We talk about maturing, and I'm very much a different person, I think, from my overt spiritual understanding now, than I was 12 years ago. Maybe there was a lot of turmoil in the early '80s between a religious framework which perhaps didn't really fit the world in which I worked. I mean if we talk with a Christian metaphor, the night before Jesus was crucified he went through agony in the 'Garden of Gethsemane'. Well you could say that many of our patients, using a Christian metaphor, are going through their own agony before their death, their own 'Garden of Gethsemane', and I think if you are working in the 'Garden of Gethsemane' through which patients are coming, then it's going to have a certain impact on you. And when the Church generally reflects the culture in which it is, for better or for worse, it tends to be health-oriented, youth-oriented, death-denying and all the rest, triumphalistic we call it, then I think if your – if your support system from infancy, the Church, is out of tune with the reality in which you find yourself, it's going to be a major negative influence. And I think if you want to look at my spiritual pilgrimage, well you won't see the pilgrimage – but the new theology which emerged out of the late '80s will be found in a book called *Mud and Stars* which was, OK it's got a curious subtitle, it's called *The Church's Ministry of Healing in the light of Hospice Experience*. Now you can write a Christian book about hospice theology without talking about the Church's ministry of healing. But part of the challenge was to get something within the Christian world which challenged the overoptimistic, naive, miracle-oriented theology of those people who called themselves, well, you know, were interested in the ministry of healing, sort of thing. So I think my new theology manifests in the book called *Mud and Stars*. I was Chairman of the group, I was the ghost editor, majored several of the chapters and that sort of thing, and I think it's that fundamental rejection of an unrealistic interpretation of the Christian faith and accepting a more rugged one which is based on a theology of suffering, which has undoubtedly given me a firmer foundation.

For many people drawn towards hospices, it was the spiritual dimension of care which was the added attraction. Rita Beattie explains:

I think this is what appealed to me about hospice philosophy and care. Like, when I went to St Christopher's it wasn't just the physical/psychological/emotional care, but you were including the spiritual care, which I felt was an area that had been neglected throughout my training and experience. And it was, to me, a key part of holistic care that had been missing, certainly in the rest of my training and my experience. And that's what really attracted me, if you like, to hospice care. It wasn't just the holistic approach in terms of the whole person approach, but the approach holistically to … spiritual care.[8]

Sister Seraphine Bermingham, a member of the Sisters of the Cross and Passion,[9] outlines her view of whole person care in a religious setting. She explains how spiritual care at St Gemma's, Leeds has attempted to become more embracing, more Christian in outlook rather than focus exclusively upon the needs of Catholics:

In the early days there were a number of Sisters involved in the hospice. Added to this – well they had a variety of roles. Sister was the Matron, and there were quite a few Sisters working and, well, they saw their role as getting this hospice established, established in a way that truly met the needs of the people who would come in, and trying to look at all the needs, you know, as I said before. Over the years, as it is happening in so many places, there are fewer Sisters now. Sister Brigid is the only one actively involved in the hospice at the moment, and her role is Coordinator of Spiritual Care. And that would be a very important element in our work, our commitment to the hospice, and spiritual care is a very wide thing as you probably know, it's not just caring for Catholics and Catholic needs, it's caring for the whole person, and for all religions,[10] and she is involved in that. And that's an important, a very important aspect of the hospice work as far as we're concerned.

The institutional provision of spiritual care raises complex issues of definition, access and inclusivity.[11] Patricia Scott outlines how the search for a broader, inclusive model of spirituality at Sir Michael Sobell House, Oxford, ended with the creative therapies becoming encompassed within the spiritual dimension of care:

The spiritual care role is a vital one, and it's something that as a team we have struggled with over the years, recognising that all of us have a spiritual element, not necessarily a religious one, but a spiritual element, and the need to recognise that in our patients and our families, and, indeed, in ourselves. And I say we've struggled with it, because over the years we've had many discussions, formal and informal, and opportunities to look at what we mean, and to throw it around. And this has been greatly facilitated since we've had a more chaplaincy presence, because she has the focus, now, of spiritual care. She is somebody who, yes, OK, she's an Anglican chaplain, but she has the ability to be quite comfortable with people of different faiths, and none, and to explore all sorts of other possibilities. There's a great awareness in the House of the need for spiritual care, and

St Gemma's Hospice, Leeds

The origins of St Gemma's Hospice can be traced back to a decision by the Second Vatican Council that all religious orders should reappraise their origins and purposes. In response to this challenge, the Sisters of the Cross and Passion, in 1971, came from all over the world to a General Chapter. Taking a fresh look at the needs of people in the UK and seeing that state provision of Catholic education was good, they decided to phase out their private schools. One of these was St Gemma's, Moortown in Leeds which had been a girls' grammar school since 1957. Turning down the offer of a million pounds for the site and buildings, Sister Seraphine, Provincial Superior, with her Sister councillors, decided to serve the most pressing need of the times. Research showed that hospital wards were occupied with patients with advanced and terminal cancer, many of them suffering from unrelieved pain and spiritual or mental distress. At this time Sisters Olivia and Cecily Mary attended a conference on Hospice care where they were greatly impressed by the speakers, particularly Eric Wilkes and Tom West. The dedication of these two men provided the final impetus to the decision to establish a hospice. Three of the Sisters undertook specialised training at the London and Sheffield hospices. The architects who had built these two institutions were engaged and a working party was formed. On 12 October 1977 a public meeting was held and an Appeal Fund launched. Six months later, on 12 March 1978 (the centenary of St Gemma's birth), the former school was rededicated as a hospice. The official opening of the Hospice took place on 12 April 1978 by Bishop Gordon Wheeler. Initially a nine-bed in-patient unit, providing day care and a home care service (begun in February 1978), was opened in the old school house but by the end of 1978, in response to the large numbers of patients who had to be turned away, it had been decided to construct a 45-bed purpose-built extension at an estimated cost of £1 million. Work on the new building started on 4 July 1979 and was completed in just under two years. On 30 March 1982 it was officially opened by the Prince and Princess of Wales. In 1988 an appeal was launched for a new study centre which was completed in 1989. See www.st-gemma.co.uk.

we have quite a breadth of it, in recognising that, as I've said, that it isn't just religious care. We've got things like music therapy and art therapy and massage and aromatherapy, and many sort of other options on offer, to recognise all the many different sides. And we're still, we're still, as a team – and I guess it'll be ongoing – searching and looking and trying to help ourselves and each other develop in that way.

On the theme of institutional provision, Marjory Cockburn describes the architectural significance of a centrally located chapel at St Luke's, Sheffield, which resulted in widespread accessibility for both patients and staff:[12,13]

Eric Wilkes recognised the importance of faith in people's lives, the spiritual aspect. And so, in the plans of this building, it was so designed that the chapel is actually in the centre. And when people come in through reception, before they go down the corridor to the ward, or into the day room, or into the additional buildings of the Day Unit, or into the dining room; they see the chapel with the door always open, and that was a policy I emphasised. The chapel is designed with three double doors, so that if it's overfull the doors are opened and reception becomes part of the chapel, which it has done on numerous occasions. Normally two sets of doors are closed, one is open. The chapel is very simple; it's very beautiful. It has a very, I think, attractive cross which was specially designed on the wall. And many people as they pass go in, perhaps not for spiritual reasons, but perhaps just to look. But at the same time, there are those who go in on their way into the hospice to visit somebody, who will go in, sit down, and have some quiet in there, usually taking themselves over to the far side so that they're not visible as you go past. But that's one important aspect of the physical structure. The chapel was actually dedicated as an interdenominational place of worship, so that whatever the faith of the patients, within the Christian sphere, they can come to a service in the chapel and not

feel embarrassed. The services were so designed to be acceptable for people of different religions. So the Thursday morning communion service, and Sunday afternoons was a short half-hour service, very much 'do-it-yourself', sometimes taken by clergy, but more often taken by, perhaps, a member of staff, or someone who would be invited in to do it.

Personal sources of spiritual support

Contributors to this section highlight the ways in which personal sources of spiritual support have contributed to a sense of calling or commitment on the part of hospice activists. Carolyn Brodribb tells how her strong faith enabled her to regard all individuals as precious and unique:

You know I have a strong faith, and from that point of view, I suppose probably considered quite unorthodox in many ways – but [I have] a belief that there is a life beyond here, very different, and some strange experiences have reinforced that for me. You know, people talk about phenomenology, but some, you know, some things that [pause] have been very helpful for me – because they're part of me in terms of being able to see people as individual and precious and unique, and, whatever their difference, the fact that they are still precious and unique. And that however, you might say 'bad' a person, there's a kind of sense that actually there is a real person there, but waiting, perhaps, to be given permission to emerge, and sort of respecting the structures of other people's beliefs, but I would always open up the spiritual dimension, and the phenomenological dimension. And so for many and most people, they probably wouldn't know what my belief, beliefs were. But there's a sense I do see it as being part of

– part of a kind of assessment, an exploration for everybody. So that, you know, I wouldn't want not to explore areas that people opened up, however controversial it might seem to be.

For Patricia Scott in Oxford, it is the relationship between the living and the dead – as articulated by the Greek Orthodox Church – which gives her a source of spiritual strength; the sense of continuity resulting from centuries-long connectedness between past, present and future and the awareness of a larger context that eases the shedding of everyday burdens:

I was Anglican for many years, and 18 years ago I joined the Greek Orthodox Church, and that has been very, very important to me and has provided me with a great strength – a great strength. It's the relationship between the living and the dead, that sort of thing is fairly explicit and has been a great strength. And for me, the opportunity to go on a weekly basis to just be part of the services that have rolled on through the centuries, have provided an enormously positive time to, to just stand and reflect and to let go of, of what one carries, from the day-to-day things. I guess this is another huge thing, slightly off the spiritual point, but the other huge thing about coming to Sobell, to be able to not feel one was losing face to cry in front of one's colleagues. And this was something that was not part of, well, definitely drummed out of us as junior nurses. You know – nurses don't feel; nurses don't cry; stiff upper lip, and all that. And of course that's so wrong and so damaging. And I think, you know, that it was here, in the sluice, in front of an auxiliary, the first time I cried on duty – ever. And it was a huge lesson to me, and it's something that I would want others to be able to do, and I don't think the young have the same problem that those of us that trained 30 years ago do. The ability for us to be able to share together is very important 'cause we're all, we're all human. The day we don't, the day we don't feel what we're doing, is the day we should stop doing it, I think,

because, you know, it makes us less than human. So yes, I think the spiritual side is very important to recognise. It's very important not to force people into a particular way, or to – I mean they're trapped, as patients and families, there's no way we should be forcing them into a particular religious aspect or whatever, but just having available, and the acknowledgment that we all have a spiritual dimension, and there are many ways of looking at it and experiencing it.

Recalling a different experience, Mary Butterwick speaks of the task of raising funds and of the intervention of what she perceived as a personal call from God. Surprising yet irresistible, it caused her to step out 'in faith', sell her home and, from the proceeds, finance a hospice project in the North-East of England:

At that point I was 54 with a grown up family. How was I going to open a day care centre for the terminally ill? I mean, I knew people would laugh at me. They really hadn't – they didn't want to know some of the things I was saying at that point so – and that's no detriment to them – it's just that they didn't understand it. I'm not criticising them, I'm just stating a fact. And you see, I thought, 'Well how is a 54-year-old going to raise that kind of money?' And I thought, 'At 54 I haven't got five years to take out of my life to basically, just to raise the money you know – and £75,000'; I thought, 'Well, goodness me! It'll be more like £100,000 by the time I start getting it built!' So I thought, 'Well how I am I going to do it, God; really, how am I going to do this? You're going to have to show me how I'm going to do it.' And God did because – I even thought, you know – a vicar of my early days, my young days, was a vicar that had raised enough money to build a church school and he had stood – this was before I went into the army so you can tell how young I was – I remember this man sitting on Stockton High Street out, well just at the foot of the crossing that we had in Stockton High Street, and he basically used to bring his little stool every day and sit with his black cassock, and his little black hat with his pompom, and sit there with a bucket, and that's how he raised the money in this town to build a church school. It took him years and I thought, 'I haven't got this time, I really haven't got this time!' I was getting a little bit angry about this 'cause I thought, '[At] 54 you don't feel as if you've got that much time to waste,' you know, in that sense so, I thought, 'Well, I don't know how I'm going to do it.' And then again the Good Lord spoke. He said, 'Everything you've got I gave you – everything you've got I gave you!' And then started to point out through the scriptures. So I had no alternative did I? So I sold my home and everything in it and basically bought another house with the money, and proceeds, and with what I had in the bank, because, like I said, I had more money at this point in my life than I'd ever had.

Prue Clench speaks of the impact of the Christian tradition on the hospice movement and of the ways in which St Columba's Fellowship supports Christian hospice workers. Founded in 1986 (and with around 700 members worldwide) it aims to sustain and promote the Christian foundation of hospice care through courses, retreats and the ecumenical sharing of faith. For Prue Clench, the hospice ideal is rooted in the Christian concept of service and it is a tradition that she fears is in danger of being obscured in modern, secularised palliative care:

It's necessary to flag up the Christian roots of [the] hospice movement, not as being forefront and leader only, any more than the medical, but because it's in danger of being overlaid and forgotten, and that means you can actually lose something of quality. And I think the whole tradition, over the centuries, which comes from [the] Judeo-Christian tradition, of the value of a person as being a unique individual, that they matter as long as they live, that it isn't on the basis of somebody's worth and the contribution they make, but simply because they're human, the tradition of caring for the unattractive and the unwanted and so on, these things are largely rooted in our Christian heritage – and Jewish – but essentially in perhaps our British viewpoint, in the Christian heritage of previous generations, and the whole concept of service. We are, in my generation, a bit apt to forget and take this as read. And you have only to go to other countries who haven't had that tradition to realise that there is a chunk that we take for granted, that is very valuable. So I would want to say, right at the beginning, St Columba's Fellowship is not about trying to make people Christians. It's not an evangelical organisation trying to get people to say yes to three questions; it's not anything to do with that. It is about sustaining the people who are Christians, within hospice, who want to talk about their care that they're delivering in terms of what they as a person find most meaningful. But it's also about remembering that hospice care has a spiritual component, dying has a spiritual component, and most people with very unformed ideas of faith find it very threatening and very difficult to be able to operate as competently in areas of spiritual care as they would do in physical care or social care.[14]

The nature of hospice chaplaincy

Historical links between caring for the sick and the work of religious orders were incorporated into the newly established NHS in 1948, when the Ministry of Health advised hospital authorities to provide spiritual care by appointing paid chaplains from different traditions. Subsequent guidance advised hospital authorities to set aside a room for use as a chapel and to arrange schedules so that nurses and hospital workers could attend services of their denomination.[15] As a result, hospital chaplains came to occupy a central place in spiritual caregiving.

Within hospices, spiritual care evolved along different

lines. One source of inspiration to Cicely Saunders was that of the ancient Christian 'hospes' tradition, welcoming the sick and performing the works of mercy contained in the gospel of St Matthew 25.35–36.[16,17] Spiritual care, therefore, was not devolved to a specific group of people, but became a shared responsibility of the multidisciplinary team, the workings of which we have explored in Chapter 3, above. Consequently, the chaplain represented one group amongst many that was concerned with spiritual care.[18]

The following extracts give an insight into the nature and breadth of chaplaincy models. They record the rewards, the challenges and pressures of the chaplain's role and highlight both the benefits and difficulties inherent in its institutionalised form. Here Cicely Saunders recalls the ministry of Phillip Edwards, St Christopher's first whole-time Chaplain:

The Chaplain: how on earth did I acquire him? Oh, I know. Somebody wrote and said, 'Will I preach at Oundle School?' And I've done quite a lot of preaching in boys' public schools in my day, and I went there and one of the house masters who was a priest was very interested and he came as our first whole-time Chaplain. That was Phillip Edwards, he's now very retired down in the West Country somewhere, but we're still in touch, and he was with us – he must have been with us five or six years. He did a little teaching outside but he was basically whole-time here. And he used to think of himself as a shop steward. He used to say, 'The Chaplain's job is to be rather "untidily around".' And he was a wonderful 'listening ear' and he supported a number of people among the staff as well as among the patients. He was an important person at that time of setting up the chaplaincy.

By contrast, Edward Daly, working in Northern Ireland, tells how he became involved in hospice care in later life, after a stroke in 1993 brought about his retirement as a

bishop. Despite a wealth of experience, Edward Daly explains how his chaplaincy role became the most demanding, yet fulfilling, of his ministerial career:

I worked as a priest here in Derry since 1962, or thereabouts, I ministered largely in the Bogside area which was a very deprived area at that time. And strangely Dr [Tom] McGinley arrived in Derry around the same time, started his work as a doctor. We both knew one another and we worked in largely the same geographical area, he as a doctor, I as a clergyman, as a Catholic priest.

And he invited me to a public meeting in the Guild Hall which Tom called here and that was the first meeting this hospice was, the idea of hospice was launched and discussed and I attended that meeting and from day one I was very, very enthusiastic about the idea I think. I always felt that answering a need, a particular need in our society that was not being met, but people who were in that situation, terminally ill, and the families of people who were terminally ill deserved some kind of specialised care and therapy at that time in their lives. So I was enthusiastic for it. The need that Tom McGinley and myself and others felt was confirmed by just the sheer demand for home care nursing of the terminally ill.

Wilf Walton also speaks of challenge. Notwithstanding a sense of fulfilment, the theological pressures of working with the dying as Chaplain at St Luke's, Sheffield caused him to re-examine his own beliefs:

In Holy Week 1983 I had a telephone call from the Matron of St Luke's saying that someone told them, one of those kind friends that lands you in the soup, you know, that I was a retired clergyman doing nothing. The Chaplain of St Luke's had had to retire on health grounds. They were without a Chaplain: would I take the Easter Communion? So I knew of St Luke's existence, but had never been to the hospice, so I said I would need to talk to Matron before I agreed to do it. So we, I remember, we had a long talk on Good Friday afternoon. And to my surprise she didn't talk about the Easter Communion, she talked about my becoming Chaplain, you see, which rather shook me as it had never entered my head that this would happen. Anyway, I took the Easter Communion and then they asked me would I carry on, perhaps, for six weeks until they'd decided about chaplaincy, you see. And that six weeks lasted 11 years, and I became part of St Luke's. Chaplaincy at that time was – what shall I say – shall I call it a fringe thing? It was not, the chaplaincy was not developed here, really. And as I've already said, I didn't know anything about St Luke's, and I was very nervous. And any staff of that time will, I'm sure, endorse that – because how do you approach terminally ill people? How do you talk to them? How do you treat them? All this kind of thing was quite new to me. So I was very nervous at the outset, and needed help, and the person who gave me that help was Eric Wilkes. And any success, if you like to call it that, that I had as Chaplain is due to a great extent to Eric Wilkes, you see. Because when you come into a hospice … it's natural that you ask yourself questions: what do you yourself believe? Because again and again one is faced with the question from relatives, 'Why me?' And I had to rethink the whole of my own theological position, if you like.

Len Lunn, Chaplain of St Christopher's, speaks of a different challenge: of the mystery of the spiritual task. He acknowledges difficulties when explaining the nature of his role and recalls how patients come to find peace in their pain – and in their dying – in ways that are beyond human understanding. Yet he does not use the presence of mystery as cover for uncritical practice and suggests that research can be a useful tool for the development of more skilful responses and care:[19]

Tom West gave me a brief of ceasing to be a chaplain and to create a chaplaincy department, and he gave me some resources to do that, and to employ some assistance. And looking back, that was a great

Len Lunn: 'I still find it hard to tell people what I do and to explain the task of spiritual care to patients and families.'

privilege. And part of the brief was to create courses for clergy and to share in the teaching side of the multiprofessional side of things. They were very keen to have a teacher, and that's one of the things they grabbed me for, I think, because I had that background. I was at ease talking in groups and so on. So I had that brief to create something which was a great privilege, and quite exciting, and that's what I set about, really. One challenge was the incredibly difficult task of interpreting spiritual care to one's colleagues. I still find it hard to tell people what I do and to explain the task of spiritual care to patients and families. I feel a failure in that, although at times I justify it. It's so nebulous because it doesn't fit into the highly professionalised structure of the clinical scene. I'm beginning to think that chaplaincy has to exist as something a little bit apart, which goes against the grain in many ways, but it's what my experience keeps telling me.

So to be part of a multiprofessional team is to be part of it – working alongside and with – but because the spiritual task is so different from the clinical one, in its usual sense, one doesn't work in a linear way from a problem to a solution and one comes to it in a very generalised sort of way, and sometimes in a mysterious way because sometimes patients will be comforted, will grow, or will find peace in their dying, and in their pain, in ways in which you cannot comprehend. You were just there with them and something happens which cannot always be described, at least I can't describe it. But I don't want that to sound like a cop-out. One of the things I did do, which I think in the long term will be quite influential, I got a grant for someone to do a PhD – Rachel Stanworth as she was then – and she did a study which was based on listening to patients and how they actually describe their feelings, their situation and their experience of terminal illness and dying, and I think that kind of research will give us more handles on which to hold and develop the spirituality.[20] It will teach us how to listen to patients better and to interpret the symbols they're using, and the metaphors they use to ask for help, hopefully, and for us to respond more carefully and more skilfully.

Moving away from a traditional model of chaplaincy, Sally Campalani, interviewed in 2000, explains the benefits of appointing a non-denominational, non-ordained chaplain at the Marie Curie Centre, Belfast:

I think [there was] some lack of understanding of the role of chaplaincy in a health and social care environment. They tended to confuse chaplaincy with religion, and spirituality with religious denomination – so the feeling was by the people who were here before, that we couldn't have a Chaplain because it'd be better if everybody just accessed their own minister, and better if we avoid any political incorrectness. That has actually not proved to be the case because, while there's a lot of people who are churchgoers here and belong to a faith, equally because of the difficulties of the last 30 years, a lot of people actually want nothing to do with organised religion and so

have a lot of both religious and spiritual needs. And we find that our Chaplain, because it is a non-denominational, non-ordained person, other people access her who wouldn't actually dream of going to an established minister or religion. Because people have had – you know, you cannot remove Northern Irish people from the collective grief over the last 30 years and in fact in a lot of our work it's very clear that the issues are there, you know, a lot of the parents are dying, have already lost the other parent to the Troubles, and there's collective griefs in the family and there's different experiences. So it's proved really, really useful to have somebody who's a non-denominational person.

Ann Cooney, Administrative Director with Southern Area Hospice Services in Newry, Northern Ireland, also envisages the possibility of lay chaplaincy – a development which could become problematic in the future:

We've always had a Chaplain but it happens to be a Sister now and it always was a priest before that, so now we have a Sister which is different and I think in fact it's more the Catholic community who are concerned about it because the Catholic community have a big, I suppose, dependency on their priest and to find that it's not going to be a priest is you know – so a Sister isn't really a priest, no matter that she's a religious Sister. I think in the future it'll be a lay person and that'll be quite difficult as well particularly in what was a very Catholic organisation. We have tried over the years, to not be less Catholic, but be more Christian, to be more all-embracing, to be not sort of identified with any one religion and I think in the future, regardless of the religion of the Chaplain, it'll probably be a lay person and that will bring difficulties as well, so this is probably step one. There isn't the priests and there isn't the religious and it may not be a Catholic person who would apply. We'll be looking for somebody with qualifications in pastoral care and whatever, and we would just look at whoever applies and they don't necessarily have to be of religion, but that will be a difficulty I imagine.

Striking a different note, Derek Doyle is sceptical about the value of chaplaincy and raises concerns about the capacity of chaplains to find a team-based niche which includes both religious and non-religious spiritual care. While the importance of religion for the religious is not in question, he considers that within hospice care, difficult issues arise which relate to existential questions: the meaning of pain; the presence of a listening God; and why suffering happens. In the presence of a team approach wherein many members have an underlying faith, he is concerned that the Chaplain may become isolated in the presence of a different language, different training and different patterns of thought:

Chaplains: I think we've got a problem. Many chaplains that have come into this work are not – a) they're not natural researchers and, b) they're not writers. I don't want them to sit down and do a 'Quality of Life' scale for us. I'm not asking them to be 'quasi' scientists. Thank God they're not, most of them. But I do wish they would teach the rest of us; tell us what people ask them, what people expect, what are the commonest dilemmas that they get. This is a bit trite now, I wonder whether all our chaplains of whom we have some very, very outstandingly good ones, haven't we, I wonder if all of them, however, are as clear as many of us are beginning to be on the difference between 'religious' and 'spiritual'. And I think many chaplains still see themselves as performing a 'religious' ministry, which is very important, but I don't think it is the same as, and sometimes hardly comes into the 'spiritual' care.

After all, what I think we need is not somebody who will, if you like, make sense of the Bible, or pray with them, or read with them, or take them through our doctrines and dogmas, and perform the sacraments – very important for believers, all of them. I think we want people that will help us, as well as the patients, to make sense of the deep spiritual problems in this work: why does this happen? Existential meaning if you like. Why is this? Who am I? Why suffer? What's the meaning of pain? Can we change as a result of this? Why pray? Is there a God who listens? Is God deaf? And so on. This is what happens all the time. I'm interested, wherever I've gone talking to chaplains, I hear them saying, 'People seem to ask the doctors all these things more than they ask us. I never seem to get asked these questions.' I don't think that's … because they're bad chaplains, I think it's because they're seen as the 'religious' men; the religious practitioners, rather than the spiritual ones. And I don't think for one minute that most chaplains in this country, part-time or full-time, are envious of the rest of us. That's not in them, they're too nice people, but I think they find it difficult working in an environment where our language is different, our mode of thought is different, our training is totally different, where apparently our goals are different and where many of us have got some sort of faith, almost doing part of their ministry.

Now I'm not saying we do it as well, of course I'm not, but I think they sometimes find themselves very uncomfortable in a group where everybody seems to be on that same wavelength too. I mean I've been in team meetings where the Chaplain has sat absolutely silent and one of the doctors would be saying, 'And he asked me if I'd just have a word of prayer with him,' and I said, 'Well I'm not very good at doing it but, yes, let's do that, let's do that just now.' And a nurse said, 'Well, last night I said to her, you know, "Can I get you a commode?" and she said, "Well I'd rather you read the Bible to me, dear, because I just can't read it and I must have somebody to read it to me before I went to sleep" so I did, I did that before I brought the commode to her.' And you can see, sometimes, the Chaplain thinking, 'Where do I fit in here?'

Colin Murray Parkes however, speaking from the perspective of the psychiatrist in the hospice, is more optimistic. In the following extract he explains how chaplains may well transfer their hospice experience to other professional situations that ultimately impact upon wider social arrangements:

A lot of people come for training to a hospice, work in a hospice for a few years and then they go off and do something else. And that's great because they may find that what they learnt in hospice is relevant when they're caring for amputees, is relevant when they're caring for people in other settings. And the clergyman who, having worked as a hospice Chaplain, goes and works in the community and meets people who are suffering the effects of divorce and other losses in their lives, again, has opportunities to use the lessons that he's learnt in one setting to improve the care in another. I hope I'm not being romantic in suggesting that the long-term influences of hospice may well extend far beyond the medical care systems, and maybe have important implications for the entire social structures that we live in.

Stories about patients

Like other areas of life, experiences in the spiritual domain range from the surprising and amusing to the disturbing and deeply moving. In the following extract, Barbara McNulty, who helped set up the first home care service out of St Christopher's, tells of a patient's request for a faith healer – which had an unusual outcome:

Anthony Bloom was somebody I remember very clearly, now the Metropolitan Anthony, whose mother had recently died. And he had a great interest in the problems of dying people and people with cancer, and he came and talked to us quite a few times, by memory, a very remarkable person. One of the things I remember

him saying was, 'If somebody asks you to pray for them, then that is your responsibility for life.' That's always intimidated me. You think of the number of people who've said, 'Oh please say a prayer for me?' and you've said, 'Oh yes, yes.' Do you remember them? Another one was David Shepherd,[21] whom I remember. That's a story I'm not sure that I can – perhaps I can tell you part of it: People often, in their last weeks and months, begin to turn to the Church, or to ministers, or to some outside help they think will save them from something, or help them through a difficult time. And there was one man, who was certainly suffering deeply in his inner self, at home, and he said to me one day, or he couldn't speak so he wrote on his little pad; 'I know you can't save me but do you know, you must know someone who can, or you can't help me.' And I said, 'Like who?' And he said, 'Well, like a faith healer,' to which I could only reply, 'Well I don't know anybody, but I'll find out.'

And such was the urgency in my mind for this that I went racing back to St Christopher's at lunchtime, and ploughed into the dining room to find Cicely and said, 'Do we know a faith healer?' And she was sitting at the table with a couple of ministers there, and one of them I later learned was David Shepherd, and Cicely said, 'Well, do you know a faith healer?' And one of them said, 'Yes,' which was David Shepherd, and he gave me a name and number ... 'Well I won't give you the name, I'll give you the number ...' And then – I dialled this and the answer came: 'This is Buckingham Palace.' So, I hesitated and said, 'I'm so sorry,' and put down the phone. I dialled what I'm sure was the right number again and had the same reply. And, in fact, it was one of the Queen's Chaplains[22] who came out and saw this man, and was absolutely wonderful, wonderful. He came out regularly, every week, or every other day I think, until [the man] died, and had an enormous influence. But that's the kind of thing that happened. There was always somebody there who knew something, or knew someone who knew something.

Appearances can sometimes be misleading, as Wilf

Walton discovered while at St Luke's, Sheffield. In the following extract, he speaks of a patient who seemed deeply moved after hearing the American evangelist, Billy Graham.[23] Yet on closer examination, there was a different reason for the patient's sense of peacefulness:

Billy Graham came and [this patient] was well enough to be taken by her husband to one of these meetings at Bramall Lane. He had the front seat of the car taken out and got the wheelchair put in, you see, and she went. And, the end of that week when I came in the staff said, 'She's changed, she's completely different, and we don't know why. Must be Billy Graham,' you see, rather jokingly. So I went to see her and her attitude was completely different, you see. So I asked her how she got on at this rally, if you like, with Billy Graham, and she said, 'The choir sang in a most heavenly way,' she said, 'and then afterwards Billy Graham spoke.' And I thought; this is it, this is something Billy Graham's said to her, that's touched her, you see. So eagerly I said, 'What did he say?' 'I don't know – I was asleep!' But that taught me, or, you know, it reinforced what I'd believed for a long time; that one can find God or spiritual calm – call it what you like – in more ways than by listening to sermons or by going to church. And I found some people find spiritual peace by going into Derbyshire. And others I found, and I think she was an instance of this, through music – it was the music.

At the Northern Ireland Hospice, Belfast, patients from across the region's religious divide frequently attend each other's services. Liz Atkinson recalls how one occurrence led to an unexpected consequence:

One thing I can say hasn't really come into the situation in the hospice, it's something we've managed to overcome – that both sides of the community have taken the hospice on board. Our staff is a wide mix from both communities. Patients are from all communities and they mix together and we have – we would see ourselves as

Anthony Bloom – Metropolitan Anthony of Sourozh (1914–2003)

Born in Lausanne, Switzerland, where his father was a member of the Russian Imperial Diplomatic Corps, André Borisovich Bloom grew up in France after the 1917 Revolution changed the social structure in Russia. Drawn to the Orthodox priesthood, he studied theology, practised medicine, embraced monastic vows, and in 1949 moved to London after his appointment as Chaplain to the Fellowship of St Alban and St Sergius – an ecumenical society which sought to further relations between Anglicans and the Orthodox. In 1957 he was consecrated bishop of the diocese of Sergievo, becoming elevated to Archbishop in 1962. In 1963 he was given oversight of all patriarchal parishes in Western Europe as Exarch of the Moscow Patriarchate and in 1966 raised to the office of Metropolitan. These were difficult times for the Orthodox Church: in the Soviet Union, Nikita Khrushchev instigated a persecution of Orthodox Christians; churches were closed and believers imprisoned. Metropolitan Anthony responded by focusing on the eastern tradition of prayer and spirituality, although he was publicly outraged when Alexander Solzhenitsyn was expelled from the Soviet Union. Over the years, Metropolitan Anthony became regarded as a spiritual leader of great stature, particularly among intellectuals, and came to play a leading role in the life of the Orthodox Church in the UK. In 1960 he began an association with the newly formed project to establish St Christopher's and had contacts with the hospice over many years, including serving as one of its Vice-Presidents.

a hospice with a Christian ethos and foundation, and patients who come to us are welcome from whatever denomination. We have a daily lunchtime prayer time at 12 o'clock every day, and that's taken by various chaplains from the denominations. And that would be attended by patients, no matter who was taking it. I can tell you one funny story where a gentleman went up one day to prayers, and he was from a brethren, some sort of brethren gospel hall background, and the Catholic priest was leading the prayers that day. So when this gentleman came back down into the ward I said, 'Well, did you enjoy the devotion time?' He says, 'I did, but I didn't know it was the priest taking it.' And I said to him, 'Well I'm sure God wouldn't mind.' And the patient said, 'It's not God I'm worried about, it's my pastor!'

Finally, Jo Hockley, interviewed whilst working at St Columba's, Edinburgh, but with many years' experience in hospital palliative care, recalls how her involvement in the spiritual care of a patient came to have an effect upon both of them:

[This lady] just wanted to die. And she had the will to die but she just couldn't die. And so I thought, well, 'Why aren't you dying?' you know, 'Are there unresolved issues?' … And I actually do believe it was a spiritual issue and we struggled for six weeks with this lady and, you know, in the end I was going on holiday, and, this one time if somebody had been sitting next door to me I would have said they had said it, but obviously I said it, and I was just about to leave and I said, 'Before I go would you like me to pray for you?' Well, nurses are not meant to, you know, do these sorts of things, but I just felt there was a spiritual issue there and I didn't know how else to try and work it out. I, I was praying for her just, just a very simple prayer, and said, you know, 'God, she cannot understand how there can be a God of love because of all the awful things that have happened in her life, and I just pray that you'd show her your love in Jesus.' And at which point I became really nervous, and it was as though I was giving a lecture about something and suddenly the professor walks in, and I just realised something very spiritual was happening. And I opened my eyes to see her changed state, clearly having an out-of-body experience. And so I just sat there, which felt like 10 minutes but it was probably only for about a couple of minutes – really nervous – and she opened her eyes and just said, 'Jo, thank you so much.' Well I should have had the presence of the moment and said, 'What was going on, Emma?' but unfortunately I didn't because I felt so scared, I felt totally out of my depth. Anyway I went back the next day, just literally as I was leaving for holiday, because I felt I hadn't said a proper goodbye and we were chatting, and I said, 'Well, I must go,' and she said, 'Would you pray for me again like you did yesterday?' Anyway the next day apparently, while I was away on holiday, she died that night. And I think we wouldn't have grown as people without having to care for her. We wouldn't have considered a spiritual dimension if we had been able to give her euthanasia six weeks earlier – a spiritual dimension wouldn't have come into our care. And I think we as human beings would be lesser for that.

Jo Hockley: 'I think we wouldn't have grown as people without having to care for her.'

The palliative care literature often makes bold claims for its attention to the spiritual care of patients and those close to them. These extracts get beneath some of that rhetoric and demonstrate a remarkable involvement in the spiritual dimension of care in hospice and other settings – and the varied forms which that can take. They point to a rich tradition within the hospice movement; a flow of committed activists whose particular contribution has been to recognise the importance of spirituality to both their patients and themselves. By being prepared to address the spiritual issues surrounding death and dying, 'palliateurs' such as these ensured this important dimension of care became an historical and present reality.

Some commentators have been inclined to describe this shift in emphasis from 'religion' to 'spirituality' as an unintended, even unwelcome aspect of the 'routinisation', 'secularisation' and 'bureaucratisation' of hospice and palliative care. Better informed by historical analysis, however, we may see the shift as a conscious response to changing social circumstances and a necessary adjustment within a changing health care environment. At the same time religion has been central to early articulations of hospice philosophy and we might speculate that the transition to an apparently more inclusive model of 'spirituality' may have wider ramifications: in patterns of staff recruitment and retention; in public perceptions of the work of hospices; and in the experience of patients, particularly those who do endorse a formal religious tradition. We can see from these extracts the way in which those working in hospices have tried to address the question of how to acknowledge the Christian tradition of hospice care while at the same time demonstrating equity towards spiritualities expressed through other religions, belief systems, or indeed no faith at all.

Notes

1. For an analysis of these issues, developed within the Hospice History Project, see C. Humphreys, '"Waiting for the Last Summons": the establishment of the first hospices in England 1878–1914', *Mortality* 6 (2): 146–66, 2001.
2. D. Clark, 'Religion, medicine and community in the early origins of St Christopher's Hospice', *Journal of Palliative Medicine* 4 (3): 353–60, 2001.
3. For a résumé of the principles of contemporary spiritual care, see Spiritual Care Work Group of the International Work Group on Death, Dying and Bereavement, 'Assumptions and Principles of Spiritual Care', *Death Studies* 14: 75–81, 1990.
4. A wide-ranging exploration of spiritual issues at the end of life may be found in M. Cobb, *The Dying Soul: Spiritual care at the end of life* (Buckingham: Open University Press, 2001).
5. A study by Malcolm McIllmurray and colleagues concluded that patients with a religious faith were less reliant on health professionals, and had less need for information or help with feelings of guilt and practical matters than those without a faith. See M.B. McIllmurray, B. Francis, J.C. Harman, S.M. Morris, K. Soothill and C. Thomas, 'Psychosocial needs in cancer patients related to religious belief', *Palliative Medicine* 17: 49–54, 2003.
6. This is reflected in a sermon preached by Robert Twycross on Fellowship Day at Burrswood Christian Hospital in 1995: 'For the Christian hospice doctor or nurse, a God who suffers is an essential doctrine … the world's salvation is to be accomplished through weakness and seeming failure'; *Burrswood News* (No 18: Summer, 1995).
7. Working Party, *Mud and Stars: The impact of hospice experience on the church's ministry of healing* (Oxford: Sobell Publications, 1991).
8. For a nursing perspective on spiritual care, see R. Elsdon, 'Spiritual pain in dying people: the nurse's role', *Professional Nurse* 10 (10): 641–43, 1996.
9. The Sisters of the Cross and Passion were founded by Elizabeth Prout in Manchester during the mid-nineteenth century. With a focus upon education and pastoral care, the Sisters spread their activities into a variety of locations that include Eastern Europe, Africa, the Americas and Asia.
10. St Gemma's, Leeds goes to some lengths to acknowledge its multicultural, multifaith catchment area. On a visit to the hospice, one of us (MWr.) noted that visitors were greeted by a 'welcome' in 17 different languages, displays focused upon local faiths, and Islamic and Jewish advisers were available for consultation.

11. For an inclusive model of the spiritual domain see M. Wright, 'Good for the soul? The spiritual dimension of hospice and palliative care' in S. Payne, J. Seymour and C. Ingleton (eds.), *Palliative Care Nursing: Principles and evidence for practice* (Maidenhead: Open University Press, 2004).

12. This provision is in keeping with the chapel at St Christopher's. According to Shirley du Boulay, 'The infusion of a religious attitude is symbolised by the central position of the chapel. After considerable extension in 1973, it is now a long room occupying almost half the width of the building'. See S. du Boulay, *Cicely Saunders: The founder of the hospice movement* (London: Hodder and Stoughton, 1984: 9).

13. St Luke's, Sheffield opened in 1971 when chapels were regarded as a central feature of spiritual care provision. Such opinion resonated with a King's Fund report published in 1966 that gave advice relating to chapels in a hospital setting: 'A hospital with 800 patients should have seating accommodation for 120 people. Psychiatric hospitals require proportionately larger chapels' (The King's Fund, *The Hospital Chaplain* (London: The King's Fund, 1966: 37, para 15)). A telling insight into the prevailing mood is captured by the following statement: '… where the ward sister reads morning or evening prayers the patients are usually appreciative and the atmosphere of the ward is influenced for good' (*ibid*: 25, para 54). A study conducted in 1999 identified a developing trend in favour of multifaith/quiet rooms within both hospitals and hospices: see M.C. Wright, 'Chaplaincy in hospice and hospital: findings from a survey in England and Wales', *Palliative Medicine* 15:229–42, 2001.

14. Ann Bradshaw makes a similar point and expresses concern that the ethos of hospice care has become subject to routinisation. This is evident, she suggests, in an increasing focus upon management skills, greater medicalisation and a redefined concept of spirituality. Turning to the notions of 'calling' and 'service' within the Christian tradition, she asks whether the original hospice ethic has a continuing relevance in preventing modern palliative care from becoming merely a set of skills and techniques. See A. Bradshaw, 'The spiritual dimension of hospice: the secularisation of an ideal', *Social Science and Medicine* 43: 409–20, 1996 and also N. James and D. Field, 'The routinisation of hospice: charisma and bureacratisation', *Social Science and Medicine* 34 (12): 1363–75, 1992.

15. National Health Service, *Appointment of Chaplains. HMC(48 62)* (London: HMSO, 1948). This ground-breaking guidance became the bedrock of hospital chaplaincy until new publications from the Department of Health appeared during the 1990s. These included: *The Patient's Charter* (London: HMSO, 1991); and *Meeting the Spiritual Needs of Patients and Staff. HSG(92)2* (London: HMSO, 1992).

16. See C. Saunders, 'The modern hospice' in W. Wald (ed.), *In Quest of the Spiritual Component of Care for the Terminally Ill* (Yale: Yale School of Nursing, 1986: 41).

17. Although the hospice ideal of Cicely Saunders was based upon the spiritual traditions of the Christian Church, she nevertheless acknowledged the absence of any direct line between the early 'hospes' and what became known as the modern hospice movement (see her letter to Grace Goldin, 11 August 1986, in D. Clark, *Cicely Saunders – Founder of the Hospice Movement. Selected letters 1959–1999* (Oxford: Oxford University Press, 2002: 286)). Significantly, the modern hospice was influenced by an epidemiological transition in parts of Europe, America and Australia that took place during the nineteenth century, which led to a shift in the pattern of death, from primarily infectious diseases to diseases of longer duration. This in turn led to the emergence of 'the dying' as a social category and to those who became uniquely concerned with their care (see D. Clark, 'History, gender and culture in the rise of palliative care' in S. Payne, J. Seymour and C. Ingleton (eds.), *Palliative Care Nursing. Principles and evidence for practice* (Maidenhead: Open University Press, 2004). These caregivers included spiritually aware women such as Jeanne Garnier (from Lyon), who founded her first 'Calvaire' in 1842; and Mother Mary Aikenhead (from Cork), who founded the Irish Sisters of Charity – a religious order which established homes for the dying in both England and Australia. As we have seen in Chapter 1, it was in a home for the dying run by the Sisters of Charity (St Joseph's, Hackney) that Cicely Saunders worked in the late 1950s, meeting there her 'founding group' of patients and developing her ideas of what a modern hospice might become.

18. Tony Walter addresses the issue of shared spiritual care responsibilities, and suggests that such a model deepens the role of the Chaplain, widens the role of the nurse and has the advantage of being offered by those with and without a faith. See T. Walter, 'The ideology and organisation of spiritual care: three approaches', *Palliative Medicine* 1:21–30, 1997.

19. Research within the spiritual domain is considered to be problematic, due largely to the lack of a generally accepted definition of spirituality. See P. McGrath, 'Exploring spirituality through research: an important but challenging task', *Progress in Palliative Care* 7 (1): 3–9, 2000.

20. The work was subsequently published as R. Stanworth, *Recognising Spiritual Needs in People who are Dying* (Oxford: Oxford University Press, 2004).

21. David Shepherd was born in 1929 and, after studying at Trinity Hall Cambridge, he became Curate of St Mary's, Islington in 1955. As a young man, he is remembered for playing cricket for England. He was appointed Suffragen Bishop of Woolwich in 1969 and Bishop of Liverpool from 1975, where he worked closely with his Roman Catholic counterpart, Archbishop Derek Worlock.

22. There are 36 Chaplains to the Queen, who are provided as part of the Church of England's service to the Monarch – wherever she may be. Each Chaplain preaches once a year on a rota basis, usually in the Queen's Chapel at St James's Palace.

23. Billy Graham, the American evangelist; born in 1918, he joined *Youth for Christ International* in 1945. He eventually led a series of high profile international campaigns and is thought to have addressed more than 80 million people at rallies worldwide.

6   Pain, symptoms and the hospice response

'… there's so much more to be learnt about pain'
Norman Barrett to Cicely Saunders, 1951

The modern hospice movement and the modern science of pain medicine have interrelated histories which we can trace back to the mid-twentieth century. In 1953, from his base in Seattle, John Bonica published a ground-breaking treatise on the management of pain.[1] Two years earlier, in England, Cicely Saunders had begun to read medicine, inspired by a desire to help the terminally ill and to learn more about pain relief. In her pursuit of understanding the pain of the dying she was soon to turn to the work of Bonica and his associates in the United States; indeed it is Bonica's book which appears as the initial citation in the first ever publication by Cicely Saunders.[2] On both sides of the Atlantic however there were problems of recognition for this work. There was deep scepticism in some quarters that anything new could be done in this area of medicine and also a complacency that the problem of intractable pain, was just that – intractable: particularly as it related to chronic and to life-threatening conditions. Pain was seen as an inevitable part of the cancer experience and it was viewed fatalistically by physicians and patients alike. It had long been the preserve of patent remedies and quackery. Since at least the beginning of the century, the strong narcotics which appeared capable of relieving it were viewed with suspicion, and there were concerns, even for patients close to death, about the possibilities of addiction.

After the Second World War some of this began to change. Pain was becoming a new object of scientific and clinical enquiry and began to be seen as a multifaceted problem which required combined strategies for its relief. Pharmacological approaches to pain management were becoming more sophisticated, and so too was the understanding of pain at the level of perception and meaning. The early innovators of the modern hospice movement in the UK certainly had evidence that unrelieved pain among patients suffering from cancer was a significant problem. As early as 1952, the Joint National Cancer Survey, conducted by the committee of the Marie Curie Memorial Foundation and the Queen's Institute of District Nursing,[3] reported the experiences and living circumstances of 7,050 patients, 70 per cent of them over 60 years old. The survey highlighted the problems of unrelieved pain and suffering. A medical officer noted: 'My nurses all agree that ... many patients suffer much unnecessary pain, and are inadequately sedated. They attribute this largely to patients not telling the general practitioners about their pain'; whilst a district nurse observed: 'Coming into contact with a great number of cancer patients, I feel that the greatest single point that can be raised is the terrible suffering that these patients go through.' The situation appeared little better by the early 1960s, when two GPs could write:

> The popular misconception that the most powerful analgesics of the morphine group are so dangerous that they should be given only in the last resort is sometimes an unfortunate hindrance to the adequate relief of pain. The objective must be complete and continuing freedom from severe pain, not merely temporary relief with the drugs only being given when the pain has returned. When morphine is administered in appropriate combination with its antagonists ... complete analgesia can often be safe and pleasant; apprehension, fear and distress are greatly reduced and the patient can continue on these mixtures for many months.[4]

It was around this time that Cicely Saunders' work on the relief of pain and suffering in the terminally ill was beginning to gain momentum. From 1958 to 1965 she worked full time at St Joseph's, Hackney and here began to influence a generation of medical students and nurses who visited her for teaching sessions and ward rounds. In the decade up to the opening of St Christopher's in 1967 she published 56 articles, pamphlets and reviews directed at doctors, nurses and medical social workers,[5] many of them highlighting issues of pain relief in the context of terminal illness. She was also invited to speak and to give lectures at increasingly pres-

tigious meetings, and accepted these with enthusiasm and not a little courage. Perhaps one of the most crucial presentations she gave was at the Royal Society of Medicine in 1962, at a meeting of its Surgical Section where the theme was 'The Management of Intractable Pain'.[6] In their imaginative commentary on this meeting, Christina Faull and Alexander Nicholson speculate that Cicely Saunders was the only woman at the event; certainly she would have been speaking to an audience that had a formidable reputation within medical circles. Moreover she was there to 'contradict several of the myths held true by the vast majority of the audience ... to show them that what they have been taught, what they teach and what they do is wrong'.[7] Her thesis centred on the necessity of administering opiates regularly to patients with cancer pain. On the basis of systematic observation of 900 dying patients from St Joseph's, Hackney, she argued that opiates were not addictive, that tolerance was not a problem and that giving morphine orally worked by relieving pain, not by merely masking it. The paper concentrates however not so much on the drugs used with these patients, but rather the methods of their use. The 'cardinal rules' are set out: careful assessment of the symptoms that trouble the patient; assessment of the nature and severity of the pain; and the regular giving of drugs. But the paper also explores the parameters of mental distress and notes that this is 'perhaps the most intractable pain of all'. Here was a key element in Cicely Saunders' work; a willingness to go beyond a view of the body as a machine to understand that suffering is many layered and individual.

By the time that Cicely Saunders left St Joseph's in 1965, she had collected detailed descriptions of the cases of 1,100 patients and had formulated her understanding of pain as something multidimensional and which requires more than

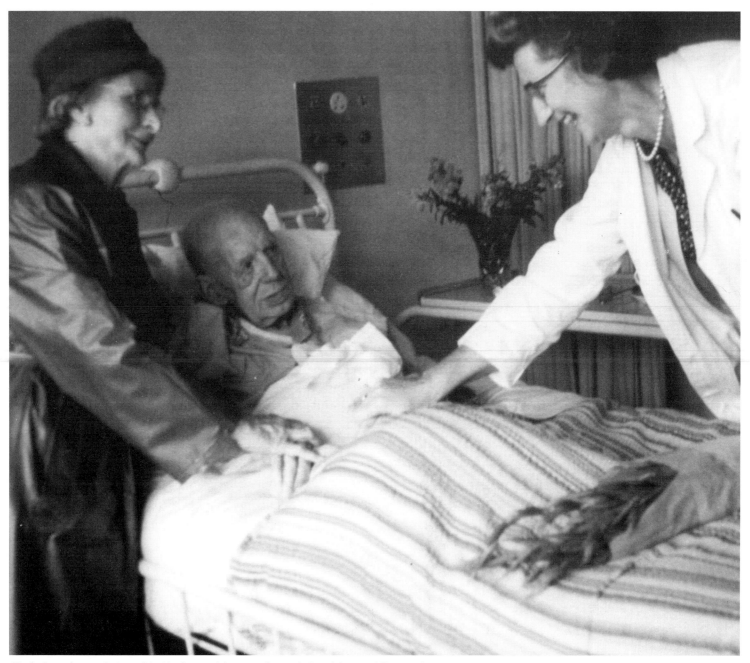

Cicely Saunders at St Joseph's, Hackney with a couple on their golden wedding anniversary.

mere attention to medical treatments if it is to be relieved. She had amassed a considerable literature concerned with the care of the dying, drawing on contributions made by nurses, doctors, psychologists, social workers and public health workers across the world. She had also travelled widely, both in the UK and further afield, exchanging knowledge and expertise with others who shared her concerns, particularly in the USA.[8] Throughout this she promoted a view of the cancer patient as a person with a story to tell about their pain and suffering and, through her case presentations, argued persuasively that patients' stories could be seen as valid sources of evidence for clinical practice, if they were listened to appropriately and attentively.

By 1964, informed with the many patient stories she had heard, Cicely Saunders had developed the concept of 'total pain'.[9] There can be little doubt that she was in the process of bequeathing to medicine and health care a concept of enduring clinical and conceptual interest. Part of our enquiry into hospice history has involved piecing together the evolution of the concept of 'total pain'.[10] The notion undoubtedly emerged from Cicely Saunders' unique experience as nurse, social worker and physician – the remarkable multidisciplinary platform from which she launched the modern hospice movement. It also reflected a willingness to acknowledge the spiritual suffering of the patient and to see this in relation to physical problems. Crucially, it was tied to a sense of narrative and biography, emphasising the importance of listening to the patient's story and of understanding the experience of suffering in a multifaceted way. This was an approach which saw pain as a key to unlocking other problems and as something requiring multiple interventions for its resolution. 'Total pain' therefore incorporated several dimensions: physical, psychological, social, emotional and spiritual.[11] After 1967

in work carried out at St Christopher's, the concept of 'total pain' was further elaborated – by researchers, clinicians, and patients themselves.[12] By 1987, palliative medicine had been recognised as a specialty in the UK and Cicely Saunders' thinking about 'total pain' had become established as a major element within the conceptual armamentarium of the new discipline. Arguably, it is the one original concept that hospice and palliative care have yet produced.

In addition to this conceptual refinement, the early days of the modern hospice movement also saw some crucial innovations in thinking about the pharmacological relief of pain. This work was of vital importance in setting a new agenda for the use of opioids – morphine in particular – to relieve intense pain associated with advanced cancer. It began with close scrutiny of some of the methods of pain relief favoured within the early hospices and terminal care homes, in particular the use of the so-called 'Brompton Cocktail'.[13] As long ago as 1896 the physician Herbert Snow[14] had described how morphine and cocaine when combined into an elixir may give relief to patients with advanced cancer. About 30 years later a similar approach was used at London's Brompton Hospital as a cough sedative for patients with tuberculosis. In the early 1950s this formulation appeared in print for the first time, containing morphine hydrochloride, cocaine hydrochloride, alcohol, syrup and chloroform water. Cicely Saunders, in her early writings, was eager to promote such a mixture. It included a remarkable combination of ingredients: nepenthe or liquor morphini hydrochloride, cocaine hydrochloride, tincture of cannabis, gin, syrup and chloroform water, and she was enthusiastic about its value to terminally ill patients. Over the next 20 years in her subsequent writing and lecturing, she did much to promote this mixture and other variants of the Brompton Cocktail.

The psychiatrist and pioneer of end of life care, Elisabeth Kübler-Ross became one of its supporters and it was widely adopted across North America. Indeed, as Robert Twycross noted, there developed a 'tendency to endow the Brompton Cocktail with almost mystical properties and to regard it as the panacea for terminal cancer pain'.[15] It was these properties he set out to scrutinise in what became a series of classic studies, among the first of their kind to be undertaken in the hospice setting. He concluded that the Brompton Cocktail was no more than a traditional British way of administering oral morphine to cancer patients in pain and urged that its use should be quietly abandoned in favour of simpler approaches. But the actions of morphine, the development of new approaches to its administration and the teaching of health care professionals about its appropriate use alongside other analgesics and adjuvant drugs – all of these became a rich territory of both research and teaching in the modern hospice and palliative care context.

In this chapter we explore three themes within this history: the problems of pain relief that were identified by hospice innovators from the 1950s onwards; the identification of 'total pain' and the appropriate responses to it; and the wider influences of ideas about pain relief first developed in hospice settings.

Recalling problems in the pre- and early hospice days

Work on pain relief had been the very stimulus for Cicely Saunders' entry into training as a doctor. She recalls a conversation, in 1951, that galvanised her into studying medicine, having already worked as a nurse and an almoner:

… and then I took over working with a Mr Barrett who was a thoracic surgeon, and I did some of his medical secretarying as well as looking, doing some social work for his patients. All this was a bit out of care, but my boss at St Thomas's not only allowed me to keep the £500, which was what David's money turned out to be once I'd given something to his friends,[16] but also to let me do a slightly unusual, sort of two-pronged job. And it was in 1951 when I was going down to Midhurst's Sanatorium where he was going to operate, and I was going to pick up some patients' notes, but I said, 'I think I'm going to have to go back and nurse, because I've really got to do, get on with this.' And he said, 'No, go and read medicine, it's the doctors who desert the dying, and there's so much more to be learnt about pain and you'll only be frustrated if you don't do it properly, and they won't listen to you.' And he was right.

Doctors themselves were clearly struggling with these problems, often with only a limited knowledge base from which to proceed. Some of our respondents were able to recollect examples, stretching back into the 1950s, of the difficulties that existed in administering adequate levels of pain relief to patients in ways that were both effective and safe. Lurking in the background was the implicit or explicit fear that any action taken by the doctor might be construed as deliberately hastening the death of the patient. John Berkeley recalls the situation in the Highlands of Scotland:

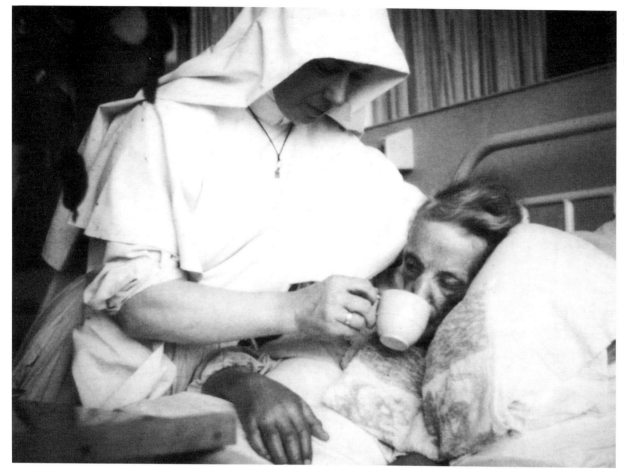

*Sister Mary Antonia at
St Joseph's, Hackney.
The patient, Miss Ford,
died next morning.*

I can very clearly remember, within the first year or two of going into practice, a lady with advanced cervical carcinoma dying at home. And we were giving quite large doses of morphine. I mean they seemed *lethal* doses to us in those days. Now, looking back with hindsight, I think we were giving adequate doses but not frequently enough and they were intermittent. And my feeling of *utter help-lessness*, of trying to help, not only this woman, but her husband and her daughters, and feeling that I had not got the skills at that time (and this was about two years into practice), to actually deal with this situation. It made quite a profound impact. I mean I can still now visualise the house, and the woman, and the many calls I made to that household. And I think it … so that must have been '55 or something like that. [And] a relatively young woman, I think she must have been in her, probably, mid-40s or something like that, made quite a profound impression on me at the time. And stimulated me to read, to see what there was that one could do to help. And there was very, very little in the literature in those days to give any indication. And indeed, as I say, using morphine; we used doses way over the recommended top dose and one really felt that one was giving a dose that could actually kill the patient. It didn't … I mean it did relieve her pain, but I was quite … my partner and I were really quite … concerned about the high doses of morphine we were using. So that was the sort of background; you went against sort of traditional teaching and therapeutics to try and help a patient. But reading around in those days, reading the literature; there was nothing else to guide you.

In the case of Gillian Ford, who as a final-year medical student had shared a flat with Cicely Saunders in the early 1960s, there were difficulties in applying ideas from the emerging hospice philosophy when working out in the acute hospital setting:

… when I was working as a 'pre-reg' house officer at Watford, I was already imbued with the ideas of regular giving of analgesia, and I found out that nothing other than pethidine, I think, had been prescribed for the six months earlier, and I did wonder how people had managed late stage pain and symptom control without using morphine. And so I used to get permission to use the morphine. Actually, I think we were using the Brompton Cocktail, which fell into disuse for very good reasons, but was actually better than pethidine. And I remember the consultant on a ward round saying about somebody who had pain, 'Well, you'd better double the dose of pethidine.' And I sort of went, 'Uuhh' [sharp intake of breath] and shuffled my feet, and he said, 'The house officer wants to manage this herself.' And if I was stuck I simply phoned Cicely, who would make suggestions.

Cicely Saunders lists some of the limitations of the available techniques and materials at this time, but also highlights the key changes that were taking place:

So we had a very limited armamentarium. And what was so fascinating was that during the 1950s when I was a medical student and I went on for about four years volunteering until I really was so busy with revising and things, but the, all the psychotropic drugs, the anti-depressants, the antispasmodics, the anxiolytics, all come in 1951. The phenothiazines, Largactil is introduced in the 1950s … and the non-steroidal anti-inflammatory drugs, apart from aspirin, started to come in then. The pain clinics were working, just began to publish, and there was a chap, Dr Maher, up in the North somewhere, who was one of the first to write.[17] And Bonica in America was coming along and beginning to write, all about the same time, and some of the earlier research on experimental pain and the earlier research on clinical pain, which was done by Beecher in Boston, was done on postoperative patients, and so was a group in Memorial Sloan Kettering in New York. So there were a whole lot of tools waiting to be used when I arrived at St Joseph's. Now they'd started using Largactil, they were giving pethidine by mouth, and they were giving morphine by injection and, but they were giving them on demand, not regularly, and it was brilliant to be able to persuade, well it didn't take much persuading Sister Mary Antonia. First, that I could keep a patient on regular giving, so that they didn't have to 'earn' their morphine, and keep a pain diary as to how pain was and [second,] sit and listen to them as a person. And of course, that was like waving a wand and Sister Mary Antonia wrote to me a few years back saying, 'I well remember the change from painful to pain free.' And the other day, two or three weeks ago (we are still in correspondence),[18] she wrote and said, 'All those many symptoms which I used to watch helplessly before you came onto the scene.' [Because] there were no patients' notes, there were no drug charts, there were no ward reports, there was only just the drug book and the Nuns, with their tender loving care, but longing, as Sister Mary Antonia said, 'To do better.'

Even in the late 1950s and early 1960s the use of potent cocktails such as 'the Brompton' was not viewed unproblematically. There was the question of to what purpose the mixture was being used, as John Hinton highlights:

… was it in fact hastening people's death, rather than just being an analgesic and euphoriant as they thought at that point? … And they said, 'Well there was nothing we could do, let's start him off on the Cocktail.' And sometimes it was very appropriate because the person was in pain … there was nothing you could do. Sometimes it was a bit inappropriate; that they were only just beginning to feel a bit of discomfort, and nowadays[19] it would have been managed differently by grading the analgesics. And sometimes one had the feeling it was used to, at least, tidy things up a bit, at least in people's mind, and this is where all the misgivings arose. And one would talk to … or go round doing a night round and a night nurse would say, 'Well, they've just started him off on the Cocktail and I don't think it's right because he's not ready for it yet' … And you sometimes wondered about the motivation.

There was also the problem of allowing pain to become established in such a way that made it then difficult to relieve. The reluctance to use analgesia was complex in character and reflected fears about narcotising the patients. Sister Mary Antonia describes the practice at St Joseph's, Hackney in the 1950s, and the impact that Cicely Saunders had upon it:

There was no such thing as proper control of pain. And you know, you'd watch them in pain, and it was agonising really to watch them. And then, thank God, I think it was in 1957, Dr Saunders came. She'd already had some experience, as she probably told you, in some other hospice,[20] and she decided she'd like to work with us … I was very privileged to work with her for seven years. And she had, one slogan of course was that 'constant pain needed constant control'. And the other was that 'you don't see the patient in isolation but in the context of the family'. Because before that we were rather inclined, I mean, it was probably part of the system which one was always influenced by, even in religion, to kind of put the visitors in the waiting room or the sitting-room and then have, kind of, certain hours for visiting, and this, that and the other. And you usually gave them an injection, particularly if you thought that visitors were coming – you wanted to save the visitors the agony of watching a person being in pain. And as a result they were usually asleep most of the time, because we didn't have the background, we didn't have the doctors educated to treat them. But, as I say, once Dr Saunders came it was like manna from heaven, she was marvellous because she had the background of medicine, nursing and social work, and she could kind of apply the three, you know, principles. And, as I say, her slogan was 'constant pain needs constant control' … And she started off with a mixture of, it was, was it morphia or heroin now? I think it was heroin we had with the mixture first. And I mean she graduated the graph up and then … and she often said as well that it was almost more difficult to get the right tranquilliser because the patient would be so anxious about the pain, you know, anticipating it, that they needed to be relaxed and quietened down. So that was another thing that she gave us and, as I say, not seeing the patient in isolation but involving the family as well.

After the opening of St Christopher's in 1967, there were far more opportunities to explore these issues in depth. Mary Baines talks here about the overall approach to drug use and symptom management and how over time, they also became more interested in the *causes* of problems – something that might not have been of much concern within the early hospice paradigm, but which became of growing interest as the medical model advanced:

We didn't go in as deeply into the family and psychological side as we do now,[21] but we looked at symptoms and we did our level best to control them. Where I think … [my] contribution perhaps was, is that in the early years, if somebody came here in pain they were given a painkiller, which at that stage of course was diamorphine or heroin that was used before Robert Twycross did his work. They were given it regularly, every four hours. They were given it by mouth, although, surprisingly, we then believed that after about 40 milligrams by mouth you had to give it by injection, so it was given by injection. How we believed that, I do not know. And they had it regularly. But what we didn't do is ever to try and analyse what the pain was. And pain in cancer was pain, and that's how we treated it. And I think, probably, one of my earlier contributions was to actually say, 'Now look, stop. Why exactly … has this patient got this pain? What anatomically, psychologically if you like, is causing this pain? What is causing this patient to vomit?' That we don't just use analgesics and anti-emetics, we need to look behind the symptom.

And looking back, you know, I think that's one of the miracles here, that whole approach, because the fact that all our patients, or the majority of our patients, are going to be dead within a week or

*Mary Baines:
'Now look, stop. Why
exactly … has this
patient got this pain?'*

two, it would have been very easy for this to become sloppy medicine. I think Cicely would probably say that, because Cicely taught us that one gave drugs by mouth, that morphine worked by mouth from her early work, and that one gave it in the dose which the patient needed, and not what a textbook said. So one gave drugs regularly, in the necessary dose. I think that I added to that, if you like, quite in the early days (and this is published), a sort of approach to it, in the 1980 Dot Summers book, Dot Summers and Cicely Saunders, *The Hospice Idea*[22] – the green book that was the proceedings of the conference in 1980 – in which I did a very early approach, and of course I'd done that well before that book came out, in an attempt to analyse why a hundred patients were in pain. What was causing it … whether it was bone pain, or liver pain, or whatever. So one looked at why, and the different approaches that would be needed, which was not just morphine. And the same was used of anti-emetics. So it was a beginning, more analytical approach to symptoms. Well, basically it is now far more available.

But the first modern hospices were also struggling internally with how to reform prevailing approaches to pain management and the use of strong analgesics – after all the early cohorts of staff were being recruited from within the very system of health care that the hospices were seeking to change. Margaret Carradice, Matron at St Luke's, Sheffield, explains some of the issues:

There was a lot to learn, and there were, I think, some nurses coming in to it who maybe didn't feel that it was right to give patients the amount of drug that we were giving, the quantities that we were giving. Because I think nurses weren't used to seeing that amount of, well, diamorphine as it was, in those days, given. And some found it very difficult that you could give that amount, and it be effective, and the patient not be comatosed … Because, you know, we were used to very small quantities, if at all. I mean diamorphine to me was

Margaret Carradice recalls the early 1970s: '… diamorphine to me was a new drug. Pethidine was the drug that was given for pain.'

a new drug. Pethidine was the drug that was given for pain, both postoperatively, and for colic, and, well for any pain that was severe, you gave pethidine. So diamorphine was a new drug. And I think, well I know nurses that have left here in the early days because they felt that it was wrong to give the amount of diamorphine that we were giving. For some patients it was given in very large quantities. I mean I can remember a patient in the very early days who was riddled with bone secondaries, who was having something like half a gram of diamorphine every four hours. But yet she was walking around and going home for the weekend, and went to her son's wedding, and having a very good quality of life. But … to try and teach someone that you can give diamorphine in those quantities, if they haven't actually seen that person, they find it very difficult to comprehend. So that was the biggest stumbling block because, you know, the average GP or hospital doctor is used to doses of 10 milligrams …

For these sorts of reasons, even when the first modern hospices had opened, it was some time before they began to have an impact upon the wider environment of general practice and acute hospitals. Gloria Day, talking about community health services in Sheffield in the 1970s, highlights the fine line between carefully administered pain relief, used progressively and early, compared to the late administration of high doses of a powerful drug. The former had become routine practice in hospices, whilst the latter was the norm elsewhere:

Often they'd be very poorly medicated, so you'd ring the GP and say, 'Professor Wilkes usually at this stage would be giving diamorphine …' The GPs were terrible at medicating, I mean I can say that honestly, I would ask any GP at that time did he think he was good, he wasn't, he was crap, you know, really … sorry! But that was the truth; they were very, very bad at medicating. Well I'd learnt about medication; I'd learnt that if you gave diamorphine regularly, every four hours, guess what? People became pain-free. GPs would often give last-minute medication, diamorphine by injection and people usually expired because they were so relieved to get some pain relief, that they just expired very quickly. And then you had the old story of relatives who would say, 'My husband died at the end of the needle.' She was right, because they gave up then.

The same resistances were in evidence when palliative care teams began to establish their work in the hospitals, though eventually the approaches to pain relief first developed in the independent hospices began to take hold in the acute setting. Janet Gahegan describes her experience in Sheffield in the mid-1980s:

By the time I came into the hospital [in 1984] people in the palliative care world were doing all these things but it hadn't filtered into the hospital and hands were held up in horror when you started trying to increase diamorphine at first and syringe drivers were … 'You can't do that … it's too much, you can't put that amount into patients,' and when doses started going up and up at first people were very frightened – as we all are – and … I suppose reluctant because of that. But it's like everything else, it's a bit like water dripping on a stone, isn't it, you see things happening and you look around you and other people are doing it and eventually it wears it away and prejudices are overrode and people start to prescribe decent amounts of stuff.

I think if it's a question perhaps of having the confidence to go in and recommend the things to people, and then if they see that it works then that's fine. So you have to get it right the first time [chuckles] because you don't always get another chance. So trying to make sure that it did work. And then I think often people were very surprised that you were giving large amounts and the patients weren't dying and all they were doing was being pain-free and more comfortable and then people got quite excited about it because you could actually do this and it was OK, and you could give better quality of life. And I think in particular it's always been the nurses that have worked on our behalf with the doctors, as well as ourselves, and general nurses on the ward who had to nurse the patients, who couldn't bear to see the patients in pain and would do anything.

And because we came and we got rid of the pain for them, then they would take that on board and the next time a similar case happened they would say to the doctors, you know, 'Why can't we give them a bit more, or do this …?' Then the doctors would succumb eventually. Because a lot of the ward sisters and the senior staff nurses knew the consultants or senior doctors very well, had worked with them for years, and there was a great deal of trust between them and so if Sister said it was all right, it was all right. And sometimes you got in that way. But I think for all nurses, it was such a joy to be able to actually get patients pain-free. When you

had nursed a few patients who had died in pain and you'd watched them die in pain, to actually be able to stop that happening again was wonderful, you know, it was really, it was one of the best things that ever happened …

Derek Doyle in the following extract demonstrates that such processes were often quite complex and were heavily tied up with perceptions of the new field, the claims that its practitioners were making and the way these were presented to doubting colleagues:

… it was just very unpleasant scepticism which made you feel that you were on your merits and you had to demonstrate every time, everywhere, every place you went to. I can't say that strongly enough. One of the stresses of the original work, which I don't think people seem to have written up, was the stress of being under a search-light or, changing the metaphor, really being under a microscope the whole time so that you often had a colleague saying, 'I'll sit with you when you see this patient because I want to see what it is you do.' Well he'd never have said that to a dermatologist or a cardiologist … it was just utter total scepticism. Very quickly, of course, followed by envy, maybe too strong a word, but a bit of kicking themselves, that, 'Damn it, it's fairly easy to do this, isn't it? This fellow Derek Doyle or Cicely or whoever they are, they're not brilliant they're just using ordinary basic stuff, they use basic drugs, there's no high technology here and yet, by gum, they're getting good results.'

A bit embarrassing when you think about it … You've got some surgeon that performs some of the most wizard technology and in comes Derek Doyle with a tiny bit of tweaking and manipulating of the morphine or the diamorphine, or just sitting for half an hour longer than the surgeon was doing, and wonderful things happening. Now that must have been quite irksome to some colleagues. They knew that they were brilliant, and they knew that people, like me at any rate, were just middle-of-the-road folks. That baffled them but I think it was really ignorance based on the wrong image that we gave. Now that is fast disappearing … I don't perceive that nowadays. So I think it's changing. I think it's changing much more rapidly than we ever thought. The interesting thing is, I think it's changing as a result of the one group of people in this country that when we started palliative medicine, nobody had any time for: I'm talking about GPs … they were the ones that really saw the need for it, who looked long and hard at what palliative medicine had to offer, and what the provision of services would do for their patients.

Identifying and responding to 'total pain'

Throughout our interviews with Cicely Saunders, as in her writing, we found a constant emphasis on the importance of learning from patients in particular by careful, active and attentive listening. In the following extract, from which we have already quoted in Chapter 1, she recalls the particular patient from whom the concept of 'total pain' was derived:

Well there was one patient who, when I said to her, 'Well, Mrs Hinson, tell me about your pain' – this was the day after she was admitted – and she said, 'Well, Doctor, it began in my back; but now it seems that *all of me is wrong*,' and she talked about one or two more symptoms, and she said, 'I could have cried for the pills and the injections but I knew that I mustn't. Nobody seemed to understand how I felt and it seemed as if all the world was against me. My husband and son were marvellous but they would have to stay off work and lose their money, but it's wonderful to begin to feel safe again.' So she's really encapsulated the whole thing in the answer to one question. And I quoted her many times and that's the start of what has gone through hospice literature: *total pain*.

Continuing with this theme, Tony Crowther provides a detailed case illustration from his own experience in the hospice setting of St Luke's, Sheffield in the 1990s:

…the patient who came in … she'd been home for a week, from the oncology hospital, came in because they couldn't manage at home because of the pain. So we knew she'd had active treatment recently, and yet her pain was totally uncontrolled, in spite of being on … something like 1,200 milligrams of diamorphine in a syringe driver in 24 hours, which isn't a massive dose, but it's big enough. And in two or three days it all unravelled … that … well first of all she'd seen the consultant who had said, 'Oh well, I can't do any more, you'd better go to a pain clinic.' When she came into us, we found that her husband had hardly been seen while she'd been in the oncology hospital; he hardly ever visited … so we needed to unravel why. She was only a youngish woman, 41 or 42. Was he too poor to travel? I mean, in fact that was what he'd said when we tackled him about it. He lived in Rotherham which was costing him, I think it was about £3.50 return and he said, 'I can't afford to come every day.' So that was easily sorted. We then found that he, while his wife was at home, had had a blazing row with her father over the care he was giving to his wife, to his daughter. We then found that [their] daughter, who lived in Birmingham with two young children and a husband in the army, had rung one evening, say the Tuesday, asked how Mum was and he had said, 'Well, I haven't visited today,' so they'd had a row; that he was neglecting mother.

So there were so many family turmoils going on, and this had rubbed off on the patient. And I'm not saying that we got her pain controlled completely, it took us a fortnight to unravel all that little lot, but we managed to get the daughter and grandchildren up from Birmingham, we managed to get enough money for the husband to travel every day, and we persuaded him to come in at lunchtime and have lunch in the unit and stay with his wife, and explained why … there's no reason why lay people should understand why; the effect that has on patients. So there is a lot more to this now and, and I'm getting more and more interested in the power of … where the patient is in their family, or in their own … I don't know, in their, their capsule of society. The influence that has on the patient I find fascinating, and on how it influences them.

Sam Ahmedzai, also working in Sheffield, but in the acute hospital rather than the hospice, draws on the concept of total pain in the following example from the late 1990s, showing how a variety of interventions and forms of support may have to be marshalled to tackle a particular problem:

What we're saying is that of course the severity determines what you offer, but really it's a case of looking at each patient's symptom now with all faces in mind. So that if you have a patient comes in with a mild cancer pain from a bone metastasis you'll say, what can we do from the anti-cancer point of view? – a shot of radiotherapy. But that's not going to work for a month so we also go to the analgesics, let's give you some paracetamol and a non-steroidal. By the way, you know this, the reason they're having the pain is because there's a fracture in their femur, well, maybe an orthopaedic surgeon can fix that and you get over night pain relief and then we can give radiotherapy to give you long-term relief. And this patient is living alone or with a very, very distressed family, we need a nurse to come in here or a social worker to come and support. Really looking at the sort of the 'total pain' concept.

Ivy McCreery, a nurse working in the Marie Curie Centre in Belfast, makes the point about pain relief quite strongly, as something absolutely fundamental to the hospice and palliative care approach:

… when people come here, you can do nothing till you've sorted out somebody's pain – so once you get their pain managed then there are other outstanding symptoms that are causing them distress that you have to try and manage, and once you get those managed then they begin to get comfortable, they begin to get their personality back and be able to cope with, with life other than just being a sick person. And from then on you have to move on into communication, because who are you communicating with, you have to be able to communicate with the patient to get them, to let them know what pain relief they're on, why they're on it, to let them know what pills you're giving them for whatever symptoms – not only them, but the relatives, you have to let, you know, keep the relatives up to date of why you're doing things. Because there's less problems then. If you have open, honest, appropriate communication, hopefully there's less barriers.

John Hunt, a nurse with experience of working in hospice and palliative care units in different parts of the country, both in the independent sector and the NHS, draws together some of the fundamental principles of pain management that by the end of the twentieth century had become orthodoxy within the field:

… one of the things I do think is that the, if you like, the underlying philosophies of the use of the medications probably haven't changed. And what I mean by that is that the, the old hard and fast ideas of looking at oral medicines, looking at trying to work from a simple base of starting with one medicine, looking at the effects of that, adding in others slowly, but also looking at – for example with pain – looking at managing pain in a very careful step-by-step way, the old idea of *by the mouth and by the clock*, and also the ideas of the goals of pain management, the old goals that we used to recite about enabling people to have no pain at night and be able to sleep, enabling people to have no pain at rest, and then enabling people to have no pain as they were able to be more active. I don't think those things have changed. I think the use of combination medications – again there may well be a much broader range of medications now – but again I think the same, the same theories apply – again if we take pain because it's probably the best one to do, looking at the type of pain, looking at the level of analgesic effect that your initial drug will get, and then thinking about co-analgesics which may not necessarily be analgesics: steroids, non-steroidals etc, etc and in particular thinking about neuropathic pain and not only being able to relieve the pain but being able to give people back some sort of function. So thinking about that in terms of the analgesic plan. So whether I am right or not, I don't know because I only have, if you like, the past to reflect on, but I don't think those theories have necessarily changed: I think some careful theories of looking at the problem and thinking about the management by using medications in a step-by-step way are still there.

Wider influences of the new thinking on pain

These more systematic approaches to pain management were built up slowly and over time, as the new interest in pain pharmacotherapy got under way and as appropriate studies were undertaken. Robert Twycross, a key figure in this area, describes the work that led to the demise of the Brompton Cocktail:

The Brompton Cocktail – well it comes in various forms but it was a mixture, it was a mixture usually of morphine plus a dash of cocaine in a so-called 'vehicle' of alcohol and syrup, and a preservative called chloroform water. Now I have already said that some people had diamorphine instead of morphine, and then increasingly in the '60s people were putting in a phenothiazine, either prochlorperazine or chlorpromazine which had both anti-emetic and sedative properties. And I not only looked at the diamorphine/morphine question, I went on to look at the issue of cocaine; whether there was any benefit in the dose we were using. And then by extrapolation and various anecdotal comments by patients, we ended up by saying, you know; 'Really at the end of the day you'd be better off just using morphine in tap water.' Well that's a slight exaggeration, you know; morphine in water, and get rid of all these fancy additives. If people don't like the taste then, you know, let them add their milk or Ribena or orange juice. So we went from a fairly sophisticated alcoholic mixture to something which was a plain aqueous solution, and that of course simplifies matters considerably in moving to one control drug from the morphine/diamorphine plus cocaine, again made it easier, it made it easier to export it.

It is clear from this that the Brompton Cocktail occupies an important place within the longer history of palliative care. Robert Twycross explains:

If you go back to the turn of the century, which is probably when it originated, the references in *The British Medical Journal* in the last decade of the last century about, well this was the Royal Marsden[23] in fact, using morphine and cocaine for cancer patients, but I think, at the Brompton,[24] it was probably developed as a cough sedative. Because you had morphine, which is a central cough sedative, you had cocaine which would be throat anaesthetic, and you had the syrup which is a local linctus. And if you imagine people dying of respiratory failure, shortness of breath, and hacking cough from tuberculosis, you can see that this might well have been the ultimate cough sedative. And, although it's not definitely documented in that form, that probably is the origin of the Brompton Cocktail. It was never in the British National Formulary if such existed in those days, or the equivalent, but it appears on scraps of paper tucked in the back of books in the '30s and that sort of thing. Eventually it came into the Extra-Pharmacopoeia known as Martindale, one or two alternative solutions/recipes. But whether it's in there as morphine/diamorphine solutions, or whether it was actually under the Brompton Cocktail, I can't remember. But basically Cicely, with her tub-thumping during the '60s in this country and abroad and the early '70s, that was what popularised the Brompton Cocktail as a regular analgesic for cancer patients at the end of life. And for years afterwards, even though I should go down in history as the man who killed the Brompton Cocktail, you know, even 10 years after I killed it, people in the States were still talking about the Brompton Cocktail, the Brompton Cocktail. So Cicely must have done her work very well in the '70s for this still to be circulating the rounds in the mid- to late 1980s.

The following remarks from pharmacist Colin Hardman reveal some of the difficulties associated with the Brompton Cocktail, but also provide evidence of how widely used it was in the UK in the 1970s in hospices, hospitals and general practice:

It was a mixture of morphine or diamorphine, cocaine, chlorpro-mazine normally (Largactil was its original trade name), some sort of alcohol – either gin or vodka – and one or two flavouring agents. But the interesting thing about it was that it was all in a fixed propor-tion. It was something like 10mg morphine, 5mg cocaine, 5mg – oh, 10mg; chlorpromazine in 5 or 10 mls. So if a patient's pain started to increase and they increased the dose, of course they increased every-thing. So as well as increasing the analgesic they also increased the alcohol, the cocaine and the chlorpromazine, which is the sedative bit – and really it was a terrible state of affairs. It was given with the best will in the world, intending to treat patients' symptoms, but it really didn't help at all because we learnt very quickly that giving fixed combinations of these drugs simply increases the side-effect.

So patients didn't have their pain totally well treated but what they did do was become sedated with the chlorpromazine and had very peculiar effects with the cocaine. Of course nowadays[25] nobody would dream of using cocaine orally in the treatment of symptoms, but it was quite common back in the '70s. And, and the alcohol equally had its own effect depending how much the patient was taking. So the hospice, our involvement [i.e. that of pharmacists] with the hospice movement at that time, was peripheral: we used to make about – I'm guessing now – but perhaps five to 10 litres a week of Brompton mixture, as a cocktail …

The eventual demystification of the Brompton Cocktail was significant in two respects. First, it transformed day-to-day clinical practice in the UK's growing number of hospice and palliative care services. Second, it provided a platform from which hospice innovators from several countries could launch an approach to the relief of pain on a much wider scale. Such interests reflected a growing concern about the need for research and evaluation of the methods used in hospice and palliative care. It was important to test out the claims which hospice pioneers were making for the new approaches to pain management and to know that they could be operationalised in practice, in actual service settings. Colin Murray Parkes describes early research at St Christopher's to establish the efficacy of the pain relief programme:

I think that the fact that the first few trials were all drug trials and trials of … studies of pain relief, enabled the hospice to get off to a good start because all of these, the results of those studies were very positive in showing how well hospice was doing. I mean, my own studies, one of the studies I carried out was a comparison of rela-tives of patients who'd died in a hospice with relatives of patients who'd died from cancer in other hospitals in the vicinity. And in the late 1960s and early '70s, there were very big differences between them, largely due to the fact that in other hospitals in the vicinity people were still dying in agony. The pain was so bad that not only the patients but the families too were very depressed and so our measures of depression which correlated fairly highly with patients' measures of pain were reflections of that issue. Once we got the pain relieved, the depression in the family improved. There's been three studies now, of evaluating hospice as compared with other hospitals in the vicinity. And one of the things that happened, fortunately I say, is that although St Christopher's has continued to improve, the other hospitals in the vicinity have nearly caught up as far as pain relief and that side of care, and physical aspects of care; other hospitals in the vicinity are still now almost on a par with a hospice.

These results began to provide an 'evidence base' that there was a science as well as an art to hospice practice. An underpinning science might also mean that the ideas and concepts of hospice and palliative care could be stimulated in other places, even in those with far fewer material resources. One step towards this was to extend teaching to the international level and to produce the kind of textbooks that could be taken up in a range of places and settings. Robert Twycross explains:

Sylvia Lack had been the Senior House Officer at St Joseph's during '71 to '73 and I was her sort of mentor. She'd then been seduced to go to the States to help set up the first Home Care Hospice Programme there in Connecticut and eventually become Medical Director of the in-patient service there. And we'd obviously met up again, and we decided that we would start running a week course, a five-day course, for physicians, one year in Oxford and one year in Connecticut, in New Haven. And that started in '79, about the same time we decided to work towards the books we eventually produced in the mid '80s. And I would be attending the triennial meetings, jamborees, of the International Association for the Study of Pain. And

I was writing quite a lot by request, chapters in books, and people were no doubt asking to come and see me and that sort of thing. So I imagine the work was just, you know, steadily developing as things do … So at the time I took over as Clinical Reader [in June 1987], we became a WHO [World Health Organisation] Collaborating Centre. By which time, of course, we'd had … *Symptom Control in Far-Advanced Cancer: Pain Relief*[26] by Twycross and Lack, came out in '83, which was a fairly unique publication in those days in this field. We'd had *Therapeutics in Terminal Cancer*[27] in '84 and then we'd had *Control of Alimentary Symptoms*[28] in '86. So, you know, there was quite a lot of activity,[29] and activity seems to attract attention.

Indeed, this attention was to prove extremely consequential and to extend the influence of the work well beyond the particular services that were developing in the UK and USA. Robert Twycross continues:

Around about 1980 Dr Jan Stjernsward was appointed Head of the WHO Cancer Unit in the WHO Headquarters in Geneva, and he had worked not only in Sweden as, I think, some kind of Professor of Oncology, not only in East Africa – well he'd worked in both, both in a developed country and a developing country – and he knew what the problems facing cancer patients around the world were going to be. So when he moved into post he set up a comprehensive cancer control programme and he said, 'There are three parts to a comprehensive cancer control programme: one is prevention, the second is early detection and curative treatment, and the third is pain relief.' And pain relief is [included] because, across the board, around the world, the majority of patients are only diagnosed at a late stage where they are incurable, and the only humane option is pain relief and general support. So that was his vision from his experience, particularly in East Africa. And he decided to develop some guidelines for the relief of cancer pain.

And so in 1982 a group of us were called together to meet in Italy, I think it was probably sponsored by the Floriani Foundation in Milan,[30] and I was fortunate enough to be one of those who was brought together. If I remember rightly the Chairman was Dr Mark Swerdlow, an anaesthetist in Manchester, Salford Hospital, or was it Hope Hospital? But let's say Salford Hospital, maybe both, you can correct that in the archives.[31] He, you know, how he was chosen – I've no idea. How he invited me – I've no idea. But there, along with others representing neurosurgery … a wide range of specialties, we sat down to produce these guidelines. Now Mark had asked some of us to prepare position papers on certain aspects, so it wasn't too difficult, perhaps, over four or five days to get a fairly good first draft of these draft interim guidelines … Now in fact those draft interim guidelines eventually reflected, fairly closely, the practice in the British hospices, and of course Mark Swerdlow – he knew the British system (and I should say about Mark Swerdlow, he was one of the founder members of the Intractable Pain Society of Great

Robert Twycross, who worked with a WHO team on a strategy for cancer pain relief.

Britain founded in 1967, the same year as St Christopher's Hospice was opened) … So, yes, he was in this because of his acknowledged expertise in chronic pain management. People at that meeting were not only representative of different medical specialties who might be interested, but they were representative of many countries and regions around the world. So, for example, there'd be an American representation, European, Asian and so on.

So these draft interim guidelines were then field-tested by a number of those who were at the meeting, who came from countries where they did not use the, let's say, the British hospice approach to pain management, which of course became the WHO method for the relief of cancer pain in time. So people like Takeda in Japan,[32] he went back and field-tested these [guidelines], and various other people did, so that when we met as a more formal group (and there were many new faces and many different faces), in Geneva in 1984 I think I was a rapporteur, which gave me an even greater potential for influencing the outcome. Now the '84 proceedings eventually were published in 1986 as *Cancer Pain Relief*, WHO: Geneva, and that included the maybe slightly modified draft interim guidelines, as I said, now styled the WHO Method for Relief of Cancer Pain. And, looking back,[33] they're fairly primitive, fairly primitive I think if people use them as the total cookbook, but if you approach them with typical medical imagination and remember that the patient needs careful evaluation before you plunge into the cookbook, then I think they are good. And they've undoubtedly proved to be good.

The WHO Global Programme for Cancer Pain Relief came to be based on a three-step analgesic ladder with the use of adjuvant therapies, and incorporated the use of strong opioids as the third step.[34] WHO representatives launched an international initiative to remove legal sanctions against opioid importation and use, relying on national 'Coordinating Centres' to organise professional education and to disseminate the core principles of the 'pain ladder'. Over time, however, some authors were critical of the principles embodied in the ladder and of the methods used to evaluate it. In particular some complained of a 'mechanistic' approach to matching patients and drugs to steps on the ladder and of the consistent failure of the ladder method to provide adequate relief for 10 to 20 per cent of advanced cancer patients with pain.[35] Robert Twycross elaborates his views on the 'ladder' and responds to some of these points:

So the concept I've tried to draw out from the three-step analgesic ladder is, well, I've tried to draw out a concept, it's not a simple mechanistic approach. If you look at what's on that ladder: you've got non-opioids (aspirin or paracetamol, or alternatives to aspirin); you've got the word 'opioid', and you've got the word 'adjuvants' (and the adjuvants include not only antidotes like anti-emetics and laxatives, not only the psychotropic drugs like night-hypnotics, anxiolytics and antidepressants, it also includes a third group called adjuvant or secondary analgesics, like antidepressants which are analgesic in certain pains, like anticonvulsants, which are analgesic in certain pains, like muscle relaxants which are analgesic in certain pains). So what I have drawn out in this consensus document[36] is the concept of broad spectrum analgesia.

We have broad spectrum antibiotics, you know, they knobble a range of different bacteria, and they clearly have a greater utility than a narrow spectrum antibiotic. And we know that there are some complicated pains, or nociceptive pains which don't appear to respond well to standard non-opioid and opioid analgesics. So, you know, just as in tuberculosis, you often have triple-antibiotic therapy to get really broad spectrum antibiosis, so I think we need to teach a concept of broad spectrum analgesia.

Now I think some doctors have intuitively seen this and picked it out and run with it, like the German group with their very excellent figures,[37] but I'm afraid there are many doctors who don't have the mind-set, and the imagination which goes with the mind-set, to

see through the ladder and to say, 'Here is a concept which I've got to develop.' So it may be mechanistic in one sense, but on the other hand it's the basis of, well … many, sort of, wheels within wheels of a very complex system of using a combination of drugs to intercept pain messages at a variety of points in different pain states.

But if you go back to the analgesic ladder and take it at its face value, again you could deny that it was mechanistic (I'm not sure what mechanistic means now), but you could deny that it was mechanistic, because a three-step ladder is what, you know, we all do in life, and what all doctors do in all circumstances. It may be a two-step, a three-step, a four-step, a five-step: if you have diabetes, the first thing you're told to do is to diet, step one. Step two, you maintain the diet and add oral hypoglycaemic agents. In step three, you substitute insulin for the oral hypoglycaemic agents. So you have a three-step approach to the management of diabetes. No doubt you have a three-step approach, or more, to cardiac failure, to cardiac arrhythmias, to atrial fibrillation as an arrhythmia in the whole body of arrhythmias. So a step-wise approach is clearly intrinsic to medical practice, and it's intrinsic to life. You know, if you are not deaf, I speak with a fairly modest voice, if you're a bit deaf I shout a bit louder, if you're stone deaf then, you know, I bellow at you. That's a three-step approach to deafness.

So whether you can just deride it as mechanistic … but on the other hand I agree you can say it is mechanistic if people use it as the magic three-step analgesic ladder and fail to use it with imagination, fail to say, 'Pain is not just a sensation,' fail to say, 'Pain is both a physical and emotional experience.' It is what I call a somatopsychic experience: it starts with a bodily hurt, always modified by the mind. Somatopsychic, not psychosomatic; somatopsychic. Provided you've got the imagination and the awareness that you're dealing with an experience and not a sensation, then you can use the three-step analgesic ladder, but if you ignore everything which is metaphysical, which includes, on my use of the word metaphysical, emotional, social and spiritual, if you ignore those dimensions of personhood and just say, 'Here's my three-step analgesic ladder, that's what I'm going to do, that's what I'm going to do, that's what I'm going to do,' then it is horribly mechanistic and it is going to throw up as many failures as successes … which is what's happening in many backwards areas of the United States and many other countries around the world.

With the 'rolling out' of the WHO pain ladder across many countries of the world, a major new phase of hospice and palliative care development was underway and one that goes well beyond the scope of this book. From the accounts presented here, however, it is clear that British hospice innovators, beginning in the 1950s, contributed to a range of developments about cancer pain relief at the end of life and that these had a widespread effect on both clinical practice and on policy. Central to this was the evolution of the concept of 'total pain' – a concept that continues to stretch the skill and imagination of practitioners. 'Total pain' moved beyond the preoccupation with pain pathways, or with pain as a phenomenon which could either be 'physical' or 'mental'. It awakened interest in the embodied and multifaceted dimensions of pain as something to be understood – and treated – in individualised ways. Strongly underpinning this were new understandings of pain pharmacotherapy, uncovered by some of the earliest research in the modern hospices. Complex elixirs gave way to simpler and more transparent methods, where careful titration of dosages was a key principle. In this way a knowledge base that might be transferable began to appear and this was seized on by those who looked beyond the immediate horizons of the modern hospices, to see cancer pain relief

as a public health issue that required the engagement and enthusiasm of a global community of policy makers, clinicians – and indeed of all those concerned to see better pain relief at the end of life.

Notes

1. J.J. Bonica, *The Management of Pain: With special emphasis on the use of analgesic block in diagnosis, prognosis and therapy* (London: Henry Kimpton, 1953).
2. C. Saunders, 'Dying of cancer', *St Thomas's Hospital Gazette* 56 (2): 37–47, 1958.
3. Joint Cancer Survey Committee of the Marie Curie Memorial and the Queen's Institute of District Nursing, *Report on a National Survey Concerning Patients with Cancer Nursed at Home* (London: Marie Curie Memorial Foundation, 1952).
4. J.H. Hunt and M.J. Linnett, 'Intractable pain', *British Medical Journal,* 4 June: 1723–29, 1960.
5. D. Clark, 'An annotated bibliography of the publications of Cicely Saunders – 1: 1958–67', *Palliative Medicine* 12 (3): 181–93, 1998.
6. C. Saunders, 'The treatment of intractable pain in terminal cancer', *Proceedings of the Royal Society of Medicine* 56 (3), March: 195–97, (Section of Surgery: 5–7), 1963.
7. C. Faull and A. Nicholson, 'Taking the myths out of the magic: Establishing the use of opioids in the management of cancer pain' in M.L. Meldrum (ed.), *Opioids and Pain Relief: A historical perspective*. Progress in Pain Research and Management, Vol. 25 (Seattle: IASP Press, 2003: 111–30).
8. D. Clark, 'A special relationship: Cicely Saunders, the United States and the early foundations of the modern hospice movement', *Illness, Crisis and Loss* 9 (1): 15–30, 2001.
9. C. Saunders, 'The symptomatic treatment of incurable malignant disease', *Prescribers' Journal* 4 (4), October: 68–73, 1964.
10. See D. Clark, '"Total pain", disciplinary power and the body in the work of Cicely Saunders 1958–67', *Social Science and Medicine* 49 (6): 727–36, 1999; D. Clark, 'Total pain: The work of Cicely Saunders and the hospice movement', *American Pain Society Bulletin* 10 (4), July–August: 13–15, 2000.
11. C. Saunders, 'Care of patients suffering from terminal illness at St

Joseph's Hospice, Hackney, London', *Nursing Mirror*, 14 February: vii–x, 1964.

12. In a 1971 publication, Cicely Saunders makes use of 35 black and white photographs, taken at St Christopher's and in patients' own homes. Three of the photographs are of artwork produced by patients; one shows a drawing of her pain made by a patient before admission to the hospice, contrasted with another made three months later when she was about to return home; a third, made four days before a patient died, shows a child standing fearlessly before a dragon (of death) which is being fed flowers. Seven photographs, with associated commentary, explore the theme of the patient's response to illness. They reveal a range of dispositions: feelings of threat, doubt, longing, anxiety, depression; denial and resolute cheerfulness; longing and weariness; and fighting back. Some photographs show how the relief of pain and other symptoms can sub-serve other important work which patients and families may need to undertake in the final weeks and months of life. One shows a patient busily writing her life story. 'Part of the art of medicine is concerned with values and therefore judgements. It is the way we look at the essence of a situation, at people with their particular needs and at what is relevant treatment for them.' This is further amplified in the distinction between 'the path of vigorous treatment' and 'the way of doing nothing', both of which are judged to be wrong. Instead, 'We are called on to find the middle way of responsibility and judgement.' See C. Saunders, 'The patient's response to treatment. A photographic presentation showing patients and their families' in *Catastrophic Illness in the Seventies: Critical issues and complex decisions. Proceedings of Fourth National Symposium, 15–16 October 1970* (New York: Cancer Care, Inc., 1971: 33–46).

13. For a full account, see D. Clark, 'The rise and demise of the "Brompton Cocktail"' in M.L. Meldrum (ed.), *Opioids and Pain Relief: A historical perspective*. Progress in Pain Research and Management, Vol. 25 (Seattle: IASP Press, 2003: 85–98).

14. Herbert Snow (1847–1930) was for 29 years a surgeon at the London Cancer Hospital (later the Royal Marsden) and is noted for his publications on cancer treatment and the relief of pain, including his innovative combination of cocaine and morphia. For a fuller account of his work, see M. Stoddard Holmes, '"The grandest badge of his art": Three Victorian doctors, pain relief and the art of medicine' in M.L. Meldrum (ed.), *Opioids and Pain Relief: A historical perspective*. Progress in Pain Research and Management, Vol. 25 (Seattle: IASP Press, 2003: 21–34).

15. R. Twycross, 'The Brompton Cocktail' in J.J. Bonica and V. Venta-fridda (eds.), *Advances in Pain Research and Therapy, Vol. 2* (New York: Raven Press, 1979).

16. See Chapter 1 for an account of David Tasma, to whom Cicely Saunders is referring here.

17. Dr Robert Maher was a consultant physician working in Lancashire, who developed a particular interest in intrathecal alcohol and intrathecal phenol for cancer pain. He wrote an early paper on cancer pain (R.M. Maher, 'Relief of pain in incurable cancer', *The Lancet*, 1 January: 18–20, 1955) and also published a lengthy review of clinical experience on the use of intrathecal injections (R.M. Maher, 'Neurone selection in the relief of pain, Further experiences with intrathecal injections', *The Lancet*, 5 January: 16–19, 1957).

18. This interview with Cicely Saunders took place in January 1995.

19. John Hinton was being interviewed in April 1996.

20. Sister Mary Antonia is referring here to Cicely Saunders' work as a volunteer at St Luke's Hospice, Bayswater, where she had observed the regular giving of opiates for pain relief.

21. Mary Baines was being interviewed in July 1996.

22. See C. Saunders, D. Summers and N. Teller (eds.), *Hospice: The living idea* (London: Edward Arnold, 1981).

23. Originally the London Cancer Hospital and renamed the Royal Marsden Hospital after its founder, William Marsden (1796–1867).

24. The Brompton Hospital, London; noted in the nineteenth century for the care of patients with tuberculosis.

25. Colin Hardman was interviewed in May 2002.

26. R.G. Twycross and S.A. Lack, *Symptom Control in Far-Advanced Cancer: Pain relief* (London: Pitman, 1983).

27. R.G. Twycross and S.A. Lack, *Therapeutics in Terminal Cancer* (London: Pitman, 1984).

28. R.G. Twycross and S.A. Lack, *Control of Alimentary Symptoms in Far-Advanced Cancer* (Edinburgh: Churchill Livingstone, 1986).

29. There had also been another work in these years: R.G. Twycross and S.A. Lack, *Oral Morphine in Advanced Cancer* (Beaconsfield: Beaconsfield Publishers, 1984).

30. The Floriani Foundation was established in 1977 with a donation from Virgilio and Loredana Floriani. Based in Milan, it has wide-ranging objectives concerning the development of palliative care: to promote the study and scientific research into new methods and techniques to be applied to palliative care; to encourage the spread and teaching of these techniques; to promote home care; to raise public awareness; to promote the academic development of palliative medicine.

31. Dr Mark Swerdlow (1918–2003) was consultant anaesthetist at the Salford Royal Hospital, and Director of the North West Regional Pain

Relief Centre. When he retired in 1980 he became a consultant to the WHO cancer programme. His obituary appeared in *The British Medical Journal* 326, 3 May: 987, 2003.

32. Dr Fumikazu Takeda, from Saitama, Japan.

33. Robert Twycross was speaking in October 1996.

34. World Health Organisation, *Cancer Pain Relief* (Geneva: WHO, 1986).

35. We are grateful for these points to Dr Marcia Meldrum and her unpublished paper 'The ladder and the clock: cancer pain as a public health problem at the end of the 20th century'.

36. International Consensus on the Management of Cancer Pain, *Looking Forward to Cancer Pain Relief for All* (Oxford: WHO Collaborating Centre for Palliative Cancer Care, 1997).

37. See, for example, M. Zenz and A. Willweber-Strumf, 'Opiophobia and cancer pain in Europe', *The Lancet* 341, April: 1075–76, 1993.

7 The family is not an optional extra: bereavement care as an integral part of the hospice

*'It doesn't end there for the family, does it, when that person dies ...
another stage is beginning for them'* **Mary Butterwick**

In the second half of the twentieth century, understandings of the effects of bereavement and the possibilities of a therapeutic response emerged in a variety of ways: from the contemplation of individual experience of loss; through theoretical exploration into the processes of grief; and in the lessons learned from trying to develop services.

We shall see in this chapter how bereavement care has emerged as an important aspect of the work of hospices. The crucial notion here is that the death of the patient does not see an end to the process of care – for those left behind, those who have been bereaved, may also have needs, and these can be met in a variety of ways. Of course human beings have always known of the sorrow of loss and the impact of grief, but in the years after the Second World War there was an emerging understanding of two new things. First, that grief might be manifest in problems amenable to professional help; and second, in a developing perception that professionals were ignoring, even shutting off, the bereaved person's expression of grief in ways likely to be detrimental. The implications of these insights and observations

were considered by those working within the developing hospice movement, and the results have been wide-ranging and have taken many different forms. This recognition of the importance of bereavement care is an important characteristic of the modern hospice movement, such that the two sit together in ways that shape each other.

In this chapter we examine the impact of loss and the expression of grief at various levels: as part of a professional life; as an aspect of intellectual engagement with the challenge of fashioning a response; and as an attempt to improve care for the bereaved and develop networks of support for those involved. We will look at how the hospice multidisciplinary team came to be involved in bereavement care and also consider the particular contribution of volunteers.

Since the mid-1940s there has been a series of influential research studies and thoughtful writings concerned with aspects of bereavement.[1] Several important themes have been explored: 'acute' grief; widowhood; professional and cultural avoidance of death; bereavement and mental illness; the role of the professions; and the experience of bereavement. We will see how such work helped shape the accounts of professional development given to us by several of those we interviewed for this book.

There have also been a number of initiatives, some started by individuals we have interviewed, that have either developed services for particular groups or have provided a forum for professionals to seek support and guidance in the work they do. This chapter reveals a series of shifts in concern: from identifying the rationale for services, through refining the focus of interventions and considering the sorts of services that should be developed, to an interest in filling gaps in provision.

The development of interest in loss and grief

In this first section we draw heavily on interviews with Colin Murray Parkes as his story captures especially well the personal insights and intellectual engagement we want to highlight. Instrumental in the development of bereavement services in hospices, he worked closely with Cicely Saunders and so we later include material where the two consider the link between their emerging interests. He has also contributed much original research that has, in turn, proved influential to many others. Later in this chapter we will show how Colin Murray Parkes has pursued an interest in what have been lasting international professional associations. He has also been instrumental in the development of bereavement services with other groups, through the development of Cruse Bereavement Care and then in services directed specifically at those who have suffered traumatic loss.

At the time Colin Murray Parkes was a medical student

in the early 1950s there was a prevalent attitude in medicine of detachment towards patients. This was actively encouraged at medical school and widely practised in hospitals. Colin Murray Parkes recounts how guilty he felt at the care he was able to give a mother on the death of her child and how angry he became with the shortcomings of medicine:

When I was delivering my very first baby, for me it could have been a great experience, but the woman they chose as the first mother for me to deliver was carrying a microcephalic child, a child who had no top to his head and who was going to die within a few hours of birth. They all knew that, they'd had X-rays, they knew what the situation was. Because the child had a very small head, it was going to be an easy delivery and they thought, 'Well, a medical student could do that alright.' So I was allowed to deliver this woman. I was told beforehand on no account was I to talk to her about her baby, that as soon as the baby was delivered it was to be covered up and removed from the ward so that she wouldn't see it, and again afterwards I was not to say anything to her about it. And the myth was that somebody else would talk to her. The truth was nobody talked to her about this. I mean she had been warned that the baby would probably die. She knew that this was what the situation was. But I knew that nobody was supporting her, it was so sad. As was common in those days, her husband wasn't allowed on the ward while the baby was being born. She was totally on her own and I'd been excluded, I'd been told not to mention it. And after the baby was born she thanked me most profusely, and I felt so guilty that I'd failed this woman at a time when I knew she needed me.

After this student experience, there was a shift in the focus of his interests as he determined to take forward some positive framework in order to shape a research agenda for himself. We see Colin Murray Parkes first getting excited by the potential of new studies of stress as a way to move forward understandings of the link between mind and body, and then going on to consider bereavement as a specific form of stress:

There were some very important discoveries being made in the area of mind/body relationships. Stress was the buzz word, a man called Hans Selye had produced a series of volumes on stress, collecting together research from animal studies and studies of human beings into this whole area.[2] He developed a thing called the General Adaptation Syndrome which was supposed to explain the relationship between mind and body … we had a feeling that this was a new area that was beginning to come together, and that within a few years we'd have all the bits tied up and we'd understand the relationship between mind and body in a coherent way. So it was natural enough that a young medical student would become enthusiastic about this psychophysiology which somehow brought together, not just the mind and the body as an area of study, but also the two parts of myself; the psychology and the love of medicine as a science. So I began to read very avidly in this whole area of trauma and stress, with the idea that eventually this was something in which I would want to do research of my own.

While undertaking psychiatric training at the Maudsley Hospital in London, both the experience of caring for patients and the discovery of research on grief helped Colin Murray Parkes identify a clear direction for what became 'a life's work':

I had two patients who were severely depressed because of a bereavement, I started reading the literature on that subject. It didn't take me very long because there were only about two or three papers at that time that had been written on the subject of bereavement. There was Eric Lindemann's famous study of survivors of the Coconut Grove nightclub fire, which described grief as a psychiatric syndrome, and, being a psychoanalyst and a psychiatrist, he

had applied diagnostic procedures to try and list the symptoms of grief. And I'd never thought of grief in that way before, and here it was clearly laid out in a beautifully written article which is still a classic, that I think most people working in the field will have read, describing, 'The Symptomatology and Management of Acute Grief' – that was the title of the paper, and that was an eye-opener.[3] And it suddenly seemed that here was one area where one could actually find something that looked like a mental illness but at that stage certainly wasn't considered a mental illness, which was nevertheless a consequence of a particular life event, or stress, which we could focus on.

From this coming together of professional observations and his reading of the limited literature, Colin Murray Parkes began to see a programme for his own research:

The interesting thing was that even Eric Lindemann's paper wasn't very clear on the distinction between what you might call 'normal grief' and mental illness. And it occurred to me that what was needed was some studies to look at, first of all: how do people in the psychiatric setting present; what are the symptoms they bring; what are the problems they bring. And secondly: how does that relate to the normal process of grieving which people, most people, go through when they suffer a loss.

This was a potential direction that did not immediately win over his academic supervisor:

I remember going to see my Professor of Psychiatry about this. He was interviewing me about my dissertation and I started talking enthusiastically about all this. He said, 'Well, hang on, Colin, I've got two things to say. First of all, what you're describing is not a research project, it's a life's work. And secondly, it's not psychiatry. You know, grief is not a mental illness, and it's not really the job of the psychiatrist to study it.' And with those two sorts of damning statements, he tried to rubbish the whole project. And I wasn't going to be rubbished. I don't know whether it was the way he put it to me, but there was a sort of challenge there, and he was saying, you know, 'Either you've got to drop this idea, or you've got to be a bit more humble and sort of take another look at it and present me with a simple little bit of research that might be of use.'

The 'bit of research that might be of use' now began to take shape. The first focus was on the link between mental illness and bereavement:

I did two studies, one was a review of the case notes; I spent hours and hours in the basement of the Maudsley going through every single file I could find looking for bereaved people. I wanted to do two things; first of all I wanted to find out what proportion of people seeking help from the Maudsley had suffered a bereavement prior to the onset of their mental illness. I wanted to know the incidence of bereavement as a precipitating factor in mental illness and then, having identified a group with mental illness, to see how they differed from the rest. So the first study I published on bereavement was this study of case notes, looking at the difference in diagnosis between the two groups, looking at the incidence of different types of bereavement in the pre-illness histories of patients presenting at the Maudsley. At the same time I began collecting interviews with patients who'd been bereaved ... The word got around at the Maudsley that I was studying this subject, and if anybody came across a patient who'd been bereaved they would call me in, and I'd come along and start interviewing them and carrying out detailed case studies. So I collected a bank of bereaved psychiatric patients whom I'd interviewed myself, and that led to a series of papers about psychiatric aspects of bereavement.

One thing these studies revealed was how little was known about ordinary grief:

While I was doing this, I became more and more aware that we knew virtually nothing about normal grief and that, for instance,

if somebody said, 'Ooh, I'm having hallucinations of my dead husband ...' I didn't know whether that meant she was schizophrenic ... I strongly suspected that the frequency with which these bereaved psychiatric patients were talking about seeing or hearing their dead husbands, and the fact that they had absolutely no other evidence of schizophrenia or other diseases which were thought to produce hallucinations, that maybe this was normal, that maybe all bereaved people had hallucinations. At all events, I thought the obvious next step must be to try and study an unselected group of bereaved people. I managed to get a post with the Medical Research Council, Social Psychiatry Unit. I was working under Maurice Carstairs who was the Director of the Unit. The Unit was mainly concerned with studying schizophrenic patients who were being discharged from mental hospitals.

Colin Murray Parkes was about to experience a 'meeting of minds' and to cross a 'divide' into a different sort of psychiatry:

Colin Murray Parkes: 'I became more and more aware that we knew virtually nothing about normal grief.'

John Bowlby[4] was a great discovery. In the course of my reading around bereavement, I developed my own theory: I called it a 'biological theory of grief'. It was an attempt to understand grief in terms of animal behaviour. I was interested in the way in which animals separated from their young cry aloud, and search restlessly for the young that they've lost, and this sort of thing. I began to put together a few ideas about the psychological basis for grief which very much drew on that kind of thing. I knew nothing. A friend then lent me a couple of papers written by John Bowlby that were both in draft form which he'd circulated for discussion among his friends at the Tavistock Clinic,[5] and they were absolutely on the same field. I mean, he'd reached virtually the same conclusions that I had, except that he was three steps ahead of me. And I was very excited by this, so I rang him up, and it was very much a meeting of minds. He invited me to dinner and we got together and he said, 'Look, you must come and join my research unit at the Tavistock because these are exactly the kinds of things I want to study. I'm studying loss in childhood, you're studying loss in adulthood, it's logical for us to work together.' And that really set me on course for the next 13 years, because after a couple of years in the MRC Unit I was ready for a change. And I stepped, in a way, across the great divide between scientific psychiatry at the Maudsley, into the more 'soft' side of psychiatry; the psychoanalytic schools at the Tavistock.

Comfortable with 'soft' psychiatry Colin Murray Parkes now encountered sociology, in the form of the work of Peter Marris:

Peter's book, *Widows and their Families*, was a rarity at the time. He was one of the first people to enter this field, and it was a useful piece of work. Peter is a sociologist … who has looked, not just at bereavement by death, but many other types of loss, and his book *Loss and Change*,[6] is very important … he manages to combine the sociology and psychology in a very effective way. His ideas about

'structures of meaning' and the way in which, when you suffer a major loss, your structures and meaning collapse, that sense of your world collapsing, like a pack of cards, and then having slowly and painfully to build and find new meanings in life.

Getting a bereavement service into the hospice

We have so far followed Colin Murray Parkes from initial encounters with death in his professional life to an emerging recognition of an intellectual interest and research agenda. We have seen how the work of others and the opportunity to work together with John Bowlby helped shape a widening understanding of the complexities of bereavement and grief. The subsequent extracts quoted here chart a progression of ideas concerning the necessity of provision for bereavement care, and how this was initially implemented.

Cicely Saunders recalls meeting Colin Murray Parkes and John Bowlby whilst she planning what would become St Christopher's Hospice:

I read an article of his in 1965 and I wrote to him saying (and I've got my first letter, it's in his file here),[7] I wrote saying that I was working with the Sisters who … worked with families very intuitively, but that I was starting a hospice and I knew the staff needed to look very carefully at our families, and the needs of bereaved people, although I felt that really good terminal care would make quite a difference to the course of bereavement. And he was really excited and rang me up and I went and had lunch with him and John Bowlby. And that's how he came on board, as part of the steering group, part of St Christopher's. From '65 he went out and spent a year in Harvard.

And I met him out there and we shared some of the ideas then. And in '67 he started coming one day a week and also started the evaluative research on the patterns of terminal care locally, and that was a very important study.

Colin Murray Parkes recalls the prospect of working with Cicely Saunders and illustrates using the importance of a practical approach to the achievement of lofty ambitions:

She'd learned of my work in bereavement and clearly valued what I was doing, and I sent her all my papers and so on. And then, when I was in Boston,[8] she came and stayed for three days … with us in our home in Boston, and brought with her the plans for St Christopher's Hospice which was beginning to take shape. Somebody once drew a picture of Cicely Saunders with a castle in the clouds, it was called 'St Christopher's Hospice' and she was there pulling the castle down to earth. And that was very much what she was doing, and I was impressed by this lady.

For both Colin Murray Parkes and Cicely Saunders the family was not an optional extra, rather their shared vision was of a family orientated hospice:

I remember Cicely saying to me, 'The worst time for me is when I have to say goodbye to the families because during the patient's illness I've often got to know those family members very well and then the patient dies and they all come and say goodbye and I realise, just when they need me most, I'm losing them, or they're losing me.' And she said, 'I want to change all that. I want somehow to retain a link with the families, particularly those who need it, so that we can continue to help them.' And that was just what I needed to hear because … I was interested in the idea that if we could only reach bereaved people before they were bereaved we'd have further opportunities to prevent some of the problems that follow bereavement, and that preparation for bereavement might be a useful thing to do. So I wanted somehow to get across the idea that the unit of care in a hospice is not the patient, with the family as a sort of an optional extra that you take on if you've got time, but that the unit of care should be the family, which includes the patient. And that if we try and look at it as a turning point in family life, if we can somehow focus on family needs and recognise that the family will help the patient, and the patient will help the family, and that you can't really separate the two.

The way bereavement services developed

In the contributions from Colin Murray Parkes we see the lessons learned in the care of patients and the intellectual engagement with an emerging field of bereavement research. We now consider the reflections of a wider group of individuals who contributed to the development of bereavement care in hospices. One overriding theme of this section is the recognition that the development of bereavement services depended on multidisciplinary teams and in particular the growth of social work and volunteer input in hospices.

Tom West outlines some of the advances in terms of the involvement of families at St Christopher's and links this with the development of the social work contribution:

When I joined St Christopher's the concept of 'total pain': physical, mental, social and spiritual, was of course already inscribed, and remains, I think, one of the clear guidelines for the approach of the care for hospice patients. The second thing was, of course, the involvement of families. When I joined St Christopher's in 1973 there was one untrained social worker. When I left, I think I'm right in saying, there were seven fully trained social workers. And this is a clear indication of the enormous increase in the importance with which families have been held from the first days, when I think it was a staff/patient relationship, the staff very much headed up by the doctor, to 1992, when I left, when it was far more the patient's condition, the tumour if you like, surrounded by the patient, the patient surrounded by the family, and the family sitting round the patient's bed surrounded and supported by the staff. This spread of responsibility, which I think is completely appropriate and extremely helpful and constructive, actually also takes a great deal more time and organisation and understanding to achieve.

Elisabeth Earnshaw-Smith recalls the significance of concentrating on the strength within family units. Having the St Christopher's 'family' meet the patient family involved teamwork that was not common elsewhere in the 1980s and certainly had not been a focus of professional training:

I was working on the wards, and thoroughly enjoying my returning to clinical work. And one of the things that struck me most forcibly was that there, on the wards, we had tremendous resources and strengths, but weren't using them; in the form of people's personal strengths, patients and families around them, and their friends and relations outside. And I suppose this is something that I thought about a lot before, but it is so easy to almost infantilise people when they become ill: they're depressed, they're [at the stage patients were admitted], they were feeling helpless, and it seemed that life was coming to an end, and the family as it knew itself was coming to an end, or a relationship was coming to an end. And I felt the thing to do was to begin to work with that and to demonstrate, by talking to the families together, by talking to partners together, by talking to children together, how you could dig out that these helpless people were, in fact, people with immense resources and strengths. Actually asking people, 'What is your particular strength?' And asking a family, 'Who are the strong people in this family? What have you got

through in the past? What have you been good at?' And I felt, also, that it was important that the hospice 'family' met the patient family, and I began to build up a habit of getting a nurse, or ward sister, and the doctor looking after the patient … and myself, to see a family or a couple together so that we could work together, as a team really, and they could actually hear families talking about their strengths, and they could have the experience of the power of working in little groups. Because I think this is something that, in those days, doctor and nurse training didn't touch on, and they had to carry so much of the weight themselves because they didn't see patients as strong, or families as resourceful. And so it built up from there. And I think I particularly remember some of the experiences I had with Tom West and the ward sister on that ward, Madeleine Duffield. And we saw some tremendous families together who were going through very bad times and yet managed to get themselves together and become confident and cope. And this gradually spread.

Mary Butterwick, founder of the Butterwick Hospice in Stockton-on-Tees, restates the shared notion of hospice care that family members, and not only patients, are given utmost consideration and that the reach of the service grows as people have personal experience of the work that is done:

We were the first in the community for terminal care, well the first in the North-East really … We'd started drop-ins for bereavement care and I always believed, having had the experience that I'd had, that the family needed to offload afterwards and they do need … continuous care for a long time, you know. Afterwards for the family it doesn't end by a long shot, by anybody's imagination. It doesn't end there for the family, does it, when that person dies? It's just beginning, another stage is beginning for them. They've got to learn to adjust without their person, they've got to come to terms with their loss, whatever that person's meant to them … We'd always given that follow-up care. Being a trained bereavement counsellor I was the one that went out for years to the day patient's family when we lost a day patient. I would go along and see the family, I would go to the funeral and I would go along then and phone up and ask permission to come along and see them and invariably they gave it me. I don't know, I can't remember, any one person that didn't in all those years and basically we would give them bereavement follow-up care.

Marilyn Relf, from Sir Michael Sobell House in Oxford, then identifies the logical extension of an approach that considers the family context of care of the dying into a family approach to offering bereavement care. If the place of the family within the hospice is emphasised then legitimate expectations for continuing care are fostered. She points out some of the implications of this approach and also the important requirement of preparing and supporting volunteers appropriately. What is described is a hospice world where there is a variety in the range of services. Hospices are not some uniform entity. As we have seen in the words of Mary Butterwick above, they offer different things in different places and settings. Marilyn Relf elaborates:

Hospices have been set up with the family as the focus of care, but no provision for ongoing care after the patient had died. And because of the quality of relationships that were being set up, people had become used to having a degree of support, and they didn't realise that it stopped with the death. And ... I think the hospice planners hadn't realised that for some people being able to talk to a nurse in the first few weeks after the death would not be enough, that they would want to carry on ... as they worked through their feelings, worked through, adjusted to their new situation, coped with all the changes. So a lot of people were interested in trying to do something ... so that it felt as though the hospice world was poised, wanting to move into bereavement in a bigger way. Of course there were some

hospices like St Luke's [Sheffield] that were doing things already, but not in a very structured way. And I think we were perhaps one of the, following St Christopher's, one of the few who set up quite structured approaches quite early on. And ... I think our ideas really were borne out; that the volunteers need a solid structure behind them if they're going to be able to work in any meaningful way with people. If they haven't got it, I think they go as far as they can, but they will pull back if they don't have the support to help them stay with the pain ... of people's feelings.

The balance between what the professional staff can and should do and what properly falls within the remit of the volunteer has also been marked by a process of development and change. Eric Wilkes, the first Medical Director at St Luke's, Sheffield, recalls what his years of involvement with the bereaved have taught him and yet sounds a note of caution about the ability to identify who will need what. There is a great benefit, he suggests, in self-help groups; indeed he appears to be wary that there may be some unnecessary provision of professional services to the bereaved:

When we had the social workers dividing the bereaved into those distressed enough to have a visit from the social worker, this was a very select tiny proportion of cases. The majority of bereaved relatives would be visited by volunteers who had received training, and again, almost an equal proportion would be given a phone call to say, 'How are you getting on?' because they had been classed as, really, people who would cope very well. They were busy in full-time work, the bereavement had been a very genuine burden for them but in a way it would allow them to pick up their threads of their life and get on with it. And what I found, which is not fashionable wisdom at all, is that ... humanity is infinitely unreliable and that a lot of the predicting of how difficult a bereavement will be, we found the ones that merited a telephone call only were having just as hard a time [as] those who were visited. Obviously the social worker visits a tiny proportion of cases, obviously complex and difficult, but you can't tell. And I think that one of the things that's impressed me most again over the years is how much more useful it is to have self-help groups going, in whatever form, however organised, than professional input. And I think the bereaved are tremendously assisted by the bereaved if you can give them the right forum and the right environment and, therefore again, one is a little worried of the tremendous empire building of bereavement and almost the encouragement of 'grief ill-health' to give people a role.

But others saw a need to be cautious about the bereaved helping the bereaved. Ros Beetham, Volunteer Coordinator at St Luke's, Sheffield, reveals the common problem of the newly bereaved wanting to volunteer:

… like the woman who … came to see me for a job and I didn't accept her at the time because she was fairly newly bereaved. And I felt, you always feel terrible when you don't take people on, because you know they've got terrible needs, but they're misplaced at the time. And she was crying a lot and I mean, she just couldn't cope. And we couldn't cope with her, either. But we had a very long chat, and I said to her, 'Do come back, give six months or so … when you feel right.' She did, and she is a volunteer now. And she wrote to me and she said, 'I really enjoyed coming to see you …' I thought she would send me a horrible letter saying, 'How dare you?' But it doesn't work like that, and she said, 'I was so pleased to come to see you. You are the first person who has actually listened to me and spoken to me about my husband's death.'

As well as having to sensitively support volunteers, hospices have also been required to recognise the bereavement and related needs of staff. We conclude this section with Elisabeth Earnshaw-Smith recalling the beginning of multidisciplinary courses at St Christopher's. She describes how recognition was given to the needs of professionals working in this area and the growing understanding of the often considerable burden they may carry:

Gradually we began to have multidisciplinary courses at St Christopher's … One of the things we were enormously struck by was how, if you get a group of professionals together, of one specialty or another, or a multidisciplinary group; if you give them the opportunity, they will share together their own pain. And gradually through these informal ways of teaching, we unearthed a huge pain that professionals carried with their work: unresolved bereavements, griefs … enormous family burdens people were carrying, and going to work every day and picking up the burdens of their patients and families, and how little support there was in the community, in hospitals, how little opportunity for professions to talk to one another. And I think one of the great strengths of these courses was shown to be that people could 'let their hair down', could be themselves, could let themselves be known as a, competent professionals, but with human problems through which we could learn, and from which we could use our insights in the work we were doing.

The need for new ways of working

The focus on the family and the recognition of its resources and strengths in turn prompted thoughts about new ways of working. Elisabeth Earnshaw-Smith describes how 'family trees' became a much used tool in work with terminally ill and bereaved people:

One of the things that we had done a little with, in the children's unit I'd worked on before, was use 'family trees', first of all as a way of helping a family to see visually that they belonged together: it was not one person, it was two, and when you think about the two, it was a whole lot of twos, whole families put together, and then a new family being created. And I noticed, more and more, what an enormously powerful effect this visual demonstration had on patients in helping them to get themselves together, and communicate, and believe that they could stay together, and belonging was a very important thing to all of us as human beings. And from there, gradually, it became a habit that whoever saw the family first, be it doctor, nurse, or social worker, sometimes before the patient was even admitted, when they came on a visit or a member of the family came on a visit, to draw a 'family tree' with them. And from this you could discover all kinds of things. We discovered miscarriages, or stillbirth, that had never been recognised, or grieved, or mourned over, or even talked about. We discovered previous deaths in the family, from cancer, which had perhaps been not very well managed, and people came to us with this tremendous fear that it would be the same again; or a death that had been traumatic and sudden, and all kinds of experiences that came through the 'family tree', passed down as myths in a family, through generations, of fears about certain things and certain kinds of people, which you could lay to rest right at the beginning, or at least bring into the open. And so this became, in a way, a 'shorthand' way of writing a whole family history.

As well as within the family trees, persons could also be located within a social network:

The other thing I used to do a lot with families, perhaps … single-parent families, or an elderly couple who felt all alone, but particularly with children, children enjoyed doing this: putting their friends round in a big circle, all the way round, and, with children, getting them to go round and get somebody to put their name, whether it's granny's home help, or our vicar, or my friends at school, or the Cubs, or the Brownies, and so [on] round their 'family tree'. They have signed names of all sorts of people who are important to them: their school teacher, their … And this has tremendously powerful meaning,

which children and adults pick up, of how important that group of people round them are, their community, their people who do things with them, for them, neighbours. And there's no doubt about it, that anything that you can do which is visual is so powerful …

As the multidisciplinary team grew at St Christopher's, and specifically as the social work department expanded, so too did the range of material they could produce. Elisabeth Earnshaw-Smith further emphasises the value of visual material for children:

When Barbara [Monroe][9] came on board, we wrote books for children when they were bereaved, and for adults, little booklets which they could take away with them, and latterly, when we were a foursome, we developed a kind of scrapbook that children could use when their parent or grandparent was in the hospice, and all sorts of questions they could fill in, and pictures they could draw, and photographs they could put in and so on. And these sort of visual things, I think are very powerful, and so often more so than words.

As well as stimulating new ways of working, the growing sensitivity to the needs of the family helped refine an understanding of the importance of endings. Elisabeth Earnshaw-Smith highlights saying a proper goodbye and describes the preparation necessary for doing so:

Perhaps sparking off from something, I was always struck by what Dr Saunders used to say about 'endings'. Something I felt we had to pay attention to, and that was the enormous importance of the time of death, and after the time of death. And that people, so often they might have met a death before, but they remember it as something that overwhelmed them, or they'd never met a death before and hadn't a clue what to do, and so all their confidence was removed. And so we began talking to families about what would happen, what might happen, and what in any circumstances they might want to do, and they would be required to do. And we talked about things like, 'Is there anything that you particularly want to say, because now is the time to say it?' One of the worst things we have found with the Bereavement Service was trying to help people who felt they hadn't said what they wanted to say, they hadn't said 'sorry', they hadn't said 'thank you', they hadn't tried to put unresolved problems right. And so we started helping people to go right ahead to the time when the death would come and to gain confidence and to know what to do.

Some needs related to practical matters about what the bereaved family will have to organise following a death:

One of people's great fears, too, was how they would manage with undertakers, and what you do about registering a death, and what physically happens to the body. And knowing every little detail, and what to do, seemed to help enormously. And, of course, the nurses were always brilliant at being there at the time, and helping people who were, perhaps, quite horrified by the idea.

Elisabeth Earnshaw-Smith: 'We started helping people to go right ahead to the time when the death would come and to gain confidence and to know what to do.'

The provision of a time and a place so that people can make their own endings has also been emphasised:

Yet to sit by somebody who was dying, and discover for the first time how peaceful death can be, and what a resolution in some ways for the patient and for themselves. And to spend times after the death with their loved one and, even then, it's not too late for last words. I learned an awful lot on this children's unit I'd worked on, about children dying and the importance of, perhaps, leaving the baby, the child with the parents, for a whole day if necessary, in the safety of the ward, saying what they needed to say, looking at their child, loving their child, and somehow making their own 'ending', rather than a hospital demonstrating an 'ending' which is carrying their loved one away, and a physical separation as well as an emotional one. And I think this is something St Christopher's used to do, and I'm sure still does supremely well: time for 'endings', time for last words, for caresses, for getting a family together and for just being with a family. And one of the things that was developed while I was there, was the chapel downstairs where, next door to the mortuary, where families could go and see, again, their loved one. The very beautiful way in which the nurses would prepare the body and take families down, and the incorporation, very importantly, of the Chaplain, in many cases, to come and make that 'goodbye', a memorable occasion when something actually happened. You sat there and you had time and, if you wanted to be there alone, you were there alone, and it could be quiet and nothing could happen, but at the same time so many people needed something to happen – maybe a prayer, maybe a thought, words which they could then have handed to them, or a family conversation.

After the death much contact with families has been undertaken by social workers and by volunteers. But there are examples of organised activities that help keep the bereaved in contact with the hospice team. Here two routes for ongoing contact at St Christopher's are described. First, Cicely Saunders remembers Colin Murray Parkes's aspirations for the Pilgrim Club:

Colin … very much wanted us to have a 'club' for families to come back. And it was a drinks evening, and people were coming back and it was very informal. We now have a much more formalised meeting which is, I think, a very good inheritor. There's much more structure … the old Pilgrim Club had a life of its own, but there were people who came back and back and, you know, it was too informal and it needed to be structured.

Second, Elisabeth Earnshaw-Smith recalls the emergence of Memorial Services:

We began to think about gathering together our own bereaved families for an occasion of remembering and giving thanks and, again, saying goodbye, and thinking about a future without that person, and the creativeness of that future, and the possibilities of it. And so began what became to be known as the Memorial Services. And we were amazed at the number of people who came (we decided at that time, that probably a year after the death was the right time) And every bereaved family was invited. I was struck by how many families came together, again underlining the importance of working with families and thinking 'family', and struck by how many people stayed afterwards to tea, actually wanting to meet the staff whom they'd got to know, actually wanting to reflect on the person who'd died, and where they'd got to, and tell how they'd got on. And of course these services have now developed and become a very important part of the hospice.

Prue Clench, who set up Dorothy House in Bath in 1977, specialising in hospice home care, was influenced by the St Christopher's Pilgrim Club and describes how those who have been cared for can experience a need to 'give something back'. She speaks up for keeping things simple:

It began as a sort of social evening. And it was a very big, Victorian, roomy house, so we were able to get, say, a hundred bereaved relatives together for an evening, like the Pilgrim's Club that I had seen at St Christopher's, finding that they were really the best support for each other, and I couldn't get round to everybody to follow-up. And that they, because they could identify and see that I couldn't do things, they were so glad of actually finding ways that they could work and help with me. So in fact I never did any preparations for it, everybody brought things and it was interesting that later on, when we had a more sophisticated staff, people couldn't bear this idea of a hundred people turning up for supper without laying the table or putting anything ready beforehand. So they surreptitiously started providing, and bringing just a few sausages, or just this and the other. And we had to stop it, we had to stop the evening, because it completely collapsed. The whole thing was built on the fact that these families felt they had been helped all the time that the patient was ill, and now they were doing something back, and it wrecked the self-help element of it. But we learned the hard ways on some of these things. But it left me with something which, I suppose understandably, because it's been part of my experience; I actually think that we 'oversophisticate' (that's not really a verb), we actually try to write everything into 'how to do it …' and … 'how it shall be done', and we make too many rules and everything now. I don't disbelieve in rules, but I think there is an awful lot of 'growing like Topsy' that is very healthy.

The use of research

As the lessons from developing a service were being learned in hospices in various locations, there was also an engagement with the growing body of research now available to those working with the bereaved. When new services in health and social care are established it is not always easy, or even possible, to find clear links between research and service innovation. Bereavement care is something of an exception. We have already seen how Colin Murray Parkes drew on the small amount of relevant work then available and how he looked widely for helpful understandings of what might be happening to the bereaved. He went on to undertake the work alongside John Bowlby, the Harvard Bereavement Study team, Peter Marris and others, establishing the field and augmenting its evidence base through the generation of a set of research data about the processes and outcomes of grief. Subsequently the intellectual map began to include work identifying models of grief and loss, and reporting on new services based on the specific needs of different groups of people. Here, first Marilyn Relf and then Carolyn Brodribb discuss how they identified the need to research the work they were doing – by looking to relevant previous work and also to the wider community of bereavement workers.

Marilyn Relf describes setting up a research study in Oxford:

We were very interested to learn from our experience with the Bereavement Service. It felt very much like an experiment. We … decided that we would need to evaluate what we were doing. So we started to talk to various people locally and got a small amount of money to help us to begin to monitor the work of the Service, and to plan how we might actually evaluate it in a more meaningful sort of way. And we got a grant from the Cancer Research Campaign to carry out a major evaluation. We set up a control study … We started collecting the sample in 1986, it was a prospective study. The main part of it was trying to, more or less, replicate Colin Murray Parkes's evaluation of the St Christopher's Bereavement Service in the 1970s. … From the end of 1986 through to the end of 1988 … we were collecting our sample …

The findings related to the use of volunteers and both showed the value of their work and underlined the need to support them appropriately:

We found that the support of the volunteers, actually did make a difference to people's health … particularly in their use of health care services, and in particular the GP. And we found almost significant differences in levels of anxiety and in overall outcome. We found that the level of experience of the volunteer made a difference … The inexperienced volunteers were very anxious about what they were going to do, whether they'd be accepted, and that the type of supervision that we were giving, at that time, we weren't giving enough … time to more individual supervision.

Marilyn Relf goes on to consider the extent to which she found research into bereavement and the nature of bereavement services useful in her work. This material proved helpful alongside the experience of her own practice and that of others running services:

Looking back to the beginnings of the project … William Worden had just written his book, there were all the theories, the work of Bowlby and Parkes, and … we'd been impressed with Phyllis Silverman's work in the States with the Widow-to-Widow Project.[10] We'd spent time talking to Mary Vachon about her work evaluating the Widow-to-Widow Project. We felt that from our experience of running the evening meetings for bereaved people, that probably a

Marilyn Relf: 'So "phases" and "tasks" provide an overall framework of what most people are like but the "dimensions" allowed for the individuality and diversity of grief.'

'group approach' wouldn't suit the British as much as it suited the North Americans.

Marilyn Relf found that elsewhere there were also moves to build on frameworks of understanding and models for care, particularly in the work of Susan Le Poidevin and Colin Murray Parkes:

Susan Le Poidevin ... was saying, '[These frameworks are] explanations for what grief is like, but they're not ... models for bereavement counselling, or bereavement support.' And the 'dimensions of loss' ... gave a framework which contextualised people's experience, so it gave our service a tool to help the volunteers think through what had been actually talked about in the session for the bereaved person, and to help them to get a sense of what was normal for that person ... with the ideas of 'phases' and 'tasks' in the background. So 'phases' and 'tasks' provide an overall framework of what most

people are like, but the 'dimensions' allowed for the individuality and diversity of grief.

In a similar way Carolyn Brodribb reveals that published models shaped and contributed to her work with the bereaved. For her, the works of Colin Murray Parkes, Elisabeth Kübler-Ross and Lily Pincus[11] were useful but limited. Her own practice prompted an approach that incorporated a range of models including those drawn from child development studies, psychoanalysis and cognitive analytic therapy (CAT):

I found that people weren't neat, they didn't go through nice stages, and so I actually produced a model myself, which for me meant there was a sense that people could take one step forward/two back, or two steps forward/one back. And there was a sense they could make the experience their own ...

This development of research and of theory impacted on preconceived ideas concerning the existence of 'healthy' ways to grieve. Marilyn Relf explains:

I think we did have some preconceived ideas, even though we thought we hadn't. I think we did expect people to grieve, to work through grief ... I think the ideas that were around then, were very much that if people didn't grieve openly then that would probably lead to problems later on. So there was ... a whole idea around the field (and the field was very small), that people needed to 'get it off their chest'. So I think the only preconceived idea we had was that the volunteers should help people to talk about their grief.

Attitudes toward 'healthy grieving' changed, in part through reflection on the services that were being provided, and this impacted in turn on the training volunteers received:

And we also changed the training in that we began to put much more emphasis on how to build trust, and how to develop relationships, rather than just assuming that bereaved people would be able to use what was being offered, easily. And we'd also begun to revise our ideas about the need to grieve openly … I think that's the real thing about if you're offering a proactive/preventative service, it's not the same as offering a reactive counselling service. And people haven't identified themselves as having needs and problems and they're not coming to us saying, 'I need help,' we're going out to them and saying, 'We've got this Service. We want to see if we can be helpful to you, but … it's really up to you.' So we changed the emphasis. So now volunteers talk very much more in terms of going to see the client four or five times, and then reviewing to see how helpful it is, rather than having that sense of, 'I must make a relationship with this person and help them to talk about their feelings.' And I think we've got a much more open attitude now, really much more open than we thought we had before. What we've learnt, I think, is borne out, or supports, what's now coming out of studies of bereaved people and, like Tony Walter's suggestions[12] that there are different styles of grieving, and the expressive style … is not for everybody. And just because somebody isn't talking about their grief, it doesn't mean to say they're not grieving. And there's absolutely no evidence that people who aren't open about their grief necessarily go on to have problems, we just know that some of the people who have problems are the people who find it difficult.

Expansion of bereavement care into other areas

As bereavement care came to be an integral part of hospice activity, so the potential for developing the insights obtained and translating them into other areas also expanded. At the same time insights, ideas and practices that developed outside hospices influenced developments within.

Here we consider the development of Cruse Bereavement Care as an organisation for the bereaved. Colin Murray Parkes describes his first contact with Cruse and then a growing involvement:

I was interested in organisations for the bereaved, and I learned of the existence of Cruse. Cruse was started by Margaret Torrie and her husband, who was a psychiatrist. They'd both been involved in the early days of the Marriage Guidance movement, and Margaret Torrie was a social worker who decided she wanted to work with widows. And Cruse, as it was originally founded, was 'Cruse Clubs for Widows', and it was very much Margaret Torrie's thing.[13] It was a good organisation; she was doing very good work, particularly group work with mothers with children, and using her knowledge of social work as a means of helping mothers and other widowed people. She invited me to join the council of Cruse and eventually when her husband died, she asked me to take over as Chairman of the governing body of Cruse, and she subsequently had to sell up and move out of London and largely relinquished the very major part that she'd had in Cruse up to that time.

After Margaret Torrie retired in 1976 other possibilities for the organisation began to emerge. Specifically these focused on the development of counselling:

… Derek Nuttall who was a former Methodist minister who came and worked in Aberfan[14] with me. And subsequently I introduced him to Cruse, where he became the Director after Margaret Torrie retired. So I knew Derek very well. We worked well together and our aim was to develop Cruse into a counselling service for bereaved people, and that's what it became. But prior to Margaret Torrie, prior to that time, the idea of counselling, particularly individual counselling, was not part of the model for Cruse. It only became, we only introduced the idea of using carefully selected volunteers and training them as bereavement counsellors after Derek Nuttall took control.

Cruse made great progress, although Colin Murray Parkes notes further challenges:

I gave up my role as Chairman of Cruse four years ago. We needed people with experience in managing large organisations, it had got too big for me, and too big for Derek Nuttall who was the person I'd been working most closely with … The organisation has grown and grown, and continues to grow. It's still not as big as it should be if it's going to cover the whole of the UK, but I think the policy that they've adopted of slow but steady growth is probably the right one, and each area is getting stronger, and we're able to tighten up on the criteria for selecting and training counsellors and things of that kind. So it's a much more professional body than it used to be. I use the word 'professional', not in terms of paid staff, but in terms of carefully selected and properly trained people who are doing a high quality job of work to a high standard. So I'm proud of what's happened with Cruse. I think it's a model service of its kind. And it really saddens me that it isn't adopted as a model elsewhere in the world. The only places that have comparable services tend to be the hospices. I mean it seems to be anomalous that when you go to America, for instance, you find that, if you're going to get the best bereavement service for your wife, you have to die of cancer.

Whereas people dying from other diseases don't have that kind of service available to them.

Colin Murray Parkes also describes how his role in Cruse resonated with the insight being uncovered in the USA by the Harvard Bereavement Study, set up by Gerald Caplan:[15]

[The Study] certainly taught me a lot about normal and abnormal grieving. We began to see how these sort of pathological forms of grieving could occur, and why, what were the forerunners, and what were the indicators. And we developed a bereavement risk assessment. This had obvious implications for prevention of psychiatric disorders in bereaved people, and in a way Cruse was the opportunity which we had to try and test out some of this thinking. People were coming to Cruse for help, many of them with exactly the sort of problems that we were studying, and it was obvious that I needed to be training counsellors looking at the ways in which we could actually put this helping into practice.

There were also important international networks developing from the mid-1970s. One such was the International Work Group on Death, Dying and Bereavement, which held its inaugural meeting at Columbia, Maryland in the USA in 1974. Colin Murray Parkes continues:

Cicely Saunders was there, a number of the people who subsequently went on to become leading lights in the field, both of death education and terminal care, were part of that. One of the things we started trying to do was to … specify what were the basic assumptions that we could make about our field of study based on current knowledge, you know, where had we got to? Then, having established what were the basic assumptions that one could make, what then would be the principles of care that would emerge from them? So we produced a set of assumptions and principles relating to bereavement, and I was very much involved in that group. There was another group discussing assumptions and principles about the care of the dying.[16]

Returning to a UK focus, Colin Murray Parkes remembers the meeting that eventually led to the formation of the London Hospital Bereavement Service. Its achievements were wide ranging, if long in coming to fruition:

I'd wanted to go to a hospital where general medicine was going on, because so much of my work seemed relevant to that. You know, places where you had real live cancer patients, and AIDS, and other conditions for which psychological factors play a big part. So moving to the London [Hospital] provided me with the opportunity to study a wider range of psychological stresses, particularly the kind that come to doctors. And I worked at the London [Hospital] in developing and teaching in this whole area over many years, with anybody who's been interested. There's a group of us who grew together. I started off by holding an open case conference in a different part of the hospital each week, so that in the course of a month we would have a meeting on the intensive care ward, we would have a meeting of the chaplaincy, we would have a meeting on the psychiatric ward, and then, the fourth week, we would go to St Joseph's Hospice. So some people came every week, some people just came when the circus hit their bit of the town, and other people came when they felt they had a problem and wanted to talk about it. So it was a very varied group which grew up, but over the years, of course, those of us who were permanent fixtures in the hospital, or people who stayed for any length of time, got to know each other very well. It was that group that started the London Hospital Bereavement Service. It was that group that helped to get the Macmillan nurses established in the London Hospital. It was that group that re-planned the way in which news of a death is broken, and introduced a bereavement officer, and did various things in the hospital and, I think, played a part in the establishment of a very different kind of training of

medical students, which is now crystallised in the very year that I retired. It was sad that it took 20 years to bring it about, and then it finally got through all the fences in the year that I retired. But I'm very proud of the fact that the London is now at the cutting edge in training medical students in doctor/patient interaction, and breaking bad news, support for patients and families, in a way that I don't think other hospitals do.

As well as these achievements in developing understandings of loss and grief in hospitals and in the teaching of medical students, there has been a development of bereavement services targeted at other groups of people. Sheila Cassidy describes setting up a cancer support centre and recalls her interest in work with people that conventional services found hard to reach. She also developed services for bereaved children:

I went on and trained in CAT, 1995 to '7, because I became aware of the fact that some people couldn't process … the prognosis, or the fact that there was someone who had died, because of responses that had been set up in childhood that interfered with this particular point in life. A small proportion, but nevertheless a proportion for whom, you know, there seemed to be no service that palliative care could offer.

I got together with a group of … child psychologists and various people, and we started a little charity called Jeremiah's Journey, which is modelled on Winston's Wish,[17] which is a grief programme for kids. And we run groups for … children who've lost a parent, and we see the adults in one group and the kids in another, and we're now into the third lot of groups. And that's very successful.

Marilyn Relf noticed a gap in services for child bereavement in Oxford:

A children's bereavement project … is a step forward for us because … [it is] the first time we've offered a service that is beyond cancer

… A couple of years ago I found some free money and commissioned a report on the needs of bereaved children and young people in Oxfordshire. And we found out that there's a gap, and the gap is for information and training, as well as support. So we're hoping to get the money for an independent organisation which will offer direct services to children, but also training for the people who are working with bereaved children: teachers, school nurses, health visitors. And … the 'help when you need it' service for parents, too.

Barbara McNulty highlights the different type of bereavement experienced by those who suffer loss through Alzheimer's disease:

What I'm doing now is families coping with this very slow death, and that is a kind of slow attenuated bereavement which is a new experience for me. Cancer goes on long enough, but Alzheimer's goes on forever … It has to do with families facing this very slow business of dying by inches, and how do you keep relationships alive, how do you keep loving alive when things are changing almost daily. That does interest me. And the fortitude of people is what amazes me … The fortitude of what ordinary people have and just coping with impossible situations – I'm filled with admiration, just as I was with the families at St Christopher's. The things they coped with, people are extraordinary, really wonderful creatures. And all we need is our own support of one another, and encouragement, and the sharing that goes on if you can begin to talk to people as they really are. So much of life is superficial, and to do with faces and personas and what one appears [to be] on the surface, but if you can get below that, the person underneath is always an amazing thing. I discovered that at St Christopher's and I am discovering it all over again now in this particular situation – the wonderfulness of people. The kindness that they extend to one another, I think, is amazing. I mean in the Alzheimer groups that I now participate, people are coping with such difficult problems and yet they have time to say, 'Well, give me a ring

Barbara McNulty: 'The fortitude of people is what amazes me.'

if you're bothered, I'm always there, we'll talk it over,' or, 'I'll pop in and see you' or 'If I can help one day.' How do they have time, out of their own problems, to give that much energy to somebody else? It's what's really amazed me.

Finally, in this section on the expansion of bereavement care, Colin Murray Parkes, interviewed in 1996, talks about an ongoing focus within the International Work Group on Death, Dying and Bereavement:

The work group that I'm involved with most closely at the moment is the work group on 'violent death' and the 'cycle of violence', which is a terribly important area for the world, and not just for hospice. It's to do with how trauma becomes perpetuated within a society. It's a sociological problem as well as being a psychological problem. And I work, for instance, as adviser to SAMM, which is Support After Murder and Manslaughter. It's a group of people who've all been bereaved by murder. And this is a terrible kind of bereavement. It's not surprising that when your child has been murdered on the way home from school, or you've lost a close member of your family by murder, you're likely to find your whole life is devastated in many ways. And there's been a self-help group for some time working in Britain, and similar groups in other parts of the world, where people who've suffered this kind of loss get together and support each other, and do very well. It's important, though, to learn all we can about, not only what these people need, but also, perhaps, what can be done to prevent the sort of awful situations that we're finding in places like Rwanda and countries where there's become a sort of institutionalised cycle of violence.[18]

When the impact of bereavement becomes clear a long time after a death

We will conclude this chapter with two stories of patient experiences that underline the centrality of understanding the impact of bereavement. Here we are reminded that those approaching their own deaths may be facing them through the prism of earlier bereavement experiences, often from a very long time back in their lives.

Through his story of a dying patient, Malcolm McIllmurray demonstrates the difficulties severe grief can cause:

She was very withdrawn, very difficult to please and to help, and was disassociating herself from the staff … to a degree that was plainly not normal. When we went through her background with her – and I have to say this only comes after you've been able to develop some kind of a relationship and rapport with patients – what transpired was that she had a brother that she had never told us about, and we'd known her for a long time … it became clear that this was really the source of her anguish. Because what had happened was that she and her brother had apparently been very, very close when they were growing up. When the War came her brother was called up into the Air Force. He would only have been, I don't know, 16 or 17 at the time. She was so angry about this and about being separated from her brother that she never said goodbye to him. He was stationed somewhere in Norfolk … it was on the first exercise that he went on, there wasn't even any glory in it, there was some horrendous accident with the plane and he was killed. And she never, ever talked of her brother again, apparently. Now the reason she was so distressed is plain and obvious, and it was because she never said goodbye, and she was never able to forgive herself for the way in which she behaved when he left. And it was only through discovering this, and then talking it through with her and allowing her to relive this experience and to talk to her brother as if he was there, so that she could actually explain to him, now, the way she felt at the time that this happened. And by doing this she was transformed, you know, her attitude changed … her relationships with family improved. The final weeks of her illness were very positive; she was a very happy woman when she died. And I think she had suppressed this for the most part of her life, she had functioned perfectly normally, I mean she wasn't known to be a depressive or reclusive in any way: it was the sudden confrontation with death brought about by her illness which led to this situation.

Elisabeth Earnshaw-Smith tells how the hospice team can provide some continuity of care for a family over a number of years with this example:

I remember a clergyman who rang the hospice saying that he'd been in touch with a young chap, a teenager, who'd been in a borstal when his mother died at St Christopher's of a brain tumour. And this young lad had never got over her death, and it was now I think six years later. He was married and had a son of his own … and he was having blackouts and frightening symptoms. His GP had wondered if there was some psychological reason for this and would we consider talking to him? And, lo and behold, being St Christopher's of course, we found not only the medical notes but the consultant who had known the family. Therese Vanier,[19] who was by then a part-time consultant, came in specially to see him, and this clergyman who had kept in touch with him. And it transpired that he felt that he had contracted his mother's illness and that the blackouts that he was having meant that he himself had a brain tumour. The last time he had seen his mother was when she was somewhat confused and he was very frightened and he hadn't really understood what was going on. And so Dr Vanier very slowly and carefully went through the medical notes with him so that he could see them and have them interpreted to him. And we heard later that he was a completely different person, with perhaps three-quarters of an hour spent with him. But how important it is to be aware of past patients and families, as well as current ones, and the need to have good medical notes, and nursing notes, and social work notes and to keep them somewhere safe.

In this chapter we have seen how care for bereaved people emerged as an integral part of modern hospice care. Those delivering a service in hospices were informed by a growing body of academic work and of practical wisdom. Ideas came from outside the hospices and influenced developments within, and there was also influence in the other direction. We have seen how the hospice experience helped shape services in other areas. This is a part of hospice history that has drawn on the multidisciplinary team and which demonstrates the particular input of social workers and volunteers. The model for how that care is delivered varies, but hospices remain committed to caring for the bereaved, and continue to develop innovative projects in these areas.

Notes

1. For a review of these, see J. Hockey, J. Katz and N. Small (eds.), *Grief, Mourning and Death Ritual* (Buckingham: Open University Press, 2002).
2. Hans Selye was born in Vienna and later moved to Montreal, Canada. He developed his General Adaptation Syndrome (GAS) and wrote 30 books and more than 1500 articles on stress related problems, including *The Stress of Life* (New York: McGraw Hill, 1956) and *Stress without Distress* (New York: Signet, 1975). He died in 1982.
3. E. Lindemann, 'Symptomatology and management of acute grief', *American Journal of Psychiatry* 101: 141–48, 1944. This article reports on a study of 101 patients who sought help at a clinic Lindemann set up following a fire in the Coconut Grove nightclub in Boston, Massachusetts.
4. For details of John Bowlby, see Chapter 1, above.
5. The Tavistock Clinic was founded in 1920 in Tavistock Square, London and subsequently moved to its current base in Swiss Cottage. It has a worldwide reputation for therapeutic approaches in mental health in the public sector. It has pioneered work in many areas, not least via the work John Bowlby undertook in developmental psychology, best known as 'attachment theory'. It led to a considerable body of subsequent research and impacted on professional attitudes towards child development and to the care of children in hospital. Staff from the Clinic constituted a core group who established the Tavistock Institute in 1946, which has an ongoing research and consultancy remit. See Henry Dicks, *Fifty Years of the Tavistock Clinic* (London: Routledge and Kegan Paul, 1970).
6. See P. Marris, *Widows and their Families* (London: Routledge, 1958) and *Loss and Change* (London: Routledge, 1974).
7. The letter was indeed in the file and was written by Cicely Saunders to Colin Murray Parkes on 23 March 1965; it contained the observation that at St Joseph's 'We do of course have a great deal to do with our patients' relatives during the time that they are with us but but nothing after the patient has died'. See D. Clark, *Cicely*

Saunders – founder of the hospice movement. Selected letters 1959–1999 (Oxford: Oxford University Press, 2002: 81–82).

8. Colin Murray Parkes is referring here to his time as Director of the Harvard Bereavement Study which he took over at the invitation of its founder, Gerald Caplan, the pioneer of ideas about 'crisis intervention' in the USA. The Harvard Bereavement Study was a longitudinal project involving widows and widowers in Boston, who were interviewed at intervals during their first four years of bereavement. Gerald Caplan had run a 'Laboratory of Community Psychiatry' in the 1960s and this proved to be a place out of which many innovators and innovative ideas emerged. The work of Colin Murray Parkes and Gerald Caplan in Boston was one of many influential collaborations between founding figures in the UK hospice movement and those concerned with related issues in the USA. See C.M. Parkes, 'Historical overview of the scientific study of bereavement' in M.S. Stroebe, R.O. Hansson, W. Stroebe and H. Schut, *Handbook of Bereavement Research. Consequences, coping and care* (Washington, DC: American Psychological Association, 2001) and D. Clark, 'A special relationship: Cicely Saunders, the United States, and the early foundations of the modern hospice movement', *Illness, Crisis and Loss* 9 (1): 15–30, 2001.

9. Barbara Monroe: Director of Social Work at St Christopher's and from 2000 its Chief Executive.

10. J. William Worden, *Grief Counselling and Grief Therapy: A handbook for the mental health practitioner* (London: Tavistock, 1983). Widow-to-Widow was set up in the USA in 1967. See P.R. Silverman, *Widow to Widow* (New York: Springer, 1986). Mary Vachon's evaluation can be found in M.L.S. Vachon, W. Lyall, J. Rogers, K. Freedman-Letofsky and S. Freeman, 'A controlled study of self-help interventions for widows', *American Journal of Psychiatry* 137: 1380–84, 1980.

11. L. Pincus, *Death and the Family* (London: Faber and Faber, 1976).

12. Tony Walter's books have been widely read and appreciated by bereavement counsellors in the UK. See, for example, *The Revival of Death* (London: Routledge, 1994) and *On Bereavement* (Buckingham: Open University Press, 1999). Tony Walter also established the MA in Death and Society at the University of Reading.

13. Margaret Torrie and her husband Dr Alfred Torrie founded Cruse on 5 October 1959 and for 16 years it was run from their home in Richmond near London. Margaret Torrie's book *Begin Again: A book for women alone* was published in 1970 (London: Dent) and *My Years with Cruse* was published in 1987 by the organisation itself (Richmond: Cruse). Derek Nuttall succeeded Margaret Torrie as Director upon her retirement in 1976 and saw the scope of the organisation expand considerably. In 1980 the service

was extended to widowers and then from 1986 to all bereaved people. In order to reflect these shifts in emphasis, the organisation's title was changed in 1987 from the National Organisation for the Widowed and their Children, to Cruse Bereavement Care. By 2003, Cruse was the largest bereavement care organisation in the world with over 200 branches throughout the UK and a volunteer workforce of over 6,400, including 4,400 trained bereavement counsellors. In 2002 it responded to almost 100,000 enquiries. The Cruse website tells how the organisation's name was chosen: 'It was felt at the time that no widow wanted attention drawn to her personal situation, although she desperately wanted support and encouragement … The idea behind the work of the organisation was to be positive and outward looking – a beginning again. After some thought, the idea of "Cruse" was adopted from the story in the Old Testament about a widow who shared her last jar of oil (a cruse is an earthenware vessel for holding oil) with a stranger, and by sharing found she always had more. The stranger was the Hebrew prophet, Elijah (1 Kings, Ch 17).' See www.cruse.com.

14. In 1966 at Aberfan in South Wales, 116 children and 28 adults died when a village school was engulfed by a slurry tip produced from local coal mining. Colin Murray Parkes was involved in the response to the resulting communal grief and bereavement.

15. Colin Murray Parkes took over the direction of the Harvard Bereavement Study at the invitation of its founder, Gerald Caplan. See note 8, above.

16. International Work Group on Death, Dying and Bereavement, *Statements on Death, Dying, and Bereavement* (Ontario: Kings College, 1994). The IWG continues to meet about every 20 months and membership, which is by invitation, includes people from many parts of the world. Its Mission Statement identifies it as an 'organization that seeks to advance and nurture the development of the field [death, dying and bereavement]. Further, IWG provides leadership and support to those involved in death education, in the care and support of the terminally ill, in the care of the bereaved, and in promoting research, evaluation, application, and policy development in these areas.'

17. Winston's Wish was set up in 1992 in Cheltenham to meet the needs of bereaved children, young people and their families. Its founder, Julie Stokes, a clinical psychologist, had visited the USA and Canada supported by a Winston Churchill Travelling Fellowship, and was inspired by services she saw there. In its first 10 years the organisation worked with 2,500 bereaved children and over 1,250 parents and other carers. It provides a range of responses including weekend camps for bereaved children and their parents, after school groups and individual counselling. A telephone support

service, Family Line, indirectly supported 1,600 bereaved children and young people in its first two years of operation. See www. winstonswish.org.uk.

18. Colin Murray Parkes coordinated a team from the UK that worked with the families of UK citizens killed in the attack on the World Trade Centre in New York on 11 September 2001. His work in Rwanda is described in C.M. Parkes, 'Genocide in Rwanda: Personal reflections', *Mortality* 1 (1): 95–110, 1996.

19. Therese Vanier, a haematologist, was the first woman consultant at St Thomas's Hospital in London and she also worked part-time at St Christopher's. The sister of Jean Vanier, the two founded a community of *L'Arche* in Canterbury; *L'Arche* developed as communities for people with developmental disabilities and grew from a small project in Jean Vanier's home in France in 1964, to over 120 communities in some 30 countries. In 2003 Dr Therese Vanier was honoured by the Archbishop of Westminster as one of the 'Catholic Women of the Year'.

8   Finished and unfinished business

'So there's endless interest'   **Cicely Saunders**

We began this book by exploring the process of becoming involved with modern hospice care – often through caring for patients in other settings and listening carefully to the narrative of their suffering. We considered both personal and professional experiences. For some there was a sense of religious calling; others were motivated particularly by a strong perception of social need and concerns about the shortcomings of existing provision. We then showed how ideas about hospice and the provision of services began to develop across the UK. We looked at how local groups got started, how funds were raised, how attempts were made to identify and respond to local needs and how staff were recruited to the purpose. The particular claims of hospices to multidisciplinary teamwork were examined from a variety of perspectives. We also explored the role of various professional and 'umbrella' hospice and palliative care organisations and their role in influencing policy and practice. From these our analysis turned to the spiritual dimension of hospice care, examining the motivating force of Christian faith, along with the wider development of

a broader concept of spirituality and the particular contribution of hospice chaplaincy. Important clinical innovations relating to pain and symptom management were found to be at the heart of much hospice practice – and also seen to have spread well beyond the confines of hospice services. A special place was given in this exploration to the concept of 'total pain' and the role of patient narratives in its formulation. We saw some of the obstacles to the use of powerful narcotics in the relief of pain, as well as to the development of new policies and technologies for pain relief – and how these were overcome by hospice and palliative care activists. We also considered those sometimes underexplored issues relating to bereavement and mourning: examining theoretical underpinnings, practical service initiatives and the role of research.

Many of those we spoke to closed their interviews with some personal reflections about the changing character of hospice and palliative care and its place within the wider social and health care context. For some this brought out observations concerning work concluded and a sense of

A shared moment at St Christopher's.

goals achieved and brought to fruition. But it also captured many examples of 'unfinished business' – ideas and projects that had not yet been fully realised, tasks still to be undertaken, objectives still to be met. We found that our respondents often interleaved examples and issues from their own experience, from the perspective of their local hospice service, and from a national viewpoint that took into account changing social forces, innovations in clinical practice and new aspects of policy and health care organisation. There was considerable diversity amongst those we interviewed. Some were newly retired from full-time work in hospice care, often after many years of service; others had been formally retired for some time, whilst remaining active on committees, in conducting research and in teaching. Others were still very much engaged on a full- or part-time basis. Across all of these categories were women and men with experience in independent charitable hospices as well as those who worked in NHS in-patient units for palliative care, in hospitals and in community services. In short, those to whom we spoke often had a sophisticated view about the challenges facing the hospice movement and how these might be overcome. In this chapter we therefore explore several themes that were raised, showing how they reflect on our unfolding understanding of hospice history in the UK. It is clear from much of this that hospices have become far more than 'a bit of heaven for the few'.

The positioning of hospices in the wider health care and social context

Colin Murray Parkes, at the close of an interview that took place at his home in Hertfordshire in January 1996, set out a very full picture that located hospice work in a broader historical tradition, and in so doing pointed to some of the pitfalls that might beset it, but also the major achievements it has made:

Well, let me start off, perhaps, I don't want to be alarmist, but there are certain trends I suppose one sees as time passes, changes that could lead to problems. One of the things that worries me is that, as the enthusiasm for hospice begins to decline, and, you know, when things are new everybody wants to get in on the act, and you get this terrific wave of enthusiasm, people setting things up right, left and centre. And then, after a few years, the enthusiasm dies down, and the thing either collapses or becomes routine.

He goes on to suggest a historical precedent for his worries:

… for instance, in the mental health field, during the nineteenth century, you had the so-called 'moral treatment' movement, and people became enthusiastic about helping poor lunatics, people with mental illnesses. The idea was that a lot of these illnesses were being caused by the horrors of the industrial revolution: alco-holism, overcrowding, the dreadful slums, working conditions that people were working under and living under. And asylums were set up as a retreat (some of them were called retreats), where people could escape from these dreadful circumstances and be cared for by loving, caring … people. And in the early days of the moral treatment movement, I don't doubt that there were wonderful changes, that the lunatics were being well cared for, and they responded appropriately. As the century went by, enthusiasm began to dwindle … the money began to dry up, the numbers of people preparing to work in the area, and the enthusiasm of those who did was warped. And by the beginning of the twentieth century, and by the middle of the twentieth century, we had these horrific snake-pits – the mental hospitals – which had become very little more than custodial places for the insane, and where very little active treatment was given, and the treatment that was given was largely harmful.

Now, I have a horror of the same kind of thing happening with hospice. I can imagine, for instance, that a hospice could become a dump where unwanted dying patients are put, where there's not enough money to look after them and provide the adequate staff for them, and where the staff who are there are so overworked that they can't give proper psychosocial care at all. There's a danger that the emphasis on drugs and use of medication for symptom control will be used to control depression and anxiety so that patients will be zonked out of their minds by the drugs rather than given the proper psychosocial care and understanding that they need. That's the horror side of it. That's the thing that one most dreads about a possible historical development here. I think it's very important for people working within hospice to be only too alert to that danger. To build into the hospice programmes a proper recognition of the importance of psychological, social and spiritual care, as well as physical care, because I do see, in some hospices and some necks of the palliative care wood, such an emphasis on clever palliative treatments that people are underestimating the importance of the other three. So keep the flag of psychosocial care, of spiritual care, that flag, flying.

As well as this worry, a further area of concern comes out of the very commitment to holism:

I'm a little bit worried about some of the fringe methods of treatment that seem to be drawn in the name of holism. You know, the idea that you have to treat everything doesn't mean to say that you have to adopt the latest fad or diet or whatever it may be. And without being too specific about what particular fringe approaches I approve of, I think that people need to be on their guard that something isn't necessarily good just because it's new, and that we should be critical, as I think hospice staff always have been, but as time goes by, perhaps, more critical of some of the fringe approaches. That's not to say they shouldn't be tried, but they should be tried with a proper evaluation and proper recognition of the possibility that they may actually be a waste of money or a waste of resources. So, you know, don't let's go overboard about holism. Let's recognise that there are limits, and that there are some things that are either a waste of money and time, or possibly even actively harmful.

If these are some of the negative things, there is also a positive side that relates to the wider impact of hospice care and values:

… what I think the most exciting thing about hospice, is not that it will improve our care of the dying, because I think we've already accomplished a great deal there, but that it will re-educate people throughout the caring services – medicine, social work, nursing – all these areas, to the importance of the turning points in people's lives, the critical life events where a little help can make all the differ-ence between disaster or moving forward to the next chapter of life in a more mature and effective way. A lot of people come for training to a hospice, work in a hospice for a few years and then they go off and do something else. And that's great because they

may find that what they learnt in hospice is relevant when they're caring for amputees, is relevant when they're caring for people in other settings. And, you know, the clergyman who, having worked as a hospital Chaplain, goes and works in the community and meets people who are suffering the effects of divorce and other losses in their lives, again, has opportunities to use the lessons that he's learnt in one setting to improve the care in another. I hope I'm not being romantic in suggesting that there are, the long-term influences of hospice may well extend far beyond the medical care systems, and maybe have important implications for the entire social structures that we live in.

Tim Lovel, however, speaking as a palliative medicine doctor, can see some of the tensions and difficulties resting within the hospice philosophy as it matures:

… there's lots still to do in this country to get people really to know what the hospice ethos and hospice methods can do, because we can't do it all, we – even if we could it's not desirable that we just de-skill everybody else, we should impart the knowledge to let every-body achieve what hospices can achieve, both in terms of symptom control, but more importantly personal care, because palliative care is not just symptomatology. And there's a risk, I think, that as we get closer to the NHS – and I think that palliative medicine is gradually coming back inside the fold. Cicely founded it 33 years ago,[1] and deliberately made it outside the NHS to show the difference, and they'd be free of bureaucratic control, but that battle has been won – and I think with the increased funding from the NHS, the increased acceptance of our role, Calman-Hine[2] has done a tremendous lot to bring palliative medicine inside the fold, and I think we shall get closer and closer in – within the NHS, although I hope always retaining our own identity …

Similar themes about dissonance within the hospice culture as it encountered changing external conditions and the realities of market conditions are echoed by the social worker Julia Franklin:

Hospices have had to grow up, and they've had to acknowledge that in these days, now, they are businesses as well. So we're no longer, you know, special, protected people at all – if we ever were. But we've got to function in the sort of real world which is … the purchaser/providers now, the market economy … And so we've got to find ways of growing up, really, and we can't hide behind our … halos anymore. In fact, I don't know that we ever did, but I think there's got to be a big problem, and there probably already is in hospices, 'cause I actually believe, now,[3] that a lot of the people that went into hospice movement – doctors and nurses and others – are now having to actually manage quite large budgets and institutions. And I think you've got to have different skills to manage than you have to be a clinician, although some people can really combine them.

But I actually think that there has to be some sort of maturing into sort of the management of bigger businesses, and their place within the NHS. I mean many hospices thought they were sort of precious, perhaps, little institutions in their community, but they could dispense with the NHS or the Health Authority or Social Services. And I mean they can't; we are part of it. So I think my own feeling is that for some of the hospices, perhaps like the one that I'm working at now, who in the past have been rather sort of scathing about Health Authorities and government money and Social Services, and all of that, through the Community Care Act, through the … really the pioneering work that Help the Hospices and National Hospice Council have done, they're having to stand up, be counted, communicate, you know, and look right outside their institution. So I think that's going to be painful for the hospice movement. And I think, also, that unless we can look at, as institutions, the effects of loss and change on ourselves, then we're going to come to, there's going to be unhappiness.

But I sort of fear for the hospice movement, in some ways, in the future. I think there's going to be a great stress between keeping our philosophy of care … that we've written and that we've now got, and these … what do you call them? These 'mission statements', really keeping to that, and actually becoming acute specialist care units, for example, specialist palliative care units. I think there's going to be a great tension between … those two things and I think it's going to be, you know, it'll be a difficult path. And I think what I'm saying is that there needs to be leaders, there needs to be leadership within those hospices to be able to manage those things, and I'm sad, but I don't think we have it at the moment. And that's not necessarily blaming anybody, but I just think that we've, we haven't necessarily got it. I think it's a huge task, I don't know what the answer is, but it's sort of like a bit of a sort of a feeling I've got that's a warning or something … as I sort of look back and reminisce … and look forward.

Eric Wilkes, such a central figure in the early development of the modern hospice movement, was asked at the end of series of interviews he gave in 1995 to speculate on future directions for the field:

Well, we always thought the hospice movement would be a transient, temporary phenomenon that would work itself out of a job in 10 or 20 years. I don't think this will happen because standards are changing … We have, for all kinds of totally valid and justifiable reasons, a difficult environment for the care of the dying to take its proper place … But on the whole I see, in the medium term, the need for training, the need for centres of excellence, to be as always (and slightly to my surprise), more urgent rather than less. In other words, we've filled a gap that we hardly knew existed, and now we know that we're not filling the gap because it's like the Red Queen in *Alice*; one has got to run very fast to stand still. So I see a future for it. Managerially it will tend to be more formally, bureaucratically organised, integrated into universities or into medical schools. The nursing profession is in such change at the moment; it's difficult to see what their set-up will be like in 10 or 20 years' time. The doctors I think will have, perhaps, problems of recruitment which we've not had before, in the next decade or so. But I think the specialist palliative care unit is necessary, is desirable, and will be less of a 'flash in the pan' than I thought it would be five or 10 years ago.

Hospice and palliative care as specialist activities

We have seen that what began in the UK as a form of social movement, quite quickly matured into a specialist field of health and social care. John Hinton, a psychiatrist with an early research interest in the care of the dying and whose publications did a great deal to stimulate the first generation of hospice innovators, reflects on a number of areas:

Well I haven't actually been a champion of the hospice movement, I think what I've been is a champion of what is now palliative care – that is my interest. And I think the hospice world has done it immense service and played a great part and is, and will, play a great part. To some extent public opinion has taken over and ensured that hospice, as such, will play a part perhaps rather more than the great thinkers, and so on, and planners, because people have championed having a hospice in their own area, and they want it. And despite any wise words like the Wilkes Report in '72,[4] they shouldn't increase and so on and so forth, nevertheless they have increased and people do see the need. Now I think they will shape, perhaps, differently between themselves, and different styles will emerge at different times. At the present moment they're still largely having the benefits

of the great vocational sense of the first generation. It's beginning to change hands and still, as far as I can see at the present moment, this combination of some empirical research, that indeed Cicely did to begin with, plus the vocational, including the religious inspiration, will play their part. But the balance will shift a bit, it is shifting 'cause the pattern of the whole area of palliative care has changed so much, you see, since 1960, or '58 actually I began to sort of do my first, plan my first study. And to think back over that, nigh on 40 years, the way journals have come out, special writings, the whole world, that world has altered and I think it will continue to alter. Now, so far, and hopefully it will continue, this emphasis will be in terms of improvements in the classics or factual knowledge, but also in that experiential aspect of caring, of what people feel, the quality, and not just the quantitative type study, and that will maintain it. I think people have got to be a little cautious that, on some of the smaller units, perhaps, in particular, it might be quite easy to see standards decline if they're left, and the recruitment of money, and the proper staff diminish … So far I think the record's been pretty

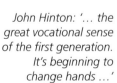
John Hinton: '… the great vocational sense of the first generation. It's beginning to change hands …'

good. I think it will probably maintain, but every now and again, I'm wondering when the first nasty blot will appear. That's a rather poor answer actually, isn't it, 'cause I finished up overemphasising a slightly negative note when I, in fact, I think the hospice has indeed played a very important part, and altered, or voiced, a component of caring in general that has altered the practice of medicine.

Ivy McCreery, a staff nurse at the Marie Curie Centre, Belfast, makes some related points, but this time in relation to the need for evidence to back up the clinical claims made by hospice services:

I think at the minute sort of palliative care and the hospice movement, whatever words you want to wrap around it, I think it's actually in a transition period. I think that looking to the future, I mean the hospice movement has got off easy in many ways in that they've had this cosy identity and they haven't had to justify it by backing it up with research, and it's mostly been done through voluntary monies and whatever. And I think looking to the future, that palliative care will have to be able to shape up professionally and every other way and stand alongside the other services by having their own research. Technology's moving on and I do think we're in transition about treatments – what treatments are good to continue and which should maybe be stopped, you know – I think we're actually in a transition phase.

Liz Atkinson, Nursing Director at the Northern Ireland Hospice, is one of many who interleave a wide range of complex issues into her analysis of future issues:

Well I certainly wouldn't be one of the people who thinks that hospices will do themselves out of a job. I know that was certainly the idea when folks thought that hospices would do themselves out of a job because they can teach these skills and pass them on. I think hospices will be here. I think there might be two different types of hospice. I think there will be the specialist palliative care unit, and I

think there will be the hospice where it's perhaps a more nursing-led unit. I think funding is going to become an even bigger problem for hospices and I think that problem is going to become widespread if something isn't done about it. I mean I do think – I know hospices have always struggled, but I think when hospices like St Christopher's and ourselves and some of the others who have always been financially quite viable, when we're meeting financial difficulty now I think, if something isn't done that could get much worse. I think there's a big challenge in the future in terms of education, professional education. Not just nurse education but professional education, to prepare clinical staff to be more ready to work in this type of environment. Some people would say hospices will become absorbed within the NHS. I hope that doesn't happen, because I think if it does we would lose a lot.

Derek Doyle, a physician who has had a global influence on hospice and palliative care development, and reflecting

Derek Doyle on the Scottish scene: '... those that started off very modestly and struggled for ages are now thriving.'

here at the end of an interview in February 1996, is able to give a sweeping overview of the hospice and palliative care scene in Scotland and the key features of its growth:

We've done a very good job here in Scotland ... Why do I say it's good? Well I don't think we've got too many units, for example they're nicely spaced. It may be questionable in the centre of Glasgow where you've got one major one, you know John Welsh's unit at Hunter's Hill in the north, and Prince and Princess of Wales in the south. There was a personality involved in that, and it's the old problem, but otherwise very nicely, logically placed around the country. And those that started off very modestly and struggled for ages are now thriving, and I'm thinking of the Borders one, which I had quite a lot to do with, and which started off with nurses, and then they managed to get a part-time doctor, and then they got a full-time doctor, and now they've got a consultant, and that's a full

going, very exciting palliative care service. The Inverness one I had a bit to do with again, and that's going fine too. And bearing in mind the difficult geography, the scattered population, and only a few areas of real dense population and conurbations, it's remarkably good. We're not getting the English picture of a hospice every five miles ... if for no other reason that it doesn't make sense to have all these specialist units, and we're going to run out of staff to staff them quite apart from the money of it all.

Why has it developed like that? Well I think probably Scottish nature, I mean the Scottish government is fairly 'couthy' and cautious as we know, and we wouldn't have been able to proliferate. I mean they would simply have said to us in Scotland, because they're very tight on the purse strings, 'Well, you can have a unit if you want to but don't come to us for money, don't come to us for help. You're perfectly at liberty to open anything as long as it meets the Nursing Home Act requirements.' And so there was, if you like, some political/ government constraints there which were very sensible. Also we had such very wise leaders, and let's never forget that Ken Calman influenced Scotland when he was a Professor of Oncology ... and then he became Postgraduate Dean, and then he became Professor of Education and then he became the Chief Medical Officer, but he's influenced all the way through from there. And we've had a lot of wise people. Aberdeen and the Grampian developed because the man who became the leading light in palliative medicine up there was John Berkeley who at the same time was senior community medicine specialist ... Well he couldn't have been a better man, ex-lecturer in general practice, ex-overseas missionary and natural administrator, so we've had very good, very sensible people. We've had the inspiration of Harold Lyon who set up Strathcarron and then Tom Scott who became administrator after that. Tom, moving from total ignorance about this work into the very heart of it, he's been a great influence.

So … Scotland has got a lot to demonstrate to the rest of the country saying: 'You don't have to have these things metastasising, proliferating all over, you can exert a considerable influence.' You've only to look and say, 'Well, look at the number of senior registrars and registrars we've got around the country. Look at the number of courses that are run.' We don't duplicate a single thing in Scotland. That's really quite something. If somebody up in Inverness says, 'We're going to run a new course …' it would always be, '… if that's OK with the rest of you,' or, 'Are any of you planning to do that one?' There's a good rationalisation there. And now it's moving logically to more and more teams within general hospitals. And you've to look at the number of people that are in palliative medicine around the country and you notice quite a significant number, certainly more than the predictable proportion, have been through Scottish medical schools, and have moved into the thing as a result of some time in their Scottish training. So I think things are quite sensible here.

The theme of specialisation in palliative care is also one explored by Gillian Ford at the end of her interview, in June 1996:

Some people would certainly feel – is death being professionalised? Are people beginning to feel that there can't be such a thing as a 'good death' unless you've had the home care team, or the hospice involved? That's one aspect. That's a question that's been aired, I think by you amongst others.[5] In Marie Curie … we used to have 'homes' and that's got a cosy sound, and they were cosy, and the Matron, as she was then known, knew all the patients and all the families and that was nice. And we are getting out of that business. We don't operate a kind of 14-day ration and then you must move on, whether it be to home, hospital or a nursing home, but the throughput's quite different from that which it used to be …

But when it comes to the crunch, I think that the professionalisation has actually been enabling. I think that there are more people,

certainly more with cancer, who are having better symptom control, are able to live quality lives, are able to be up and about, do have confidence that there's somebody at the end of the phone, end of the line, on a phone, who can give them help, can be, you know, taken and underpinned when the need arises, even if that sort of cosy, rather slow sort of aspect of some of the hospices is threatened. I think that, in the end, the benefits are there and can be counted. That's perhaps something which other people would debate.

I also think that if [palliative care] was going to have any influence on those dying of other diseases, then it has had to be specialised, it's had to present outcomes, had to be challenging, had to say there is research which shows you can treat breathlessness in this way, but there isn't enough research. Why aren't you clinicians and nursing staff who are looking after patients with severe chronic obstructive airways disease, doing the sort of research which will mean that symptoms, quality of life, are pre-eminent issues rather than simply blood gas levels?

The social worker Frances Sheldon, in an interview that took place in the last year of her life, in June 2003, is also able to describe a wide overview of developments, coupled with some personal reflections of her own role and involvement:

Well I think it's been, I mean for me personally a very exciting sort of time really because it's been, it has been so much about development and about opportunity, and opportunities there to be taken. Because it was a developing field, often opportunities were being presented to me in a way … I came into this at the beginning of a development of something that's really seized people's imagination and has grown, and so on a personal level that's been very, you know, stimulating, and I've had lots of fun with groups with like-minded people who've, you know, who've been really interesting and good to work with across all the professions.

And, looking at it more, in a sense more dispassionately, well I think, I mean I do feel positive about the development of palliative care, but also feel there is, you know, so much a continuing need to try and hang on to the essence of what that is and maintain a fresh-ness about it if you can, which is more difficult to sustain the larger something gets and the more diverse it gets. But particularly to try and sustain, you know, attention to the breadth of people's needs and wishes as they approach the end of life and as those around them approach that with them … to try and keep people's ears open to the range of what people are concerned about when they're at that stage of their lives. And I think social work's got an important role to do that, but not only social work, other professions have got to hear those, hear those messages, hear those needs as well.

So it's not just a social work responsibility, it's a responsibility of the whole of palliative care to try and maintain that listening and obviously the whole development of the user, you know, aspect, bringing in the user voice much more formally into this is one way of trying to do this. But it's not the only way because, you know, you can't just rely on that, you must have your antennae out as well for the unspoken things, the things people don't, can't quite voice because they don't feel it's legitimate to voice it, but yet you must somehow hear those things as well if you can. And to do that you need a broad range of professionals in there and you need, I think, social workers in there as part of that broad range. But ready to listen to the other professionals about what they're hearing, because people will, individuals who we're working with will tell us different things – they'll tell me different things because I'm a social worker with that label to what they'll tell the doctor. And all those things are legitimate things so we mustn't be precious about what we've got to offer.

So that's where developing education and research is really important. Research in trying to understand what we're doing and how we're going about it I'd say from my perspective particularly, you know, to inform practitioners about, well, what are you really doing? And education trying to draw on that to … but also to support people in working in a field which can be personally quite challenging, and education's a really important way of trying to help people think more about what they're doing, give them spaces to think about it and to find ways of understanding which will help them to stick with something that's difficult.

The changing character of the hospice environment

Several of our respondents talked about the changing character of the hospice environment and the shifting orientation of people working in the hospice movement as it began to consolidate and mature; there seemed to be a distinction here between the free spirits and looser working practices of the early founders and the hospices they created, and the later, more structured, climate of opinion and organ-isation. Ros Beetham, who had worked at St Luke's, Sheffield since its inception in 1971, and speaking here in December 1996, refers to this in the context of her own group – the volunteer coordinators working in hospices:

I've noticed, it started last year in our Association, that there is a new group of coordinators coming up the line. People who are much more belligerent and wanting their act together. Even more: to be recognised as people who are doing a very difficult job and are not getting suitable pay for it, which is perfectly true. And unfortunately a lot of people in the hospice movement have this idea that you should do things for love and not money, and that you can do it for a pittance because it's for charity. I'm sure you will have heard that several times, and if you haven't, that's what goes on. And a lot of staff are paid very poorly because, [whispering] 'You know, it's a charity, we mustn't be too greedy dear.' Then there are other people who say, 'I'm doing a job of work and I need the remuneration that goes with it.' In the job that we do, there is no way that you can find a balance. Nobody seems to be able to find, if you look at a scale of pay – what do we relate to? If you try and pull out the job description, it doesn't match anything. If the people who worked for you were paid, you would go up to the top of the scale and over it. The fact that the word 'volunteer' is involved is very strange, it sort of brings it down to something like clerical – absolutely ludicrous [laughter] – unless there's a fight.

So a lot of people have to fight, which is pretty difficult because they've got to be careful of the balance, as I told you earlier. But I see, creeping in now, is a realisation at long last (I'm sorry it's too late for me), of that what the job actually, really, is about. And in one or two enlightened places the Organiser or Coordinator, or whatever, Manager, whatever they're called, is suddenly being accorded a status that hasn't been set until now. In 1989 14 per cent of people were not being paid to do this job at all … nothing, not even an honorarium, or expenses. It's something like one per cent now, but it still occurs occasionally. But, this belligerent group, as I say, suddenly there was a new flavour starting last year where there were people who are young and 'with it', and who are not going to have this sort of nonsense. So that's going to create a different set-up in the future again.

A colleague at St Luke's, Sheffield, transport manager Brian Shaw, makes a related point about the changing character of the hospice as a place to work. Taking up a theme echoed by other respondents, he observes:

When I went, first went to St Luke's [in 1983], St Luke's was a lot smaller than it is now. A smallness … you're a closer knit family. I think Marjory's[6] idea was, 'We're a family.' And I'm certain that Eric Wilkes talks about the … well, I've heard him say it many times, 'the St Luke's family'. Now, whether it's a family now, I don't know.

But there were also other factors at work, as expressed here by the Newcastle-upon-Tyne-based hospice physician and educator, Claud Regnard:

If you hang on to the bits that you were doing whilst moving forward then I think you end up with a huge bulky organisation – that's always a danger. I mean we see it everywhere, you know, we see it here; we see it in all organisations. We recognise that danger. There's a danger in becoming less of a care organisation and more of an administrative organisation. There is a real danger in that where care just happens to be one department down there but really there's all this other stuff that's going on when in fact really the whole purpose of what you're doing is the care. There is a risk of that and I think it may be that we have to stop thinking that we actually hang on to what we've done in the past and that we accept that we have to move on but not just move on but leave other stuff behind. Now that's going to be very difficult and I think people have been saying it but they've been saying it for different reasons.

Education

The theme of education was prominent for several people when they turned their thoughts to future developments. Tim Lovel notes:

I think that still the greatest need is for education. It was Jan Stjern-sward[7] who said, 'What needs to be done is known; the single most useful thing we can do is for everybody to use the knowledge which now exists.' And we still need to do a lot, a lot of work in teaching all the professionals to be both confident and competent in caring for the dying patient, whether they've got cancer or some other fatal progressive disease.

But beyond this blanket call for more educational provision, there is also the major issue of extending palliative care to those with diseases other than cancer and of ensuring fairness of access to care in a society where attitudes to dying and death are changing. Mary Holland, a palliative care nurse specialist working in the Lake District and speaking here in May 2001, captures several of these points in a single passage:

I think the dissemination of education of palliative care into the community and into the hospital – I think there's still a lot of work needs to be done. I mean my particular interest really is the patients with non-malignant disease, because that is my background. I feel quite strongly that they should have access to good standards of palliative care. I don't know logistically whether that could be done by the Macmillan nurse, or what we ought to be doing is disseminating the practices of the palliative care approach so that those patients equally have access to high standards of palliative care. So that, I think that's a challenge for the future. And I'm also really enjoying being involved in the Palliative Care Congress and the [Royal College of Nursing] and Palliative Nursing Forum. So hopefully we can start to take practice in the area forward with that as well. And we've recently completed a year-long audit looking at why patients leave their home. So that might be for symptom control or for radiotherapy, or hospital admissions, and we're actually just looking at why that is, what is it that doesn't allow patients to stay in their home …

We haven't mentioned resources, and that's obviously a huge issue, and equity. And I think for the future I'd like to see that everyone had equal resources and equity to high-quality palliative care. And I think that perhaps society is perhaps changing to some

extent, that death isn't quite as taboo as it used to be. But I still think, you know, there's lots to be done within palliative care and, although people within palliative care themselves are enthusiastic about it; we've still got a long way to go with our colleagues. And that reaches into hospitals and also into nursing homes, because this is such an important area.

Claud Regnard also has some observations about education:

Cicely Saunders always said we'd be done out of a job but I think what she didn't realise was just the immensity of the people that are out there. Now we may end up somewhere at the other end and say, 'Oh gosh, we really have reached the end and gone out to all the edges now,' but I doubt that somehow. The bits I think that may be left behind, that we may still have a role in – well we should have a role in – I think are the education and resource sides. I think that won't disappear so you know I think that's where the anchor will stay but the idea that the anchor must stay in the current – you know particularly the cancer-orientated side of palliative care – I think that's very debatable. So I think we need to be a catalyst that's going forward … and education is part of that.

I think people have a rather stereotyped view of education. This has been another handicap I think in palliative care: people have seen education as something you do face to face and you do it with courses and you do it with workshops. Yes that's lovely if you can get people … So what's needed is workplace learning. I don't think in palliative care we've really looked enough at workplace learning. We need to be creating much more of that and we need to be looking at how we can not just physically face to face go and meet people in the workplace because there aren't enough of us to go and do that, but actually create materials that go into the workplace, do much more on the Internet, you know, have resources available. We've got bogged down in guidelines. Instead we should be saying, 'Look, OK let's produce some advice stuff that could be centrally driven if necessarily but let's produce stuff that we pretty well all agree with and let's get this out. Instead of producing the National Hospice Council – a great big book you know even if a big A4 sheet thing – let's produce something that's small, will go inside a BNF[8] that all house officers in the country can have you know.

It really is that sort of stuff and I don't think we're doing enough of that. Really that's a challenge because the trouble is, you know, people say, 'Oh, it must be accredited' – no it doesn't have to be. It's very nice if it is, but these days with portfolio learning people can take stuff and doctors are going to be doing portfolio learning in the future as well, so not everything has to be accredited. You can bring your portfolio and if you want to get that accredited well that's fine but, you know, show what we've done so we need more materials like that and I think that's a big challenge for the future and that's hardly being addressed unfortunately. There are lots of people doing education but hardly anybody doing work-based learning materials, there's hardly anybody doing that.

Meeting new and changing needs

In the following passage, Claud Regnard recognises that the ideas developed in the hospice environment for patients with cancer must be transplanted elsewhere, to other settings and conditions, and also notes that the character of cancer disease has in turn shifted, moving it more into the category of a chronic condition for some patients:

I think oncologists have been given more resources to do it better, I think they will want to do it better, I think they'll want to follow their own folks right the way through and you know I think we have to be doing it with them and not necessarily doing it here. We should

only be shifting across – I mean it worries me when years ago these figures but I think it was about eight or nine years ago but the figures that sort of 50 per cent of cancer patients are seen by a Macmillan nurse and I'm sort of going, 'Well, that sounds wonderful, but why? Why as much as 50 per cent? Why do 50 per cent of patients need to see a Macmillan nurse?' They're supposed to be a specialist resource, they really should only be seeing about 10 or 15 per cent. They might be advising on some of them, it might be a phone call or somebody rings them up but you know that seems to be – that's people hanging on to the past and not passing on to – not moving on really and moving forward.

The possibility of such a changing relationship with cancer and with oncologists also points the way to other potential innovations:

I think the cancer/non-cancer thing is a very good example of it I think, and I think Irene in that respect and Julia are absolutely right to push us and say, 'No look, you have got to start pioneering in this area.'[9] I think because it's been comfortable for cancer patients, we've got to know something about cancer and so we're comfortable with it and it's not just the bureaucratising it's also sort of sitting in an area that we're comfortable with. I hear people saying, 'Yeah, but I didn't know I had to think about heart disease,' and it's only when you say to them, 'But actually you don't need to, in the same way that you didn't have to be an oncologist to care for these cancer patients.' I don't need to be a psychiatrist to have an input into folks with learning disabilities because where I work over there I'm surrounded by people who are experts in learning disabilities, but they rely on me to provide some palliative care input. Alright, I'm picking up some bits about learning disabilities but I've no intention of going to train as a psychiatrist to look after people with learning disabilities nor would I want to go and train as an oncologist. Well, I'm not going to go and train as a cardiologist either or a neurologist or a respiratory physician. In the same way that I'm going to be having some input in the children's hospice as an enabler really but I'm certainly not going to train as a paediatrician, I'm going to rely on people around me who are paediatrically trained. I think that co-working and co-learning is something we need to be doing a lot more of. We've inherited cancer patients in a way and so it seemed a natural progression and St Christopher's at a very early stage was taking motor neurone disease patients. I think we need to look at other neurological conditions and rehabilitation and a number of other areas.

So I think I almost see palliative care – I'm beginning to see it more as not just a catalyst – because it does have a very direct care role – but as a catalyst in a care role that is moving through and having some roots left behind in terms of resourcing but not necessarily in terms of care. So you may end up with a very mixed population in the future which is not just cancer and could be dementia.

I'm not saying that, you know, because there are places for folks to be cared for with dementia I'm not suggesting that hospices start going forward with dementia, it's what people get very panicky about – but you know hospices will all be full of patients with dementia. I'm not suggesting that and I think some of the issues that you have to have about turnover – because if you don't have a turnover you can't deal with crisis admissions – so you're still not looking at long-term patients. I don't think there's an issue but you could – you know I don't see why we shouldn't take somebody with dementia who's got an acute problem that needs to be dealt with: whether that's a psychological problem, a physical problem or whatever. It's a life-threatening disease … it's advanced by definition usually, it's progressing … it fits all the criteria. For our folks with learning disabilities there's some dementias relating to Down's syndrome which are very fast. I mean they progress in two years and they often can die within two years, well that's faster than many cancers.

So as cancers get more prolonged – this idea that length of time is all becoming irrelevant and I think we need to start dumping this idea of diagnosis and being worried about not being able to look after non-cancer stuff and get on.

Of course, it is recognised that extending the skills of hospice and palliative care to people with non-malignant conditions might have serious resource implications, as noted by former Deputy Chief Medical Officer, Gillian Ford:

The growth of specialist palliative care to encompass disease other than cancer is a subject which, I think, is extremely important. It will have resource consequences. Have people begun to think of that? I've been in correspondence with the Royal College of Physicians who specifically asked for estimates on developments which will have revenue consequences, and I think that will have very considerable revenue consequences.

There is also the specific question of how the services offered by hospices for adults could be extended to the care of children and adolescents. Betty Irwin, the first Administrative Director of the Northern Ireland Hospice, speaking in August 2000:

You were asking about the future. I mean I think the idea of the children's hospices is tremendous and I'm very much in support of that. I know it's a slightly different service that is envisaged there from the one that we're accustomed to for adults or people who are terminally ill, in that the children who are going to be helped – it's just a different concept of help to them and help to their families. I was interested to read the other day actually in the press somewhere that Sister Helen[10] who was, I suppose, one of the leaders in establishing children's hospice, is now establishing one for adolescents – for teenagers who don't fit comfortably either with young children or with the, I suppose, predominantly older patients in the hospice so I'll be interested to see how that progresses.

The theme of how the specialist influence of hospice and palliative care could be more widely disseminated is returned to time and again in our interviews. Lyn Forbes, at the Highland Hospice:

I think we see our future work here, and our development, more about being a resource centre and an enabler for others. And I think that fits in with what people are looking for nationally, but although we've been able to help hundreds of patients we have to acknowledge that's only a small portion of the patients who've actually been receiving palliative care in the Highlands. And so what we hope in the future is, more and more, for our specialist team, to use their skills to improve the knowledge of other people. I think that is the way we'll be going in the future.

There are also those who address particular innovations in clinical practice and the ways in which these might influence future hospice and palliative care, such as Sally Campalani, Clinical Services Manager at the Marie Curie Centre in Belfast:

I think there's going to be more and more palliative care. I think the changes in cancer treatments – before it was just 'curable' or 'palliative' – now we have 'curable', 'disease-free episodes' and 'palliative'. The whole nature of the cancer treatments – we don't know the effect of it. Treatments going out into people's home, occupational health, district nurses giving chemotherapy. You now, all those sort of community services which are all going out there, or all the chemotherapy. It is all going to have a massive impact on palliative care. But I see the demand for it being greater rather than less; but then again, I think we don't know yet the impact if every health care professional practises palliative care, as is hoped – GPs saying to me, 'What will be the knock-on effect for ourselves?' I think it will get more and more complex.

Likewise, Colin Hardman offers some thoughts about changes over time, from the perspective of the pharmacist:

Yes, I think what has changed a lot again since the early days are that the majority of the products that we use are commercially advanced. We take them off the shelf, we put a label on them and we send them out to patients. So what is different nowadays is that the information that accompanies medicine use has increased; well, the term 'information explosion' is being widely used, but is an apt description. The amount of information that we have about medicines, about disease, about everything to do with patient care, really has exploded in recent years. So part of our role as pharmacists nowadays perhaps is more closely involved with providing information, with problem solving, with supporting others. So I actually do more work nowadays on information and opinion and research about particular problems than hands-on supply techniques. So there is a big change again from the early days of my career when we did more preparation and more supply and less opinion and problem solving to our current state which is almost the reverse, that we do much more direct patient care.

Local plans and ambitions

Many respondents refer to local plans and ambitions for service development, but it is not uncommon for these also to be couched in terms of a sense of caution about sustainability, in the context of a high reliance on charitable funds and voluntary giving. Edward Daly captures a sense of this in the context of the Foyle Hospice in Northern Ireland:

Well we've had day care here but it's just been very basic, and it was simply because funds I suppose were a big problem. I mean ultimately the Health Service will have to wake up to the fact that hospice care is a very integral part of the delivery of health services generally and the quicker that they treat it as such the better. I think it's a pity that people who are committed to hospice have to spend so much time and exert so much energy in raising funds when they could be more usefully occupied. Day care was something, I think that was always perceived as another need but I think up until now we were not in a position to provide such a facility. I think one of the things that one has to learn is that it's one thing to raise funds to build a hospice, the capital expenditure, but the current expenditure is the thing that people don't see, they can see the bricks and mortar and slates and a building but they don't see the services every day. It's much simpler to raise [money] for a building than for a service. And I think anybody going into this situation needs to realise that a commitment to keeping the service going is a very, very large commitment indeed, financially and otherwise. But I look forward to the new day centre, it will provide a service and also as well as giving respite care to the patients it will give respite to the families

Edward Daly:
'… a commitment to keeping the service going is a very, very large commitment indeed.'

who are caring for the patients, to the carers as well. And that's very important.

Likewise, Mary Butterwick, founder of a hospice service in the North-East of England, makes a similar point, but ties in the hospice's achievement's to her own personal horizons:

Well, we're having here I hope a time of consolidation at the moment where we're looking at everything and basically trying to grasp hold of every area of the care that we give and saying, 'Are we doing this absolutely right, is this the very best that we can give?' And so we're consolidating, taking time to look at things and I think after all that we've come through to get here … you can't keep going on spreading without taking some time … Where it'll go from here I don't know in that sense, perhaps I won't be around to see it because I can't possibly have that many years left you know …[11]

Osmond Morris of Southern Area Hospice Services in Newry also highlights the role of fund-raising and the need for local support and involvement:

… the communities have been super and they have really taken the unit to their hearts and they have backed that up with hard cash. It's a jungle out there, there's lots of other trendy charities and our funding follows the work that we do, so if we're in we do it, pull back and the funding will come, it comes from relatives, initiatives that they set up, support groups the whole network, but it takes time for that to happen. So really just to have some capital that you can actually set aside for development, for being able to implement your strategies rather than just waiting, putting it off for two or three years on occasions, so when the time's right it's important I think to plough on and go with it and we haven't actually been able to do that, so that would be nice in the future. The level of integration, the manpower issues are all being addressed so if they are addressed and addressed well and if the unit expands but still retains a character, I think our character's changed but it still has a character that marks it out as different and that the patients appreciate and their family appreciate, I think I'd be well happy if that was our future.

Eileen Kerr, a social worker in the Marie Curie Centre in Belfast, again focuses on a local development, but links this to a wider issue about the character of care provided:

Well, I mean I think it will go on developing more and more as a specialist kind of unit, and I'm not sure, I'm not sure what the future is. I would like to feel that we would be able to develop our day care, we've only one day and because of lack of resources we haven't been able to increase that. I would also like to think that we would be able to do more home care than we do, and I would like that to be, if we could do that as a multidisciplinary team. I'm not just talking about nursing, but that social work could have an input in that as well, and other disciplines. That's what I would like to see happening. I mean it's obviously all down to resource as to whether that can happen or not. I would hope that we wouldn't lose sight of the psychosocial care of patients and families, wouldn't become so medicalised that we would lose sight of that. It's difficult to know – I know there are a lot of us that would work very hard to retain that.

Personal dimensions

Barbara McNulty was one of the first to join Cicely Saunders at St Christopher's, working there from 1968 until 1978. Interviewed for this project in 1996 she reflects on her reasons for leaving. First is a concern about what being at St Christopher's might do to her:

This will sound silly: I was getting too good. I mean that, not in an inflated way at all, but I was afraid of becoming inflated. Cicely has managed to become very good without becoming inflated, that's her strength, I was afraid I wouldn't. To be quite in demand, to be at the centre of things, to be able to do things really well, to have confidence in your abilities and so forth, for me, was a frightening place to be. I thought I was getting too good, and I was afraid I was going to be built into something that I didn't want to be, a sort of 'lionised' position, and I didn't have the humility to cope with that. I knew I'd get 'lionised' in the worst possible way [laughter]. That was one of my fears. I think there was something desperate in me that needed to move on then. I was getting held into something, in a mould I was afraid of. I was not very happy [laughter].

The second reason centres on recognition of new interests and new challenges:

I had then begun to specialise in the counselling side, the family side, and I was very interested in that and wanted to do more of it. And I went and trained at the Westminster Pastoral Foundation in the Tavistock to broaden my understanding of that, and I wanted to do more of that.

One issue that some of our respondents raised is how to ease down from a busy clinical workload to new and less pressing work rhythms in retirement. Graham Thorpe retired in 1994 from full-time work as a consultant in palliative medicine at Countess Mountbatten House in Southampton. Afterwards he did some locum work, but declares that he would not become one of those within palliative care for whom retirement is almost indistinguishable from full-time work:

No, I'm not going to be one of those. It's interesting talking to colleagues, I mean they're in two groups: there are those like myself who've thought about retiring a bit before they're 65; there are other doctors, some of who I know in Southampton, who have desperately carried on until they were 65 and then they've had to retire, and then they've continued with a bit of private work or whatever. They just haven't been able to get off the hook, really, and it's been so much their life up to that time that they haven't been able to unhook themselves, and only go when they have to and so on. I haven't had that problem. I did feel it was important to, if you're going to get out, to get out and get away from things. And I probably won't do any locum work after I'm 65. So I mean it's like life, isn't it; it comes to an end. I think there is a moment when you can relinquish it.

I'm not really a pioneer, I don't think, in that sense. But they have to have this energy and to drive themselves on, and then they're an embarrassment, almost, because they go on too long … and by doing that they hamper and prevent the full development of the next group coming along to take over. I'm conscious of that. I hope I'm not, I hope I haven't done that. But the people coming after you are just as good as you and you must trust them, and they're going to get on with it anyway, you're going to go sometime. You need to get the pioneers out of the way a bit, I think. The next phase is not pioneering, it's sort of consolidating and thinking through some of the issues, and a bit more, once, you don't have to … (in the sort of adolescent phase you have to keep shouting about yourself), but now you're trying to plan in a strategy and work it all out what's appropriate for the future development, at a difficult time too, difficult time. So I'm, I'm winding it up really, and I haven't, I haven't found that transition difficult. People said to me, 'Oh, you'll find the work terribly stressful when you go to Southampton.' And within a few weeks people said, 'Oh, you're looking very well, yes you're very relaxed.' And now they say that about my retirement, which is nice [laughter].

John Berkeley was approaching the age of 70 at the time of his interview in June 1997; still active in public health work abroad and drawing on his long experience in clinical practice, he continues to have an interest in the local hospice:

I'm not interested in getting on to committees and sitting round tables and thrashing out things, I prefer to be actually implementing and doing things. Again, you might say; well, I'm on the Board of Highland Hospice, but it is only because I see there's something at this present time that really has got to be worked through. I perhaps have some of the background and knowledge that's useful to the Board in actually dealing with that.

The physician Sheila Cassidy, in reflecting on her own personal development at the end of an interview in December 1997, also draws out a number of wider points about hospice development:

… this is the phenomenon of feeding back the ethos of palliative care … into the acute system, and back … earlier in the cancer journey, if you like. And I have a vision of hospice as a prophetic movement, in the religious sense that prophets are drawn from the main body of the people to conduct their ministry and live their lives on the periphery, and then to take what they've learned and feed it back into the community. And that's what I reckon I'm doing now. And I see that as a very important thing. One of the things I've done is to set up psycho-educational groups for cancer patients. Two groups with young women with breast cancer, and that is the psychological intervention which has been shown to be, not only most effective, but also the most cost effective, and that for me is a very exciting thing to be doing; working with women in their late 20s/early 30s, with little kids, with breast cancer. And that's called Fighting Spirit. And that's been a lovely thing. It's been really, really hard working with the psychosocial team … I'm now coming to another sea change: I've just hit 60 and I'm doing psychotherapy training. So with the time when a lot of people are retiring, I'm actually beginning a whole new career … I'm still paid one session a week to lecture at the hospice. I still do a lot of lecturing there. I'm part of a pilot group, which is part of a Trust initiative to teach 'breaking bad news' to all the doctors and half the nurses in the hospital. I'm part of that. And I feel enormously optimistic. I'm very, very glad to be out of the hospice movement ... in a sense. I'm really excited to be doing something new. I value enormously the expertise and care of hospices, the hospice doctors. I think that hospices can be, I think by very definition, they can be quite dangerous places in a sense, and ... I think the structure of charitable governors is a sick structure, and I think it gives them far too much power over the health care professionals ... So I see the hospice movement as being ... technically very expert, but managerially ... very ... very wounded. And I think that if it's going to go on, I think it needs to get the balance right between ... becoming a ghetto, and linking with the hospital.

For Marjory Cockburn, who had been Matron at St Luke's in Sheffield, it's possible to look back with great satisfaction on her work there:

So as I look back over the years, they were very, very happy years ... and the constant question is always about depression [i.e. about the nature of the work], to which I reply, 'If you're doing something that is totally absorbing, totally challenging, working with a wonderful team of people, where you have a really great atmosphere ... you don't get depressed.' And always you can say, 'If we hadn't been there, how would it have been for that particular patient? Where would they be? Particularly within the quality, symptom control?' And that's not patting ourselves on the back and saying how marvellous we are. It's being realistic, being able to take up a whole family and work with them in a really, probably, tragic time, and yet being able to achieve a situation where they come out on top and turn round and say to you, 'I didn't know it would ever be so good.' And that's how I see it.

For Frances Sheldon, as her own illness advanced, so she feels her work in palliative care should diminish. Speaking just eight months before her death, she observes:

I'm still working one day a week but I'm not working in a palliative care role [at the university] at the moment, I'm still until the end of this academic year the Director of the postgraduate research programme, so I'm really involved mainly with research students, some of which are my own research students ... working on palliative care issues ... but I suppose, yes, I've withdrawn from, you know, teaching and research as I myself have become more of a patient and less of a professional ... I suppose my concentration has been increasingly to pull out of the palliative care as, you know, as I come more into that arena myself, because I don't think you're safe either for yourself or for others really if you aren't clear about ... where you're at in that.

As the work of hospice and palliative care expands in so many places, there is a growing interest in understanding more about how this field of activity first began to develop in its modern form. This book is one contribution to that endeavour. The history of modern palliative care is a short one, and many of those who have shaped it are still alive to tell their stories and to reflect on their experience. We have been privileged to listen to many of them. Learning from that history is a crucial way in which an increasingly specialised field can better understand its current dilemmas and also develop effective strategies for the future.

In the second half of the twentieth century major innovations began to take place, building on and developing some of the ideas which prevailed in the original religious and philanthropic homes of the nineteenth century. A modern 'movement' was emerging: reformist in character, advocating new approaches to old experiences, and above all opening up a space in which 'the process of dying' could be thought about in new ways – shaped and moulded by

Cicely Saunders: at home with the cat.

modern consciousness. Hospice care came to be defined in unprecedented terms: emphasising community participation, voluntary giving, quality of life in the face of mortal illness, pain and symptom management, psychosocial and spiritual care. Palliative medicine gained recognition as a specialty and advanced programmes of training developed, not only for physicians, but also for nurses, social workers and others involved in what came to be seen as the multidisciplinary activity of modern palliative care. During the last quarter of the twentieth century, and particularly in the 1990s, there was a steady growth in the number of services operating in this way, across most parts of the UK – but increasingly, also across countries and continents. By the start of the twenty-first century, hospice and palliative care had reached a stage of relative maturation, gaining a measure of recognition on the part of the public, the professions and the policy makers. Yet there was also a sense of much still to be done.

Among all these diverse voices that have characterised our oral history of the hospice movement in the UK, it seems most appropriate to end our book where we began – with the person of Cicely Saunders. Few would deny that it has been she, as much as any person, who has helped to shape and define the particular characteristics of hospice and palliative care development, not only in her own country, but also much further afield. Reflecting back over 40 years in May 2003, just before her eighty-fifth birthday, she observes:

Well I think I owe very much to Antoni, because he gave me the authenticity of having really been there, been really close to somebody who was dying, and being very close within bereavement, made me realise the potential that there is in that area and … the power of powerlessness is something that you can go on learning about endlessly, and so that you move from purely clinical into philosophical and theological insights, and there's no end to discovery

there. So whereas I don't see patients now, I do meet up with staff and I see something of their resources and how they are, have the reward of seeing patients really comfortable. A nurse was saying to me the other day, 'There's something in seeing somebody with their pillows absolutely right that is really rewarding.' And somebody who is frustrated and anxious can be made so different by just being made physically really comfortable. And so I think the implications of going on doing it, as far as I'm concerned, is the discovery, as far as other doctors coming into it now, I'm sure it's terribly important they have something going for them outside, and I think that what is so interesting is that 70 per cent of the doctors coming into the field are young women, most of them getting married, getting their consultant jobs, and immediately starting their families and wanting to do job-share. And I think that's a very good way of doing it. But they've got the discovery of a much more sophisticated medical side now, and then there's always looking at other diseases and other countries, there's the excitement of people coming to you from Africa, or Serbia, or wherever, who are just starting out or are discovering what they can do and what we learn from them about what they do with limited resources: I think that's a most exciting part of it. So there's endless interest.

Notes

1. Tim Lovel was speaking in September 2000.
2. The 'Calman-Hine' report was produced by Kenneth Calman, Deirdre Hine and members of the Expert Advisory Group on Cancer, first in a consultative document, and then in its final form in 1995. The report was in part a response to what had come to be seen as the 'cancer lottery' – disparate outcomes of cancer treatment and care across the country and significant differences in survival rates between the UK and its European neighbours. A major restructuring of cancer services resulted and the report was seized upon by the palliative care community as an opportunity for development. Nevertheless, one of our interviewees has

subsequently pointed out that just as the report appeared, many palliative care units were beginning to be staffed in a way that might enable them to widen their diagnostic base. Yet the report produced pressure for palliative care staff to take up honorary positions in NHS cancer centres – and in so doing may have held back by several years the spread of specialist palliative care to conditions other than cancer. See Expert Advisory Group on Cancer, *A Policy Framework for Commissioning Cancer Services: A report by the Expert Advisory Group on Cancer to the Chief Medical Officers of England and Wales* (London: Department of Health and Welsh Office, 1995).

3. Julia Franklin was speaking in July 1996.
4. As we saw in the Introduction (note 15), the report was actually published in 1980.
5. The interviewer was David Clark.
6. Marjory Cockburn, the Matron at the time, and quoted elsewhere in this volume.
7. From 1980, head of the World Health Organisation cancer – and later palliative care – programme; see Chapter 6 above.
8. The *British National Formulary*, a handbook of pharmaceuticals, their doses and uses.
9. See J. Addington Hall and I. Higginson (eds.), *Palliative Care for Non-Cancer Patients* (Oxford: Oxford University Press, 2001).
10. Betty Irwin is actually referring to Sister Frances Dominica, founder of Helen House, and quoted elsewhere in this volume.
11. Mary Butterwick was in her late 70s at the time of the interview, which took place in November 2000.

Appendix 1
Dramatis personae

Notes

Professor Sam Hjelmeland Ahmedzai b. 1950

After studying physiology and medicine at the University of St Andrews and the University of Manchester, Dr Ahmedzai trained in oncology under Sir Kenneth Calman at Glasgow. He then underwent specialist training in pulmonary (chest) medicine. In 1985, he was appointed Medical Director of the Leicestershire Hospice and in 1994 he was appointed as the first holder of the Chair in Palliative Medicine at the University of Sheffield, and as Director of Trent Palliative Care Centre.

Interview by Marcia Meldrum, 1 December 1999

Sister Mary Antonia 1915–2001

After joining the Sisters of Charity, Sister Mary Antonia trained as a nurse and in 1947 she was sent to London to work in St Joseph's Hospice in Hackney. After CICELY SAUNDERS arrived at the hospice in 1957, Sister Mary Antonia was involved in the development of a new approach to pain and symptom control and to the inclusion of the family as part of the unit of care. In the early 1970s Sister Mary Antonia worked closely with DR RICHARD LAMERTON in the development of home care.

Interview by David Clark, 28 November 1995

Liz Atkinson b. 1958

After qualifying Liz Atkinson worked as a staff nurse in the haematology ward of the Royal Victoria Hospital, Belfast for two years. She subsequently moved to the Royal Marsden Hospital, London, and while there had the opportunity to work in their continuing care ward and to visit St Christopher's Hospice. Liz Atkinson returned to Belfast, trained as a district nurse and worked for two years in the community. She was also involved in fund-raising for a new hospice for the city and when the Northern Ireland Hospice opened she worked as a ward sister in the in-patient unit. After three years the community team was extended and she was appointed to the post of Assistant Nursing Director to manage the service, becoming Nursing Director 10 years later in 1998.

Interview by Clare Humphreys, 31 July 2000

Dr Mary Baines b.1932

Mary Baines studied medicine at Cambridge University and undertook clinical training at St Thomas's Hospital where her contemporaries included CICELY SAUNDERS, TOM WEST and GILLIAN FORD. After qualification she worked part-time in general practice for 10 years. In 1969 Cicely Saunders asked her, together with BARBARA McNULTY, to found the first hospice home care service. Dr Baines has researched the medical management of malignant intestinal obstruction and was also closely involved in the training of registrars, many of whom have gone on to be leaders in the field. She has lectured widely in the UK and overseas, and has been able to organise further education in palliative care in the UK for many doctors and nurses from abroad. She has written extensively, including chapters in three Oxford Textbooks of Medicine.   *Interview by Neil Small, 10 July 1996*

Dr Thelma Bates b.1929

Thelma Bates studied medicine in Birmingham and qualified as a doctor in 1952. Starting out as a Ship's Surgeon, she travelled to New Zealand and Australia where she worked as a GP, before going on to study radiotherapy and oncology in Tasmania. On returning to Britain, she worked at St Thomas's Hospital, becoming a consultant in 1968. Aware of the needs of the dying through her chosen specialism, Dr Bates took regular clinical rounds at St Christopher's. Using the model of the Hospital Support Team developed at St Luke's Hospital in New York, she set up a similar unit in St Thomas's which began operation in 1977. The St Thomas's team also developed an academic function and, with money from the Lisa Sainsbury Foundation, the UK's first Professor of Palliative Medicine, Dr Geoffrey Hanks, was appointed. Dr Bates became a trustee of Trinity Hospice in 1978, a founding Trustee of the Princess Alice Hospice, Esher in 1981, and has been Chair of the International Work Group on Death, Dying and Bereavement.   *Interview by Neil Small, 19 May 1997*

Rita Beattie b. 1943

Rita Beattie trained as a nurse at the Royal Victoria Hospital in her home town of Belfast. She then completed midwifery and psychiatric training in Edinburgh before going to London where she undertook her district nurse training. She returned to Northern Ireland in 1980, working as a Community Psychiatric Nurse and became Nursing Director at the then newly established Northern Ireland Hospice in 1984.

Interview by David Clark, 17 November 1998

Ros Beetham

After working as a medical secretary and then helping her husband run first his dental and then medical practice, Ros Beetham became Volunteer Coordinator at St Luke's Hospice, Sheffield where she was responsible for the selection, training, coordination and support of volunteers. In 1990 she became the Chair of the National Association of Hospice Volunteer Coordinators, and has also held the posts of President and Conference Organiser for this organisation.

Interview by Neil Small, 19 December 1996

Dr John Berkeley b. 1927

John Berkeley qualified in medicine in Edinburgh in 1949. After house jobs and a short period in the Royal Air Force, he joined a general practice in Fort William where he worked from 1953 to 1966. Between 1966 and 1977 Dr Berkeley and his wife, also a doctor, spent periods of time in Bhutan with the Leprosy Mission, and here gained an interest in the planning and administration of health services. Dr Berkeley gained a Diploma in Social Medicine in 1971, and in 1972 was appointed Senior Lecturer in General Practice at Aberdeen University. In 1977, now a consultant in community medicine, he was involved in discussions about the use of GPs at the newly opened Roxburghe House, a hospice unit attached to Tor Na Dee Hospital, Aberdeen. This involvement developed into a clinical role as he became Medical Director at Roxburghe House, a post he held from 1981 to 1992, combining the position with his consultant post in community medicine and public health. Dr Berkeley has been involved in medical education, in needs assessment and in quality of life research and was the Vice-Chairman of the Scottish Partnership Agency for Palliative and Cancer Care between 1991 and 1993.

Interview by David Clark, 18 June 1997

Sister Serephine Bermingham b. 1923

Sister Seraphine joined the Sisters of the Cross and Passion in the early 1940s. After studying for an arts degree at Manchester University she taught in a Dublin school and undertook a university diploma in education. After 10 years in Dublin she returned to England where she taught in a grammar school near Huddersfield from 1958 and in 1970 she was asked to go to Bolton to be a head teacher. Three years later she was elected to be Provincial of the Sisters of the Cross and Passion and, as Provincial, Sister Seraphine was involved in the decision to set up a hospice in Leeds. She has also been involved in the Sisters' work in Sarajevo which involved setting up a palliative care centre, from which a home care team of doctors and nurses works in the community.   *Interview by Clare Humphreys, 11 July 2000*

Mary Box b. 1926

Mary Box studied pharmacy, qualifying in 1952, and moved to London where, from 1954, she worked in community pharmacy. From her base in Sydenham, South London she became St Christopher's Community Pharmacist which involved working closely with the home care service, and regularly visiting the hospice.

Interview by Sylvia Paz, 3 August 2002

Carolyn Brodribb b. 1948

Carolyn Brodribb trained as a social worker and subsequently worked at St Bartholomew's Hospital in London. After moving to Plymouth in 1978 she attended the inaugural meeting of a group wishing to establish a hospice. When that hospice, St Luke's, opened in 1982 she became its Principal Social Worker and while in that post she taught social work students from Exeter and Plymouth Universities. In 1993 she gained an MA in Policy and Organisational Studies, focusing her thesis specifically on independent hospices, and was then appointed Macmillan Social Work Lecturer in Palliative Care at the University of Plymouth. Carolyn Brodribb has also been Chair of the Association of Hospice Social Workers.

Interview by Neil Small, 2 December 1997

Mary Butterwick b. 1924

Mary Butterwick became a secretary after leaving school. She joined the Land Army as soon as she was able after the outbreak of the Second World War, then spent most of the war years as an ambulance driver for the Royal Army Services Corps. By the time her children married Mary was working for Tetley's Tea as a machinist instructor. After her husband John Butterwick died after a very short illness in 1979, Mary Butterwick began to do voluntary work for Stockton Voluntary Services. She did this for seven years, then becoming a Cruse bereavement counsellor and also at this time living out her religious beliefs by assisting the hospital chaplain. Mary then turned her attention specifically towards providing help for people with terminal illness, forming the John Butterwick Trust and opening her home as a day care centre for people with terminal illness in 1984. Three years later, after continuous fund-raising, a larger house was acquired which would eventually become a six-bedded in-patient hospice with day care. After another 10 years the present Butterwick Hospice was opened in Stockton-on-Tees. Mary Butterwick has also worked as a bereavement counsellor in the community and as Assistant Chaplain in Butterwick Hospice.   *Interview by Nic Hughes, 22 November 2000*

Sally Campalani b. 1957

Sally Campalani trained as a nurse in Belfast in the 1970s. After working in orthopaedics at the Princess Grace Hospital she was appointed to the post of Director of Nursing at a small hospital performing open-heart surgery. Sally Campalani has held senior posts in cardiac care in India and in Italy, and secured a two-year grant from the European Resuscitation Council to study problems associated with cardiac arrest. After holding a post in Milan as a Director of Nursing she returned to Northern Ireland where she worked, from 1997, as Clinical Services Manager at the Marie Curie Centre, Belfast.   *Interview by Clare Humphreys, 7 August 2000*

Major General Sir Michael Carleton-Smith b. 1931

After school at Radley, Michael Carleton-Smith was commissioned into the Rifle Brigade. He retired in 1985 with the rank of 'Major General' after a military career that had taken him all over the world. Following his retirement he was approached by Marie Curie to become their Director General and presided over the charity's expansion and its participation in the growing national scene of palliative care. Knighted for services to cancer care in 1997, Michael Carleton-Smith subsequently became Chairman of the Leicester Royal Infirmary NHS Trust.
         Interview by Neil Small, 26 September 1995

Margaret Carradice b. 1942

After qualifying as a nurse Margaret Carradice spent two years working in Sheffield's first renal unit at the Royal Hospital. She joined the team at St Luke's Hospice, Sheffield working first as a ward sister then as Assistant Matron and finally as Matron. She was centrally involved with St Luke's development within the city and contributed to national and international developments in hospice care.
         Interview by David Clark, 3 February 1997

Sister Cecily Mary Case b. 1921

Sister Cecily followed a career as a teacher and joined the Sisters of the Cross and Passion in 1956 when she was 35 years of age. She then took up the post of Superior at the convent attached to Trinity and All Saints Training College. Whilst there she served as a councillor to the Provincial Superior and was heavily involved in the decision to set up St Gemma's Hospice, Leeds, and in the 1980s she became a member of the Hospice Board. After 13 years teaching in Bradford, she retired and was sent to be Superior of the Convent in Bolton. Five years later in 1993, she came to St Gemma's where she worked as a volunteer fund-raiser.
         Interview by Clare Humphreys, 11 July 2000

Dr Sheila Cassidy b. 1937

After school in Australia and then medical training at the University of Sydney, Sheila Cassidy completed her studies at Oxford. There then followed a variety of junior jobs in accident and emergency departments, and plastic surgery. Dr Cassidy went on to practice medicine in South America where in 1975 she was held prisoner and tortured for treating a political suspect in Pinochet's Chile. After periods of religious retreat in both a monastery and a convent, she resumed her career in medicine in 1980 in the radiotherapy department of Freedom Fields Hospital in Plymouth. Two years later, she was appointed Medical Director of the new St Luke's Hospice in Plymouth, a position which she held for 15 years. Dr Cassidy then went on to set up a palliative care service for Plymouth hospitals as part of the Oncology Directorate, and has developed an interest in psycho-oncology and in bereaved children. She has written and lectured widely about her life and work.

Interview by Neil Small, 3 December 1997

Prue Clench (Dufour) 1942–2004

Prue Clench trained as a nurse at the Middlesex Hospital. After taking a break to raise two children, she returned to nursing and worked on radiotherapy Ward 9 at the Royal United Hospital in Bath. In 1975 she undertook a month's training at St Christopher's, and sought to bring this experience back to Ward 9. In addition she developed a vision for hospice care in the community and formed a steering committee in 1976 to develop this idea. In 1977 she became Chairman/nurse of Dorothy House Foundation, which subsequently opened a six-bed unit in 1979, and by 1982 she had become a freelance, full-time, national adviser for the hospice movement. She worked closely with the National Society for Cancer Relief, in the areas of hospice management and Macmillan Nursing, both in the community and in hospital support teams. In the early 1990s Prue Clench spent three years as Director of Thames Valley Hospice. She had a long standing involvement with St Columba's Fellowship, an organisation that promotes Christian perspectives on hospice care, and towards the end of her life was ordained into the Church of England and served as a parish priest.

Interview by David Clark, 9 December 1996

Marjory Cockburn b. 1927

Marjory Cockburn undertook a variety of nurse training: orthopaedic nursing at Nuffield Orthopaedic Centre, Oxford; general nursing at King's College Hospital, London; midwifery at Nuffield Maternity Centre, Oxford; and finally health visiting in Oxford. After several years working in this country she spent 12 years, from 1961, in Nigeria with the Church Missionary Society. While in Nigeria she first heard of the ideas being developed in the UK about a new sort of hospice care from DR TOM WEST. After returning to the UK she began as administrative sister at St Luke's Hospice, Sheffield in 1974, rising to Assistant Matron, and then Matron after the departure of Eileen Mann in 1976.

Interview by David Clark, 17 January 1997

Ann Cooney b. 1953

Ann Cooney began her involvement with hospice care – working in finance and administration – at the St John of God Hospital in Newry. Subsequently she was involved with Newry Hospice from its inception and then with Southern Area Hospice Services, Newry.

Interview by Clare Humphreys, 14 August 2000

Dr Tony Crowther b. 1935

Tony Crowther studied medicine at Queen's College, Cambridge. His clinical training between 1958 and 1961 and his first house jobs were at the Middlesex Hospital. Post-qualification he took an obstetric post in Blackburn, and, in 1963, went into general practice in Sheffield. Dr Crowther and ERIC WILKES provided medical cover at St Luke's Hospice, Sheffield for some years and, as Eric Wilkes's national role flourished, Dr Crowther increased his involvement, taking on the medical directorship in 1986.

Interview by David Clark, 3 December 1996

Bishop Edward Daly b. 1933

From 1962, Edward Daly worked as a Catholic priest and subsequently as Bishop in Derry. He was invited by DR TOM MCGINLEY to attend the first public meeting regarding the establishment of what became Foyle Hospice in Derry and was subsequently involved in its development. After retiring as Bishop in 1993 he became Chaplain to Foyle Hospice.

Interview by Clare Humphreys, 9 August 2000

Gloria Day b. 1939

Gloria Day qualified as a State Registered Nurse in 1961 and began her nursing career as a staff nurse on a medical ward at the Royal Hospital, Sheffield. Shortly afterwards she married, had her first child and left her job to care for her family. On returning to nursing she took a post at a school for children with spina bifida, and then worked as a district nurse. She undertook a six-month secondment to St Luke's Hospice, Sheffield afterwards returning to district nursing where she was frequently called on by nurses and GPs to assist with dying patients. When ERIC WILKES secured funding from Macmillan for nursing services, Gloria Day was asked to return to hospice work and enthusiastically accepted. With Shelagh Bellamy, she became involved in developing the Macmillan service in Sheffield in the mid-1970s. Post-retirement she worked as a volunteer at St Luke's.

Interview by Michelle Winslow, 9 October 2001

Sister Frances Dominica b. 1942

Sister Frances Dominica is the founder of the first children's hospice, Helen House in Oxford. She initially trained as a paediatric nurse, working at Great Ormond Street Hospital for Children, London. In 1966, at the age of 21, she joined the Holy Community of All Saints and was elected as the youngest ever Mother Superior in 1977. As well as her continuing role at Helen House, Sister Frances is involved with Douglas House – the first specialty hospice for patients between the ages of 16 and 40.

Interview by Kirsten Lund, 3 April 2002

Dr Derek Doyle

Derek Doyle studied medicine at university and after various junior house jobs he was sent to South Africa by the Scottish Mission where he specialised in general and chest medicine. After 10 years in South Africa he returned to the UK in 1966 and settled in Edinburgh. Dr Doyle then turned to general practice and combined this with a part-time consultant post at Corstorphine and Beechmount Hospital. In 1968, the hospital Matron, Miss Ann Weatherill, encouraged him to help form a founding committee to plan a hospice for Edinburgh. St Columba's Hospice finally opened in 1977, and he became Medical Director where he not only developed clinical services but also research and education. He was involved with the journal, *Palliative Medicine*; The Association for Palliative Medicine; the establishment of the specialty of palliative medicine in 1987; and as an editor with the publication of the *Oxford Textbook of Palliative Medicine*, the first edition of which was published in 1993. He has also been centrally involved with the European Association for Palliative Care, the National Council for Hospice and Specialist Palliative Care Services and the Scottish Partnership Agency for Palliative and Cancer Care.

Interviews by David Clark, 28 December 1995
and 13 February 1996

Elisabeth Earnshaw-Smith b. 1929

Elisabeth Earnshaw-Smith's early career was in teaching. However, in her mid-30s, she decided to study social science at Edinburgh University and she was employed subsequently as a social worker at the Royal Infirmary, Edinburgh. Moving to London she worked for Kensington Social Services at St Charles Hospital where for 10 years she did family work in a children's unit and became Principal Social Worker. In January 1980 she took up a newly created social work post at St Christopher's. She founded, and chaired until the late 1980s, the Association of Hospice Social Workers.

Interview by Neil Small, 30 January 1996

John Easun b. 1952

John Easun held the post of Acting Administrator at Pilgrims Hospice, Ashford, Kent. Prior to its opening, he was Appeal Administrator and assisted in raising the £3.5 million needed to realise this third hospice in the region. His role as Acting Administrator involved responsibility for building maintenance, financial management, purchasing of non-medical supplies, and overseeing non-nursing/medical staff, including administrative and kitchen personnel, and volunteers.

Interview by Michelle Winslow, 13 December 2002

Lyn Forbes b. 1948

Lyn Forbes' career spans a variety of administrative, management and small business positions within different organisations including National Opinion Polls, Derby Aviation, British Midland Airways and the Young Farmers' Association, as well as a spell running a tea room/shop/post office as a family business. After moving to the Highlands she became involved with a group planning a hospice to cover the needs of the Highlands' scattered population. Lyn Forbes was employed as Administrative Manager in 1986 to help with fund-raising and planning services and became General Manager in 1991. On leaving the hospice she worked as an independent consultant on hospice management.

Interview by David Clark, 14 February 1996

Dr Gillian Ford b. 1934

Gillian Ford went to Oxford to study medicine, and to St Thomas's Hospital for clinical training, qualifying in 1959. After house jobs in ophthalmology, her early career involved her in the Oxford/Reading ophthalmology circuit. In 1965 she was appointed as a medical officer at the Ministry of Health, later DHSS, where she became Deputy Chief Medical Officer in 1977. During the late 1950s and early 1960s her flatmate in London was CICELY SAUNDERS. Dr Ford was able to help promote hospice care within the Department, working in the early days with Dame Albertine Winner. From 1968 she worked at St Christopher's as a weekend volunteer and was seconded there as Director of Studies between 1985 and 1988. She retired from Marie Curie Cancer Care from which post she retired in May 1997.

Interview by David Clark, 6 June 1996

Julia Franklin b. 1936

After working as a medical records clerk at the Hammersmith Hospital, Julia Franklin studied for a diploma in sociology, worked as an assistant social worker at Northwick Park Hospital in Harrow and, between 1977 and 1979, did social work training at Buckinghamshire College of Higher Education. Between 1982 and 1989 Julia Franklin set up the Bloomsbury Support Team, a new social work service for the terminally ill backed by University College Hospital and Camden Social Services. Between 1986 and 1990 she spearheaded a campaign to enable terminally ill people to be able to apply for state financial support via Attendance Allowance or Disability Living Allowance. From 1989 she was employed by St Barnabas Hospice in Worthing, where she set up its social work department. She chaired the Association of Hospice Social Workers from 1990 to 1993. In 1991 Julia Franklin obtained a postgraduate diploma in counselling from Brighton University, reflecting an increasing interest in family therapy, drama therapy and a concern with issues related to children and grief.

Interview by Neil Small, 9 July 1996

Janet Gahegan b. 1939

Janet Gahegan qualified as a State Registered Nurse in 1960 and began her nursing career as a staff nurse on a medical ward at the Royal Hospital, Sheffield. On returning to nursing after a break to start a family she took a part-time post in an intensive care unit. In 1970 she transferred to community work and worked as a district nurse for 11 years. She found the terminal care part of this job very satisfying and, after a short interlude training and practising as a midwife, applied for and gained a post as Macmillan nurse at the Northern General Hospital in Sheffield in 1984. Janet Gahegan retired in 1999.   *Interview by Nic Hughes, 19 March 2001*

Dr Maddy Gerrish

Maddy Gerrish studied nursing at the University of Maine. Her first job was in Boston where she was involved with the developing mental health movement in the city in the early 1960s, and was one of the founders of the Boston Family Institute. After a Masters in Psychiatric Nursing she worked at Tufts Medical School as the Director of Family Care in the

oncology department. ERIC WILKES was impressed by her family systems approach and, unable to find this expertise in Britain, invited Maddy Gerrish to St Luke's Hospice, Sheffield in 1970/71, and again in 1973. Here she advised on some of the early management and staffing problems in the new hospice. Back in the USA, she gained a PhD in Psychology in 1988 and worked as a Geriatric Mental Health Consultant.

Interview by Neil Small, 31 May 1996

Patricia Gilbert b. 1947

After training as a nurse, Patricia Gilbert spent some years working as a staff nurse on a surgical ward. In 1978 she became part-time staff nurse working on night duty at St Gemma's Hospice, Leeds, After nine-and-a-half years holding this post she moved to the St Gemma's Home Care Team.

Interview by Clare Humphreys, 12 July 2000

Dr Ann Gilmore 1934–1998

Spending most of her life in Glasgow, Ann Gilmore first graduated in music and then took medicine as a second degree. Her early interests were in psychiatry and geriatrics, working for Ferguson Anderson on a three-year study of elderly people living in their own homes, for which she received her MD in 1976. At the end of the 1970s, Dr Gilmore was the first Medical Director appointed by Marie Curie, at their Hunter's Hill 'Home' in Glasgow, and then moved into general practice. However, her knowledge and skills were welcomed by a group of clergy in the early 1980s seeking to establish a hospice in the Glasgow area. Dr Gilmore became the first Medical Director of the Prince and Princess of Wales Hospice when it opened in Glasgow in 1986. Subsequently she developed an interest in psychoanalysis and group therapy.

Interview by David Clark, 10 December 1996

Dr Ann Goldman b. 1949

Following her undergraduate degree in medicine Ann Goldman spent the late 1970s working in Boston, USA. She developed an expertise in the field of paediatric oncology, an area that she turned her attentions further towards, from both a research and clinical perspective, when she returned to London. Dr Goldman's move to Great Ormond Street Hospital for Children saw her interest in psychological perspectives of terminal illness develop. Her work led to the establishment of a palliative symptom care team in 1986 as part of the hospital's oncology unit and its success resulted in Dr Goldman becoming recognised as the first British paediatrician dedicated solely to the field of paediatric palliative care. She was involved with the Royal College of Paediatrics and Child Health and other national committees in the growth of paediatric palliative care and with the development of a new organisation – the Association of Children with Terminal Illnesses (ACT).   *Interview by Kirsten Lund, 2 April 2002*

Dr Peter Griffiths b. 1932

Peter Griffiths studied medicine at King's College Hospital (1950–56). After three years in the Royal Air Force, he returned to Swansea where he worked in obstetrics/paediatrics at Morriston Hospital. He then went on to join a general practice, developing an interest in pain and symptom control in dying patients, and from 1978 he spent three years working at St Christopher's. Back in Swansea he helped set up an appeal committee and, by 1981, with monies from the Regional Health Authority, the National Society for Cancer Relief and local fund-raising, the hospice for Swansea, Ty Olwen, was ready to open. Dr Griffiths was appointed Medical Director in April of that year and the first patients were admitted in October. Nationally, Dr Griffiths was one of the founders of Help the Hospices.   *Interview by Neil Small, 11 June 1996*

Sheila Hanna

Although trained as an architect, after marriage and children Sheila Hanna worked as a volunteer family visitor for the Inner London Education Authority. She was invited to visit St Christopher's before its opening by a neighbour, COLIN MURRAY PARKES, and was subsequently asked to become the Volunteer Coordinator, where she was involved in the recruitment, interviewing, support and education of volunteer hospice workers. This role led to considerable involvement with the local community but also led to links with other hospices including the New Haven Hospice, Connecticut, USA, where Sheila Hanna visited in 1977/78.   *Interview by Neil Small, 17 January 1996*

Colin Hardman

Colin Hardman studied pharmacy from 1969 at Portsmouth Polytechnic and subsequently worked as a trainee pharmacist at Withington Hospital in Manchester, his home town. His involvement with cancer care started in 1975 when he was appointed to the post of Pharmacist in Charge at the Christie Hospital, Manchester, a regional and international cancer treatment centre. In 1977, the first Medical Director of St Barnabas Hospice in Lincoln invited Colin Hardman to join him on hospice ward rounds which constituted his first real exposure to palliative care. As well as his continuing participation in Lincoln he has been involved on the Palliative Care Committee for the Mid-Trent Cancer Centre; in the Royal Pharmaceutical Society of Great Britain (the local branches of which provide postgraduate education to pharmacist members); and he has had a research involvement with the Academic Palliative Medicine Unit, University of Sheffield.   *Interview by Silvia Paz, 23 May 2002*

Dr Richard Hillier b. 1940

Richard Hillier's early medical career was spent at St Bartholomew's Hospital London, where he trained from 1958 to 1964. In 1966 he went to Antarctica for a year, where he researched his MD as part of the British Antarctic Survey. Dr Hillier then moved into general practice and sought further training in care of the dying at St Christopher's in 1972/73, as well as visiting a number of other hospices. In 1977 he became Medical Director of the NHS unit in Southampton, Countess Mountbatten House, where he continued to work until 2003.   *Interview by David Clark, 18 December 1996*

Professor John Hinton b. 1926

John Hinton undertook his medical training at King's College Hospital in London. He qualified in 1949 and after further medical training and some psychiatric experience, finally opted to study psychiatry at the Maudsley Hospital (1955–61). He then moved to join Dennis Hill's new Unit of Psychiatry at the Middlesex Hospital where, in 1966, he became only the ninth Professor of Psychiatry in the country. Although Professor Hinton's main career has been as an academic/hospital psychiatrist, an interest in the experiences of dying patients has constituted a strong research theme, contributing significantly to the world of hospice/palliative care.
Interview by David Clark, 25 April 1996

Julia Hitchens b. 1932

Julia Hitchens studied English literature and language, and then librarianship, at Glasgow University. After moving to Sheffield she attended a meeting for volunteers in 1971 led by Eileen Mann, Matron at St Luke's Hospice, Sheffield. After initially volunteering as an auxiliary nurse her skills as a librarian were eventually called upon in 1986, when she took up post as head of the hospice's own library.
Interview by Paul Lydon, 12 December 1996

Jo Hockley b. 1950

Jo Hockley's nursing career began in the 1970s when she trained at St Bartholomew's Hospital, London. After four years of general training she then qualified as a midwife and pursued this path for a further four years with plans for a career in midwifery. However, after visiting St Christopher's Hospice she changed direction and began working as a staff nurse at the hospice. Six months later she became a ward sister. In 1982 she returned to St Bartholomew's, taking up a research post that examined care of the dying on acute respiratory wards. She went on to establish a multidisciplinary palliative care team that, by 1991, included four nurses and a full-time doctor, social worker and secretary. She then left to complete a Masters degree at the University of Edinburgh, before moving to the Western General Hospital in Edinburgh, again to set up a palliative care team. From here Jo Hockley moved to St Columba's Hospice, Edinburgh to take up the post of Clinical Nurse Specialist and Research Fellow.   *Interview by Lorna Campbell, 19 September 2001*

Mary Holland b. 1958

After nurse training in the late 1970s in Manchester Mary Holland held posts on a medical ward, as a midwife and, after moving to London, as a sister on a renal ward at St Bartholomew's. There was a palliative care team in the hospital and she developed an interest in the specialty. She subsequently went to Addenbrooke's Hospital, Cambridge as a specialist pain nurse, and was also used as a resource for palliative care. She undertook further training, completing a BSc honours in palliative care, and on moving to the Lake District in 1995 she took up a post as a Macmillan nurse.

Interview by Sara Morris, 15 May 2001

John Hunt

After nurse training in 1978 John Hunt became the first male staff nurse to be appointed at St Christopher's Hospice. He left St Christopher's for acute oncological settings in Nottingham, Sheffield and Leicester. By the mid-1980s, John Hunt returned to palliative care and joined St Christopher's home care team as a clinical nurse specialist, a post he held for five years. He left St Christopher's for a second time to take on a managerial role developing a palliative care service in Derby, where he was appointed to the post of Senior Nurse Manager. After 10 years in this post he moved to Cumbria to establish a day care centre. His subsequent move to Sheffield was to work alongside PROFESSOR SAM AHMEDZAI in setting up a palliative care team at Weston Park Hospital, and developing the Trent Hospice Audit Group.

Interview by Sylvia Paz, 29 May 2002

Betty Irwin b. 1925

Betty Irwin was the first Administrative Director at the Northern Ireland Hospice, Belfast and held this post for four years until her retirement. For almost 30 years prior to this she had worked in the Northern Ireland Public Service Alliance.

Interview by Clare Humphreys, 2 August 2000

Eileen Kerr b. 1943

Eileen Kerr worked initially as a nursery school teacher and then became involved in a family centre in Belfast run by Bryson House. From there she gradually moved into social work and after qualifying she worked for another voluntary organisation before joining the North and West Belfast Authority to work with disturbed children and families. Eileen Kerr also worked with Barnados and piloted a new method of working with children and their parents in the worker's own home – the 'Care Givers Scheme'. This was followed a few years later by a move into hospital social work. During that time Eileen undertook training with Cruse in bereavement counselling and became a Cruse counsellor. In 1990 she was appointed to a social worker post at the Marie Curie Centre in Belfast

Interview by Clare Humphreys, 7 August 2000

Steve Kirk b. 1955

Steve Kirk has a long history in nursing and nurse management and much of his work has focused on neurology and oncology. His previous posts include Senior Nurse Business Manager of the Oncology and Breast Care Unit at Guy's Hospital, Senior Nurse of the Cancer Unit at Oxford and five years as Hospice Director of Harestone Marie Curie Centre in Surrey. After a short period in the Marie Curie Centre in Newcastle, followed by 18 months back in the NHS, he took up the newly created post of Chief Executive and Director of Nursing at St Gemma's Hospice, Leeds in the late 1990s.

Interview by Clare Humphreys, 30 August 2000

Peter Laidlaw b. 1934

Peter Laidlaw was educated at the Edinburgh Academy and carried out his National Service with the Royal Air Force in Singapore. A qualified combustion engineer, he worked in industry until 1982 when he responded to an advert for the position of Assistant Secretary to the Marie Curie Memorial Foundation, Scotland; Peter Laidlaw had a long-standing interest in charities. He worked as Assistant Secretary until 1985 when he became the Secretary of Marie Curie Cancer Care, Scotland, as it had then become.

Interview by Gerry King, 11 April 2000

Dr Richard Lamerton b. 1943

Richard Lamerton studied medicine at St Bartholomew's Hospital, London and then worked as a junior doctor at St Christopher's. He moved to a post as physician at St Joseph's Hospice in Hackney, where he and SISTER MARY ANTONIA developed the home care service. After working in general practice, Dr Lamerton undertook a grand lecture tour in the USA in 1983. Subsequently he has been Medical Director at St Michael's Hospice in Hereford, and then at the Hospice of the Marches, also in Hereford. He has played a role in hospice development in Germany, New Zealand, India, Trinidad and Japan. *Interview by Neil Small, 30 January 1997*

Professor Tim Lovel b. 1935

Tim Lovel went to the University of Oxford in 1945 intending to study law, but quickly changed to medicine. He held posts in endocrinology at Hammersmith and Whittington Hospitals during the early 1960s and in 1964 he became a partner in a general practice in Hampshire. His interest in caring for people with terminal illness began with the influence of a charismatic consultant obstetrician and gynaecologist, continued in his work as a GP and was cemented by attending a course at St Christopher's in the early 1970s. In 1985, stimulated by a lecture by ERIC WILKES, Dr Lovel began to explore the possibility of working exclusively in palliative medicine, and in 1988 took up a half-time post as a consultant in palliative medicine at St Benedict's Hospice in Sunderland. Additional part-time work followed as Medical Director at Butterwick

Hospice in Stockton, at the Hartlepool Hospice and at St Clare's Hospice in Jarrow. In 1995 Dr Lovel became Professor of Palliative Care at the University of Sunderland. He retired from clinical practice in 2000.

Interview by Nic Hughes, 27 September 2000

Rev. Leonard Lunn b. 1942

After an early career as a teacher, Len Lunn trained for the Anglican ministry at Trinity College, Bristol. He was ordained in 1972 and thereafter took up the post of curate in the parish of Walthamstow St Mary in the Diocese of Chelmsford. He remained in parochial ministry until 1987 when he became Chaplain of St Christopher's Hospice, London and stayed there for 16 years. While at St Christopher's he adapted his role from that of being the Chaplain to creating and then leading the chaplaincy team. He retired in 2004.

Interview by Michael Wright, 1 October 2003

Ivy McCreery

Ivy McCreery trained as a paediatric nurse. After some time working in the UK and abroad, both in Australia and America, she joined the Marie Curie Centre, Belfast as a volunteer in 1992. She subsequently took up a nursing position in a local nursing home and from there moved back to the Marie Curie Centre as a staff nurse.

Interview by Clare Humphreys, 3 August 2000

Ciaran McGinley b. 1964

Ciaran McGinley trained as a podiatrist but, being the son of DR TOM MCGINLEY, the founder of Foyle Hospice, Derry, he has been involved with the hospice movement most of his life. His first substantial input began in fund-raising for the

Hospice in the mid-1980s and he organised his first major fund-raising event in 1990 when he took part in the London Marathon with his father and two others. Ciaran McGinley was Project Coordinator for the establishment of a new day centre within Foyle Hospice.

Interview by Clare Humphreys, 10 August 2000

Dr Tom McGinley b. 1934

Although born in the USA Tom McGinley returned with his family to Ireland where he attended secondary school in Letterkenny and then went to university to study medicine. Dr McGinley moved to Derry around 1960, spent a few years at the hospital and then moved into general practice. He started visiting St Joseph's Hospice, Hackney, for a few weeks each year. He then decided that anaesthetics might be the way forward into providing pain relief so, at the same time as continuing in general practice, he worked towards obtaining a fellowship in anaesthetics. It had always been Dr McGinley's intention to start a hospice locally and this he began in 1983 when, with others, he worked to establish Foyle Hospice in Derry where he subsequently became Medical Director.

Interview by Clare Humphreys, 11 August 2000

Professor Malcolm McIllmurray b. 1945

Malcolm McIllmurray went to the London Hospital to study medicine in 1962. Through the course of his training and early career he developed interests in gastroenterology, colon cancer and immunology, and became a Senior Registrar and Lecturer in therapeutics in Nottingham. In 1978, he moved to a post in Lancaster as a consultant general physician with an interest in medical oncology. Dr McIllmurray became interested in palliative care through developing local cancer services in Lancaster, and helped establish a local hospice, St

John's, in 1985. He served as its Medical Director and also as Chairman of another local charity he helped form, Cancer Care. He also holds a chair at Lancaster University.

Interview by David Clark, 11 July 1997

Barbara McNulty

Barbara McNulty trained as a nurse at St Thomas's Hospital in London, and then became a district nurse in the Cotswolds in Gloucestershire. She joined the St Christopher's Planning Committee before the hospice was opened, and subsequently become a ward sister. When St Christopher's decided to develop home care in the early 1970s, Barbara McNulty, with her district nursing experience, was the obvious choice to set about liasing with GPs and district nurses. She was also involved in spreading hospice ideas, travelling and giving talks in Britain, Holland and the USA. After 10 years she left the hospice and went on to study counselling, working particularly with families of Alzheimer's patients.

Interview by Neil Small, 23 January 1996

Dr Osmond Morris

After medical training Dr Morris entered general practice and first became involved with palliative care in the late 1980s when he was given the responsibility of looking after the 12 terminal beds in the local cottage hospital. After undertaking a number of hospice-based specialist courses, he took up a post at St John of God Hospital in Newry where his remit was to take the lead in setting up a hospice service. In 1998 he also took on the post of Consultant at the new cancer unit at Craigavon Hospital. His subsequent work included the development of services at the hospice that was created, Newry Hospice (now Southern Area Hospice Services).

Interview by Clare Humphreys, 14 August 2000

Michael Murphy b. 1948

Michael Murphy's career in administration began in the accounts department of the local paper mill where his father worked. His first job in a health care setting was at Coombe Hospital in Dublin in 1967 and in 1972 he became Administrator at Our Lady's Hospice in Dublin. A year later Sister Ignatius Phelan arrived at the hospice and a modern palliative care approach was introduced. Michael Murphy has played a role in many subsequent developments including the separation of terminal care and rehabilitation functions, the building of new palliative care facilities, the change in medical cover from part-time GPs to a full-time consultant post, and the introduction of the Sisters of Charity Mission Effectiveness Programme in 1995.

Interview by David Clark, 20 November 1997

Sue Osborn (Duffing)

Sue Osborn worked as ERIC WILKES's secretary and as such was involved in early fund-raising, organising building work and the opening of St Luke's Hospice, Sheffield in 1971.

Interview by David Clark, 31 September 1996

Dr Colin Murray Parkes b. 1928

Colin Murray Parkes undertook his medical training at Westminster Hospital. Having undertaken various house physician posts, and a period in the Royal Air Force as a medical officer, he turned his attentions exclusively towards psychiatry. In 1956 he became a trainee psychiatrist at the Maudsley Hospital where his DPM focused on bereaved psychiatric patients, and he subsequently followed up this work by looking at 'normal grief' for his MD thesis entitled 'Reactions to Bereavement', submitted in 1962. He was invited by John Bowlby to join the Tavistock Institute of Human Relations and remained there from 1962 to 1975. In the late 1960s he was Project Director of the Harvard Bereavement Study in Boston, and it was here that he first met CICELY SAUNDERS, who invited him to become Honorary Consultant Psychiatrist at St Christopher's Hospice. He has also been centrally involved in Cruse's bereavement work, the International Work Group on Death, Dying and Bereavement and SAMM: Support After Murder and Manslaughter.

Interview by David Clark, 10 January 1996

Graham Perolls

After a varied work life that included his family business, working in education and a long involvement as a voluntary worker with young people, Graham Perolls developed an interest in hospice care. That interest arose from his father being cared for at St Christopher's Hospice and was further strengthened when, four years later, his mother died suddenly of a brain haemorrhage. With support from a GP who wanted a hospice service in Dartford, Kent, his local Director of Community Nursing, and the Tudor Trust, Graham Perolls was instrumental in establishing a hospice service in 1984. The Ellenor Foundation Home Care Service took its name from a combination of Graham Perolls' parents' names – Ellen and Norman. Graham Perolls had a long-standing contact with Brasov in Romania, dating back to 1975, and in 1991 an appeal was launched to raise funds to develop a hospice service in Brasov with the Tudor Trust once again supporting the venture. The involvement of the Ellenor Foundation was crucial in assisting with clinical and managerial support in the initial years in Brasov and by 2001 the service 'Casa Sperantai' had a new in-patient unit and a new UK charity to support it, 'Hospice of Hope Romania'.

Interview by David Clark, 15 September 2001

Gillian Petrie b. 1929

Gillian Petrie studied social science at the London School of Economics, and then began an English degree at Oxford but left to get married. Then followed a career that included work as an administrator in the charitable field. After several jobs (including a period with the Samaritans) she was appointed Welfare Officer for the Marie Curie Memorial Foundation in 1979. After leaving the organisation she was invited by ROBERT TWYCROSS to be Director of the International School for Cancer Care in Oxford. She then became involved in a voluntary capacity with both the Nairobi Hospice, and the Polish Hospices Fund.

Interview by David Clark, 16 September 1997

Rev. Jean Radley b. 1940

Jean Radley is an ordained minister and, until her retirement, was a district nursing sister and team leader at a large GP practice in Kendal, Cumbria.

Interview by Sara Morris, 8 May 2001

Malcolm Rapson b. 1938

Malcolm Rapson studied civil engineering at university and his career took him to the Middle East where his emphasis moved from engineering to management. He returned to Yorkshire and took up the post of Administrator at St Luke's Hospice in Sheffield in 1989.

Interview by Neil Small, 4 March 1997

Dr Claud Regnard b. 1950

After studying medicine at the University of Dundee, qualifying in 1976, Dr Regnard took up a post in general practice. He gained experience in palliative care at Roxburgh House, Dundee. Following a period as a clinical assistant at a Macmillan Unit in Dorset, Dr Regnard became the first Macmillan Fellow in Palliative Medicine. This was essentially a training post which Dr Regnard undertook with DR ROBERT TWYCROSS at Oxford between 1983 and 1986. Having trained and gained experience in palliative medicine he took up the post of Consultant Physician and Medical Director at the newly established St Oswald's Hospice in Newcastle-upon-Tyne in 1986.

Interviews by Nic Hughes, 20 November 2000 and 17 January 2001

Marilyn Relf

Marilyn Relf gained a degree in sociology from Sussex University in 1973. Her first job was as a development worker for Community Service Volunteers that led to a special interest in the training and support of volunteers. She became the first full-time Volunteer Coordinator at Sir Michael Sobell House, Oxford in 1982, and together with Ann Couldrick, a Macmillan nurse, she went on to develop a bereavement service. A recognition that there was a lack of research prompted Marilyn to seek funds to conduct an evaluation of the bereavement service. Her job has evolved from Bereavement Service Coordinator to Research Fellow in Bereavement Studies and then to Bereavement Service Manager.

Interview by Neil Small, 26 November 1997

Paul Rossi

After spending the early part of his career in politics and public administration, Paul Rossi was appointed to the post of Press and Parliamentary Officer for Help the Hospices in 1984. At Help the Hospices he undertook a variety of duties including those of secretary and administrator as the organisation advocated for hospices with the government, NHS and other national organisations. In 1991 he helped to establish the National Council for Hospice and Specialist Palliative Care Services before moving to Macmillan Cancer Relief in 1992. From the early 1990s he was also a trustee of the British Soviet Hospice Society, founded by Victor Zorza, to support the development of hospices in Russia and the Soviet Union. *Interview by Michael Wright, 18 March 2003*

Bill Rourke

Bill Rourke has been involved with the Northern Ireland Hospice as a volunteer since it opened in 1985, just after his retirement. His contribution was principally in two areas: the organisation of transport for day care and working on reception on alternate Saturday evenings. In the early 1990s he served on the hospice council for six years as representative of the volunteers.

Interview by Clare Humphreys, 31 July 2000

Dame Cicely Saunders b. 1918

In 1938 Cicely Saunders went to St Ann's College, Oxford to read philosophy, politics and economics. However, after the outbreak of war she left Oxford to study nursing at St Thomas's Hospital. A recurrence of back pain caused her to stop nursing, and she returned to Oxford for a year, gaining a 'war degree' and Diploma in Public and Social Administration. In 1945 she took up training as a medical social worker, and in 1947 returned to St Thomas's as a lady almoner. It was through this work that she met David Tasma who was dying of cancer at Archway Hospital. Cicely Saunders was subsequently accepted to study medicine at St Thomas's, qualifying in 1957. Whilst still a medical student she worked as a volunteer at St Luke's in Bayswater and then as a research fellow at

St Joseph's Hospice in Hackney. Developing a clearer vision of the role of medicine in the care of the dying, Cicely Saunders began to plan for a 'home' that was to become Britain's first modern hospice. St Christopher's became a registered charity in 1961, and building work commenced in 1965. Meanwhile Dr Saunders campaigned to raise awareness of the need to improve the care of the dying, and to promote St Christopher's: a series of six articles on 'Care of the Dying' was published in *Nursing Times* in 1959; and in 1963 she took her first trip to the USA. St Christopher's opened in 1967. The hospice's activities were expanded with home care (1969); research (1969); the Study Centre (1973); and the Hospice Information Service (1990). Despite two illnesses in 1969/70, Dr Saunders maintained an active programme of work, for example her annual lectures to the London Medical Group which began in 1970, and she was involved with St Christopher's own international conferences. As well as publishing widely and speaking throughout the UK, she made many visits to other countries including to meetings of the International Work Group on Death, Dying and Bereavement.

Interviews by Neil Small, 24 and 31 October,
7 and 14 November 1995, 10 July 1996,
interview by David Clark, 2 May 2003

Patricia Scott

Patricia Scott trained in children's nursing at Queen Mary's, Carshalton and general nursing at Stoke Mandeville where she continued as a staff nurse on a medical ward, then as a night sister, and finally as a sister on a medical ward (1968–82). She had one month's experience as an observer at Sir Michael Sobell House in Oxford in the early 1980s, and one year later she became a ward sister there, subsequently becoming Matron. *Interview by David Clark, 22 July 1997*

Brian Shaw b. 1931

After National Service in the Royal Air Force and a career in insurance, Brian Shaw was encouraged by June Emerson, a night sister a St Luke's Hospice, Sheffield and fellow church member, to apply for the position of transport manager there. His work in this post was central to the ability of the hospice to deliver its full range of services as the role of volunteer drivers is crucial, especially for day care patients.

Interview by Paul Lydon, 17 January 1997

Frances Sheldon 1940–2004

Frances Sheldon took a degree in history at Cambridge before embarking upon a career in social work. Beginning in the probation service, she worked in several posts across the North of England, mainly in psycho-geriatric care. In 1977 she moved to Hampshire and there began working in a newly established NHS continuing care unit at Countess Mountbatten House, Southampton. Here she became actively involved in teaching and writing about palliative care, eventually taking up a full-time university post in 1991. She was involved in several key palliative care groups and organisations: the Association of Hospice Social Workers; the board of the European Association for Palliative Care; the editorial board of the journal, *Palliative Medicine*; and the executive committee of the Palliative Care Research Forum.

Interview by David Clark, 25 June 2003

Dorothy Summers

Dorothy Summers commenced her general nursing training at the Royal Northern Hospital, Holloway in 1944. She undertook a nurse tutor's course in Battersea after spending several years as a ward sister. While tutoring at the South

London Hospital for Women and the Mayday Hospital she became a volunteer at the newly opened St Christopher's. After several years as a volunteer she was invited in 1974 to become Coordinator of Studies at St Christopher's Study Centre which had opened the previous year, a post that she held until 1984.

Interview by Neil Small, 13 December 1995

Dr Graham Thorpe b. 1932

Graham Thorpe trained in medicine at Charing Cross Hospital Medical School between 1951 and 1956. He then pursued a career in hospital general medicine becoming a consultant on the Isle of Wight in 1968 where he was part of the founding group planning Earl Mountbatten Hospice. As Dr Thorpe decided to leave hospital medicine for a career in palliative care in 1980, before the opening of Earl Mountbatten House in 1982, he joined Countess Mountbatten House in Southampton where he worked alongside RICHARD HILLIER for 14 years before retiring in 1994.

Interview by David Clark, 25 October 1996

Dr Robert Twycross b. 1941

After studying medicine at Oxford University Dr Twycross gained general medical experience, including cardiology at the Manchester Royal Infirmary, before joining the nascent field of palliative care. In 1971 he was invited by CICELY SAUNDERS to undertake a study of the relative efficacy of morphine/diamorphine as a Research Fellow at St Christopher's, a time in which he gained clinical experience as visiting medical officer at St Joseph's Hospice in Hackney. This background led him to one of the new posts emerging in palliative care in the NHS in the mid-1970s, and in 1976 he was appointed Consultant Physician in Sir Michael Sobell

House in Oxford. Dr Twycross has published widely, worked with the WHO, had a close involvement in the Association for Palliative Medicine, and played a central role in the development of the specialty of palliative medicine in the UK and overseas.

Interviews by David Clark, 4 January and 25 October 1996

Rev. Wilf Walton d. 2002

Reverend Wilf Walton studied at Durham University before working in the diocese of Lichfield during the Second World War. He also worked in Kenya, but finally settled in Sheffield where he became involved with the Soldiers', Sailors' & Airmen's Families Association. His first contact with St Luke's Hospice, Sheffield came when the then Matron, MARJORY COCKBURN, invited him to take an Easter Service in 1983 and he subsequently took up the position of hospice Chaplain.

Interview by Neil Small, 7 March 1997

Miriam Warren b. 1949

Miriam Warren qualified as a social worker in 1980. She worked in Adoption and Fostering and Family casework before moving into the specialist area of palliative care in 1988. She is Head of Social Work at St Gemma's Hospice in Leeds.   *Interview by Clare Humphreys, 10 July 2000*

Dr Tom West b. 1928

Tom West's family returned to Britain from Africa in 1938. He studied medicine at St Thomas's Hospital in the same set as CICELY SAUNDERS, qualifying in 1957. After a period in West Africa with the Church Missionary Society, Dr West joined the St Christopher's team in 1973 as Dr Saunders' deputy.

Interview by Neil Small, 28 January 1997

Professor Eric Wilkes b. 1920

Eric Wilkes went to King's College, Cambridge in 1937 to read English. He left Cambridge in 1939/40 with a war degree and joined the Army as a signaller. After the war he followed through earlier thoughts of a medical career by returning to King's College, Cambridge to study medicine and carried out his early medical training at St Thomas's Hospital, London from 1947 to 1952. After experience of general medical, obstetric and paediatric training he decided to leave hospital medicine for a career as a country GP in Baslow, Derbyshire. He was instrumental in establishing St Luke's Hospice in Sheffield in 1971, then played a national role, including as Professor of Community Care and General Practice at the University of Sheffield (1971–84), during which time he wrote the 'Wilkes Report' (1980). He was also involved in the formation and management of Help the Hospices as well as the creation of the National Council for Hospice and Specialist Palliative Care Services.

Interviews by David Clark, 12 September, 13 October, 10 and 17 November 1995

Paul Williment

Paul Williment first became involved with St Gemma's Hospice, Leeds in February 1985 when he joined as a volunteer working on reception. A month later he was employed as the Home Care Team Administrator. In December 1989 he was ordained in the Catholic Church, after which he joined the Hospice Chaplaincy team as part-time Catholic Chaplain. He also has a background in computers and provides all the IT support for the Hospice.

Interview by Clare Humphreys, 11 July 2000

Introducing our interviewers

The Hospice History Project has benefited from the help of a number of people who have undertaken interviews. In addition to the authors of this book the following have contributed interviews directly used in the text. We are grateful for their help. (We have identified the post they held when they did their interviews.)

Lorna Campbell: Doctoral student, Edinburgh University.

Clare Humphreys: Research Associate, University of Sheffield.

Gerry King: Nurse Researcher, Highland Hospice.

Kirsten Lund: Undergraduate medical student, University of Manchester.

Paul Lydon: Archivist, Hospice History Project, Sheffield.

Marcia Meldrum: Historian of Pain, University of California, Los Angeles.

Sara Morris: Researcher, Institute for Health Research, Lancaster University.

Silvia Paz: Visiting Fellow, Trent Palliative Care Centre, Sheffield.

Appendix 2
A timeline of hospice developments

• David Tasma, an émigré from the Warsaw ghetto, dies in London's Archway Hospital. He later becomes known as the 'founding patient of the modern hospice movement'. • The National Health Service (NHS) is founded. • The Marie Curie Memorial Foundation is formed. • In August, just one month after the foundation of the NHS, *The Practitioner* journal devotes a series of papers to the question of care for the dying.	**1948**
• A Voluntary Euthanasia Bill is introduced into the House of Lords. It seeks to legalise euthanasia for willing adults with fatal and painful disease. Four medical peers speak against it and the motion is withdrawn without a division.	**1950**
• The newly established Marie Curie Memorial Foundation working with the Queen's Institute of District Nursing conducts a survey of 7,050 cancer patients at home, which highlights the need for improved institutional care.	**1951**
• Cicely Saunders commences her medical studies, age 33.	**1952**
• The British Medical Association's annual meeting, held in Newcastle-upon-Tyne, contains a plenary session on terminal care and is reported in *The British Medical Journal*.	**1957**
• Cicely Saunders publishes her first paper in the St Thomas's Hospital Gazette, London. It becomes a manifesto for what should be done to improve terminal care. • Cicely Saunders commences work as a research fellow at St Joseph's Hospice in Hackney, under the direction of Professor Harold Stewart of St Mary's Hospital School of Medicine, London.	**1958**
• Cicely Saunders writes to key individuals with ideas for the creation of St Christopher's Hospice. • *Nursing Times* publishes a series of six articles by Cicely Saunders on the care of the dying. They provoke a huge written response from the readership, as well as an editorial in the *Daily Telegraph*. • The widows' organisation, Cruse, is formed. • Mark Swerdlow establishes the UK's first pain clinic in Salford. • A key meeting takes place between Cicely Saunders, Colin Murray Parkes and John Bowlby. • Harvard Bereavement Study gets underway in USA.	**1959**

• H.L. Glyn Hughes produces a major report on institutional care of the dying: *Peace at the Last. A survey of terminal care in the United Kingdom*.	**1960**
• An editorial in the *The Lancet* gives a major impetus to efforts to promote improved care of the dying.	
• Cicely Saunders makes her first visit to the United States, covering the east and west coasts and making connections with a wide range of individuals who will become influential in forging the modern hospice and palliative care movement. Subsequent lecture tours follow in 1965 and 1966.	**1963**
• The St Christopher's Hospice planning group produces a key document entitled *Aim and Basis*, providing the hospice with a statement of underpinning motivation which is reviewed from time to time in subsequent years. • A paper by Cicely Saunders uses the phrase '*all of me is wrong*' to introduce the concept of 'total pain': to include physical symptoms, mental distress, social problems and emotional problems.	**1964**
• The gate-control theory of pain is published by Ronald Melzack and Patrick Wall in *Science*. • Florence Wald, Dean of the Yale School of Nursing, invites Cicely Saunders to become a visiting faculty member of the school for the spring term.	**1965**
• In the aftermath of the Aberfan disaster, Colin Murray Parkes is engaged in work to support bereaved family members.	**1966**
• St Christopher's Hospice is opened in Sydenham, South London. As the first 'modern' hospice, it combines three key principles: excellent clinical care, education and research. • First meeting of the Intractable Pain Society of Great Britain is held at the University of Salford.	**1967**
• Home care service begins at St Christopher's Hospice, taking hospice skills and philosophy into the wider community. • Elisabeth Kübler-Ross's ground-breaking work *On Death and Dying* first appears in the USA and quickly becomes an international best seller.	**1969**
• St Luke's Nursing Home is opened as a purpose-built hospice in Sheffield, one of many established during the 1970s.	**1971**
• The Department of Health and Social Security holds a National Symposium on 'Care of the Dying'.	**1972**
• The International Association for the Study of Pain is founded by John Bonica in Issaquah, Washington, USA.	**1973**
• Balfour Mount, surgical oncologist, establishes Royal Victoria Hospital Palliative Care Unit in Canada. The term 'palliative care' is first adopted in the context of a hospital based service. • The first Macmillan nurse posts are established. • Supported by the National Society for Cancer Relief, the first purpose-built 'continuing care' unit opens in the grounds of a Christchurch general hospital, bringing hospice practice close to hospital care. • The first hospice day care unit opens at St Luke's, Sheffield.	**1975**

• English National Board for Nursing and Midwifery establishes its course on 'Care of the Dying Patient and Family'. • First specialist palliative care support team is established in the UK at St Thomas's Hospital, London. • The 1st International Congress on the Care of the Terminally Ill is organised by Balfour Mount and takes place in Montreal, Canada.	**1976**
• Publication of report by the Working Group on Terminal Care (the 'Wilkes Report') encourages the spread of terminal care principles in all health services and collaboration between services. • International Conference on Terminal Care held at St Christopher's attracts representatives from 16 nations. • International Hospice Institute is formed by Josefina Magno and colleagues, renamed International Hospice Institute and College (1995) and International Association for Hospice and Palliative Care (1999). • £2.5m is allocated by the National Society for Cancer Relief to expand Macmillan community nursing teams, nationwide.	**1980**
• Report by Barry Lunt and Richard Hillier shows that 58 hospice in-patient units and 32 home care teams exist in the UK – and recommends that home care teams take priority over in-patient units.	**1981**
• World Health Organisation (WHO) Cancer Pain Programme is initiated by Jan Stjernsward.	**1982**
• Help the Hospices is established as an umbrella charity supporting developments in the hospice movement.	**1984**
• National Association of Health Associations (NAHA) holds a conference on terminal care and guidelines are published in 1986. • Cicely Saunders retires from full-time work at St Christopher's Hospice.	**1985**
• Appointment of first Lecturer in Terminal Care Nursing at King's College London, funded by National Society for Cancer Relief. • A Medical Services Programme is set up to establish Macmillan doctors in hospitals, at home and in cancer treatment centres. • WHO publishes guidelines on cancer pain relief.	**1986**
• Palliative Medicine is recognised in its own right in the UK when the Royal College of Physicians grants sub-specialty status within General Medicine. • The new journal *Palliative Medicine* publishes its first issue. • 300 hospice projects are now in existence in the UK, with charitable income of £30 million per annum. • The Department of Health publishes its first circular on terminal care.	**1987**
• The European Association for Palliative Care is established in Milan. • The appointment of the first regional nurses for the coordination of continuing care is funded by the National Society for Cancer Relief. • Appointment of first Macmillan Clinical Reader in Palliative Care at Oxford University. • Sir Michael Sobell House, Oxford becomes WHO designated teaching centre for cancer pain control.	**1988**

• Government gives £400,000 to help 'ailing hospices'. • Publication of NHS white papers *Working for Patients* and *Caring for People* – heralding the Conservative government's reforms of health and social care and the introduction of an 'internal market' into the NHS. • Dame Cicely Saunders is awarded the Order of Merit by Her Majesty the Queen.	**1989**
• Government announces support for research in setting standards of palliative care. • Publication of Help the Hospices document, *Hospice Care – definitions and qualifications*. • The UK's first Diploma in Palliative Medicine begins at the University of Wales. • 800 Macmillan nurses are now in post in community services. • Publication of WHO guidelines on cancer and palliative care. Cancer pain and its relief are highlighted as issues of global concern. • The Hospice Information Service is founded at St Christopher's.	**1990**
• 430 hospice services now in operation in the UK. • Government allocates £18 million to health authorities for voluntary hospices under the 'partnership' funding arrangement. • The National Council for Hospice and Specialist Palliative Care Services comes into being.	**1991**
• Calman-Hine Report on cancer services is produced by Expert Advisory Group on Cancer.	**1995**
• 2,000 Macmillan nurses in post – covering almost every health authority in the UK. • Dame Cicely Saunders retires from position of Chairman to St Christopher's and adopts the role of President/Founder.	**2000**
• UK Forum for Hospice and Palliative Care Worldwide is founded by Help the Hospices.	**2002**
• A few months before her eighty-fifth birthday in June, a British medical poll votes Cicely Saunders the third greatest doctor of all time.	**2003**

Appendix 3
The work of the Hospice History Project

The work of hospice and palliative care is still developing rapidly. To engage in any analysis of its origins and subsequent progress is therefore to be caught up in a moving picture. It is to be engaged in a 'history of the present'. Nevertheless, it is likely that understanding even the recent past more clearly can lead to a better awareness of current issues and dilemmas. It was some of these thoughts that led to the creation of the Hospice History Project at the University of Sheffield, in 1995. We little imagined then, however, that the Project would develop quite so extensively.

At the outset we determined to capture now, for future generations, the voices and stories of the modern hospice and palliative care founders. We were concerned too about the need to preserve important documentary materials generated by key individuals and organisations and set out to safeguard these by drawing attention to the importance of rigorous archival procedures.

As the work grew and expanded, we came to characterise our approach to our subject matter as that of a 'critical friend': supportive of the hospice and palliative care enterprise, but also standing outside it and providing the kind of external analysis which may prove helpful to palliative care practitioners, opinion formers and policy makers.[1]

Over time we evolved three key aims for our work:

1. to undertake and to foster academic study in the history of hospices, palliative care and related fields;
2. to catalogue and help safeguard archival records relevant to hospice and related developments in Britain and Ireland;
3. to establish a hospice and palliative care digital archive, to include an oral history collection of interviews with key hospice and palliative care founders, worldwide.

Archiving and preservation

We have undertaken several projects to preserve important archival material relevant to the early history of hospice and palliative care. First among these was the cataloguing of the records of 100 hospices and palliative care units in Britain and Ireland.[2] We then created a database of all the available patient records for two early Irish hospices (St Patrick's, Cork[3] and Our Lady's Hospice, Dublin) from 1870 to 1960, yielding a fascinating insight into the epidemiological transition whereby the most common condition found among patients shifted from tuberculosis to cancer.[4]

We were also extremely fortunate to have the opportunity to undertake the preservation of the papers of Cicely Saunders. During 1997–98 these were subjected to full cataloguing, preservation and storage in some 85 archive boxes. The papers contain a wealth of information going back to Dr Saunders' earliest clinical work at St Joseph's, Hackney in the late 1950s and are an invaluable resource in studying both the contribution of one individual and the wider development of the hospice movement. They will be deposited ultimately with the archives of King's College, University of London, in close proximity to the headquarters of the Cicely Saunders Foundation.

Oral history collection

A major feature of the Project is the recording of the life stories of a wide variety of people involved in hospice and palliative care, not only in the UK, but in many other countries. In 1995 we set out to collect such stories, conscious that some of those to whom we wished to listen were already of advanced age, and wanting to capture a 'living history' of their experience whilst there was still an opportunity to do so. Some interviews with older people were necessarily rather short; others had to be continued over several sessions. By summer 2003 we had conducted over 200 of these interviews. Copyrighted to the Project, for subsequent public access, each is carefully transcribed and we are hoping to preserve the collection in two forms: bound paper copies as well as compact discs containing the sound recording and the text of the interview. Many famous individuals are represented within the collection, but we are also interested in the lives and stories of those whose role in hospice and palliative care work is less known or acclaimed. It is from this wide-ranging oral history collection that the present volume is chiefly derived.

Bibliographic collation and photographic archive

A full set of the publications of Cicely Saunders has been collated and these are being annotated by decade in a series of publications which appear in the journal *Palliative*

Medicine.[5] An edited volume of the selected letters of Cicely Saunders in the period 1959–99 has been produced[6] and readers may well find it of interest to consult this in order to gain a fuller understanding of issues raised in the present volume of oral histories. Side by side, the two books provide contrasting insights into the development of hospice and palliative care in the UK since the 1950s.

An electronic database of editorials contained in hospice and palliative care journals worldwide, since inception, has also been compiled by the Project. We also have a growing collection of hospice newsletters, annual reports, local histories, photographs, logos and other materials.

Website and exhibitions

A Project website[7] was established in 2001 and contains summaries of oral history interviews, a timeline of hospice development in Britain and Ireland and a bibliography of hospice and palliative care history. We have assisted with the permanent exhibition at the headquarters of Help the Hospices in central London, and are working with St Christopher's on plans for a free-standing exhibition to be housed there. In association with this book, we have also produced a touring exhibition of our own, depicting aspects of hospice history in the UK.

The International Observatory on End of Life Care

This interest in hospice history has now spread far beyond the discrete activities just described. Indeed the work undertaken from 1995 to 2003 can be seen as a platform for the creation of something much more ambitious in character, building on the recognition the Project has achieved and the involvement of many interested parties around the world.

In May 2002 David Clark and Michael Wright completed the first ever review of the development and current provision of hospice and palliative care in the 28 former communist countries of Eastern Europe and Central Asia. Their work was commissioned by the Open Society Institute in New York under the auspices of its Public Health Network Program and provided a comprehensive analysis of the state of hospice and palliative care provision across the whole region, country by country. When published,[8] the study made a considerable impact on policy and service developments in the region. It built in turn on other key foundations established over several years. Among these have been analyses of the development of palliative care in the UK policy context, conducted by David Clark and colleagues.[9] Also important was a comparative analysis of palliative care in seven Western European countries, covering historical, service development and ethical issues and carried out by an interdisciplinary team of historians, ethicists, social scientists and palliative care practitioners.[10] To these can be added numerous palliative care evaluations, needs assessments and related projects conducted through the 1990s.[11]

This experience of policy and needs assessment, service evaluation, historical analysis and ethical and cultural reflection, led to a major new initiative when the work of the International Observatory on End of Life Care[12] was established formally at Lancaster University in September 2003. The Observatory is the first ever research and development project to focus on comparative information relating to hospice and palliative care around the world: past, present and with the potential to influence the future. It seeks to generate data from original studies, to collate material gathered elsewhere and, above all, to turn this into useful *intelligence* which can influence current policy and practice development. The Observatory houses a growing repository of paper and digital archives relating to the global history of hospice and palliative care and is host to a steady stream of scholars and collaborating researchers from around the world. In addition to an expanding programme of work on international palliative care development, it also includes projects on the history of the Project on Death in America, on the centenary history of St Joseph's Hospice, Hackney and on the life of Victor Zorza, a key player in the development of hospice services in Russia. The emphasis on 'global analysis' and 'hospice history' form key programmes at the heart of the International Observatory on End of Life Care and illustrate how an understanding of near and contemporary history can be vital to influencing current policy and practice.

Notes

1. D. Clark, 'A critical friend? Some personal reflections on research in palliative care', Methodology Workshop, Palliative Care Research Network (South and West), Southampton, June 1997.
2. P. Lydon, *A Catalogue of Records Retained by Hospices and Related Organisations in the UK and the Republic of Ireland* (Sheffield: EAHMH Publications, 1998).
3. Later, Marymount Hospice, St Patrick's Hospital, Cork.
4. C. Humphreys, 'Tuberculosis, poverty and the first hospices in Ireland', *European Journal of Palliative Care* 10 (4): 164–67, 2003.
5. D. Clark, 'An annotated bibliography of the publications of Cicely Saunders – 1: 1958–67', *Palliative Medicine* 12 (3): 181–93, 1998; D. Clark, 'An annotated bibliography of the publications of Cicely Saunders – 2: 1968–79', *Palliative Medicine* 13 (6): 485–501, 1999.
6. D. Clark, *Cicely Saunders – founder of the hospice movement. Selected letters 1959–1999* (Oxford: Oxford University Press, 2002).
7. www.hospice-history.org.uk.
8. D. Clark and M. Wright, *Transitions in End of Life Care: Hospice*

and related developments in Eastern Europe and Central Asia (Buckingham: Open University Press, 2003).

9. D. Clark, J. Hockley and S. Ahmedzai (eds.), *New Themes in Palliative Care* (Buckingham: Open University Press, 1997); J. Hockley and D. Clark (eds.), *Palliative Care for Older People in Care Homes* (Buckingham: Open University Press, 2002).

10. H. ten Have and D. Clark (eds.), *The Ethics of Palliative Care: European perspectives* (Buckingham: Open University Press, 2002).

11. See for example: C. Ingleton, D. Field and D. Clark, 'Multidisciplinary case study as an approach to the evaluation of palliative care services: two examples', *International Journal of Palliative Nursing* 3 (6): 335–39, 1997; D. Clark, C. Ferguson and C. Nelson, 'Macmillan carers schemes in England: results of a multicentre evaluation', *Palliative Medicine* 14: 129–39, 2000; C. Ingleton, J. Skilbeck and D. Clark, 'Needs assessment for palliative care: three projects compared', *Palliative Medicine* 15: 398–404, 2001.

12. www.eolc-observatory.net.

Consolidated bibliography

– A –

J. Addington Hall and I. Higginson (eds.), *Palliative Care for Non-Cancer Patients* (Oxford: Oxford University Press, 2001).

– B –

T. Bates, 'A life of adventure', *Illness, Crisis and Loss* 9 (1): 31–34, 2001.

——, A.M. Hoy, D.G. Clark and P.P. Laird, 'The St Thomas's Hospital terminal care support team – A new concept of hospice care', *The Lancet* 1: 1201–03, 1981.

J.J. Bonica, *The Management of Pain: With special emphasis on the use of analgesic block in diagnosis, prognosis and therapy* (London: Henry Kimpton, 1953).

—— and V. Ventafridda (eds.), *Advances in Pain Research and Therapy, Vol. 2* (New York: Raven Press, 1979).

J. Bornat, R. Perks, P. Thompson and J. Walmsley, *Oral History, Health and Welfare* (London: Routledge, 2000).

S. du Boulay, *Cicely Saunders: The founder of the hospice movement* (London: Hodder and Stoughton, 1984).

J. Bowlby, *Maternal Care and Mental Health* (1951).

A. Bradshaw, 'The spiritual dimension of hospice: the secularisation of an ideal', *Social Science and Medicine* 43: 409–20, 1996.

D. Brady, *Report of meeting for those involved in libraries in hospices*, 27 November 1995.

– C –

S. Cassidy, *Audacity to Believe* (London: Collins, 1977).

D. Clark (ed.), *The Future for Palliative Care* (Buckingham: Open University Press, 1993).

——, *Partners in Care? Hospices and health authorities* (Aldershot: Ashgate, 1993).

——, 'Whither the hospices?' in D. Clark (ed.), *The Future for Palliative Care* (Buckingham: Open University Press, 1993).

——, 'A critical friend? Some personal reflections on research in palliative care', Methodology Workshop, Palliative Care Research Network (South and West), Southampton, June 1997.

——, 'Someone to watch over me: Cicely Saunders and St Christopher's Hospice', *Nursing Times*, 26 August: 50–51, 1997.

——, 'An annotated bibliography of the publications of Cicely Saunders – 1: 1958–67', *Palliative Medicine* 12 (3): 181–93, 1998.

——, 'Originating a movement: Cicely Saunders and the development of St Christopher's Hospice, 1957–67', *Mortality* 3 (1): 43–63, 1998.

——, 'An annotated bibliography of the publications of Cicely Saunders – 2: 1968–79', *Palliative Medicine* 13 (6): 485–501, 1999.

——, 'Cradled to the grave? Pre-conditions for the hospice movement in the UK, 1948–67', *Mortality* 4 (3): 225–47, 1999.

——, '"Total pain", disciplinary power and the body in the work of Cicely Saunders 1958–67', *Social Science and Medicine* 49 (6): 727–36, 1999.

——, 'Palliative care history: a ritual process', *European Journal of Palliative Care* 7 (2): 50–55, 2000.

——, 'Total pain: The work of Cicely Saunders and the hospice movement', *American Pain Society Bulletin* 10 (4), July–August: 13–15, 2000.

——, 'Religion, medicine and community in the early origins of St Christopher's Hospice', *Journal of Palliative Medicine* 4 (3): 353–60, 2001.

——, 'A special relationship: Cicely Saunders, the United States and the early foundations of the modern hospice movement', *Illness, Crisis and Loss* 9 (1): 15–30, 2001.

——, *Cicely Saunders – founder of the hospice movement. Selected letters 1959–1999* (Oxford: Oxford University Press, 2002).

——, 'The rise and demise of the "Brompton Cocktail"' in M.L.

Meldrum (ed.), *Opioids and Pain Relief: A historical perspective. Progress in Pain Research and Management, Vol. 25* (Seattle: IASP Press, 2003: 85–98).

——, 'History, gender and culture in the rise of palliative care' in S. Payne, J. Seymour and C. Ingleton (eds.), *Palliative Care Nursing. Principles and evidence for practice* (Maidenhead: Open University Press, 2004).

——, C. Ferguson and C. Nelson, 'Macmillan carers schemes in England: results of a multicentre evaluation', *Palliative Medicine* 14: 129–39, 2000.

——, J. Hockley and S. Ahmedzai (eds.), *New Themes in Palliative Care* (Buckingham: Open University Press, 1997).

—— and J. Seymour, *Reflections on Palliative Care* (Buckingham: Open University Press, 1999).

—— and M. Wright, *Transitions in End of Life Care: Hospice and related developments in Eastern Europe and Central Asia* (Buckingham: Open University Press, 2003).

M. Cobb, *The Dying Soul: Spiritual care at the end of life* (Buckingham: Open University Press, 2001).

—— and V. Robertshaw (eds.), *The Spiritual Challenge of Health Care* (Edinburgh: Churchill Livingstone, 1998).

M. Cockburn and J. Twine, 'A different kind of day unit', *Nursing Times*,18 August: 1410–11, 1982.

J. Corner, 'The multidisciplinary team – fact or fiction', plenary lecture given at Eighth Congress of European Association for Pallative Care, The Hague, The Netherlands, 2–5 April 2003.

– D –

Department of Health, *HC (87)4(2)* (London: Department of Health, 1987).

——, *The Patient's Charter* (London: HMSO, 1991).

——, *Meeting the Spiritual Needs of Patients and Staff. HSG(92)2* (London: HMSO, 1992).

——, *The NHS Cancer Plan: A plan for investment, a plan for reform* (London: HMSO, 2000).

Henry Dicks, *Fifty Years of the Tavistock Clinic* (London: Routledge and Kegan Paul, 1970).

C. Douglas, 'For all the Saints', *British Medical Journal* 303: 579, 1992.

– E –

R. Elsdon, 'Spiritual pain in dying people: the nurse's role', *Professional Nurse* 10 (10): 641–43, 1996.

Expert Advisory Group on Cancer, *A Policy Framework for Commissioning Cancer Services: A report by the Expert Advisory Group on Cancer to the Chief Medical Officers of England and Wales* (London: Department of Health and Welsh Office, 1995).

– F –

C. Faull and A. Nicholson, 'Taking the myths out of the magic: Establishing the use of opioids in the management of cancer pain' in M.L. Meldrum (ed.), *Opioids and Pain Relief: A historical perspective. Progress in Pain Research and Management, Vol. 25* (Seattle: IASP Press, 2003: 111–30).

S. Fordham, C. Dowrick and C. May, 'Palliative medicine: is it a really specialist territory?', *Journal of the Royal Society of Medicine* 91: 568–72, 1998.

– G –

H. Garner and F.P. Orelove, *Teamwork in Human Services: Models and applications across the life span* (Newton, MA: Butterworth-Heinemann, 1994).

C.J. Gavey, *The Management of the 'Hopeless' Case* (London: H.K. Lewis, 1952).

A. Gilmore, 'The care and management of the dying in general practice', *Practitioner* 213: 833–42, 1974.

– H –

H. ten Have and D. Clark (eds.), *The Ethics of Palliative Care: European perspectives* (Buckingham: Open University Press, 2002).

J. Hockey, J. Katz and N. Small (eds.), *Grief, Mourning and Death Ritual* (Buckingham: Open University Press, 2002).

J. Hockley and D. Clark (eds.), *Palliative Care for Older People in Care Homes* (Buckingham: Open University Press, 2002).

J.J. Horwitz, *Team Practice and the Specialist* (Springfield, IL: Charles C. Thomas, 1970).

C. Humphreys, '"Waiting for the Last Summons": the establishment of the first hospices in England 1878–1914', *Mortality* 6 (2): 146–66, 2001.

——, 'Tuberculosis, poverty and the first hospices in Ireland', *European Journal of Palliative Care* 10 (4): 164–67, 2003.

J.H. Hunt and M.J. Linnett, 'Intractable pain', *British Medical Journal*, 4 June: 1723–29, 1960.

– I –

C. Ingleton, D. Field and D. Clark, 'Multidisciplinary case study as an approach to the evaluation of palliative care services: two examples', *International Journal of Palliative Nursing* 3 (6): 335–39, 1997.

——, J. Skilbeck and D. Clark, 'Needs assessment for palliative care: three projects compared', *Palliative Medicine* 15: 398–404, 2001.

International Consensus on the Management of Cancer Pain, *Looking Forward to Cancer Pain Relief for All* (Oxford: WHO Collaborating Centre for Palliative Cancer Care, 1997).

International Work Group on Death, Dying and Bereavement, *Statements on Death, Dying, and Bereavement* (Ontario: Kings College, 1994).

– J –

N. James and D. Field, 'The routinisation of hospice: charisma and bureaucratisation', *Social Science and Medicine* 34 (12): 1363–75, 1992.

Joint Cancer Survey Committee of the Marie Curie Memorial and the Queen's Institute of District Nursing, *Report on a National Survey Concerning Patients with Cancer Nursed at Home* (London: Marie Curie Memorial Foundation, 1952).

– K –

The King's Fund, *The Hospital Chaplain* (London: The King's Fund, 1966).

E. Kübler-Ross, *On Death and Dying* (USA: 1969; UK: 1970).

– L –

R. Lamerton, *Care of the Dying* (Harmondsworth: Penguin, 1980).

——, *East End Doc* (Cambridge: Lutterworth Press, 1986).

E. Lindemann, 'Symptomatology and management of acute grief', *American Journal of Psychiatry* 101: 141–48, 1944.

B. Lunt, 'Terminal cancer care services: recent changes in regional inequalities in Great Britain', *Social Science and Medicine* 20: 754, 1985.

P. Lydon, *A Catalogue of Records Retained by Hospices and Related Organisations in the UK and the Republic of Ireland* (Sheffield: EAHMH Publications, 1998).

– M –

R.M. Maher, 'Relief of pain in incurable cancer', *The Lancet*, 1 January: 18–20, 1955.

——, 'Neurone selection in the relief of pain, Further experiences with intrathecal injections', *The Lancet*, 5 January: 16–19, 1957.

M. Manning, *The Hospice Alternative. Living with dying* (London: Souvenir Press, 1984).

P. Marris, *Widows and their Families* (London: Routledge, 1958).

——, *Loss and Change* (London: Routledge, 1974).

P. McGrath, 'Exploring spirituality through research: an important but challenging task', *Progress in Palliative Care* 7 (1): 3–9, 2000.

M.B. McIllmurray, B. Francis, J.C. Harman, S.M. Morris, K. Soothill and C. Thomas, 'Psychosocial needs in cancer patients related to religious belief', *Palliative Medicine* 17: 49–54, 2003.

M.L. Meldrum (ed.), *Opioids and Pain Relief: A historical perspective*. Progress in Pain Research and Management, Vol. 25 (Seattle: IASP Press, 2003).

——, 'The ladder and the clock: cancer pain as a public health problem at the end of the 20th century' (unpublished).

B. Monroe and D. Oliviere (eds.), *Patient Participation in Palliative Care: A voice for the voiceless* (Oxford: Oxford University Press, 2003).

B. Mount, 'The Royal Victoria Hospital Palliative Care Service: A Canadian experience' in C. Saunders and R. Kastenbaum (eds.), *Hospice Care on the International Scene* (New York: Springer, 1997: 73–85).

– N –

National Health Service, *Appointment of Chaplains. HMC(48 62)* (London: HMSO, 1948).

– O –

J. Øvretveit, 'How to describe interprofessional working' in J. Øvretveit, P. Mathias and T. Thompson (eds.), *Interprofessional Working for Health and Social Care* (London: Macmillan, 1997: 9–33).

– P –

C.M. Parkes, 'Genocide in Rwanda: Personal reflections', *Mortality* 1 (1): 95–110, 1996.

——, 'Historical overview of the scientific study of bereavement' in M.S. Stroebe, R.O. Hansson, W. Stroebe and H. Schut, *Handbook of Bereavement Research. Consequences, coping and care* (Washington, DC: American Psychological Association, 2001).

——, M. Relf and A. Couldrick, *Counselling in Terminal Care and Bereavement* (Leicester: British Psychological Society, 1996).

M. Payne, *Teamwork in Multiprofessional Care* (London: Macmillan, 2000).

S. Payne, J. Seymour and C. Ingleton (eds.), *Palliative Care Nursing: Principles and Evidence for Practice* (Maidenhead: Open University Press, 2004).

R. Perks and A. Thomson (eds.), *The Oral History Reader* (London: Routledge, 1997).

L. Pincus, *Death and the Family* (London: Faber and Faber, 1976).

A. Portelli, 'What makes oral history different?' in R. Perks and A. Thomson (eds.), *The Oral History Reader* (London: Routledge, 1997).

– S –

C. Saunders, 'Dying of cancer', *St Thomas's Hospital Gazette* 56 (2): 37–47, 1958.

——, 'Drug treatment of patients in the terminal stages of cancer', *Current Medicine and Drugs* 1 (1), July: 16–28, 1960.

——, 'And from sudden death …', *Frontier*, Winter 1961, no page numbers.

——, 'A patient …', *Nursing Times*, 31 March: 394–97, 1961.

——, 'The treatment of intractable pain in terminal cancer', *Proceedings of the Royal Society of Medicine* 56 (3), March: 195–97 (Section of Surgery: 5–7), 1963.

——, 'Care of patients suffering from terminal illness at St Joseph's Hospice, Hackney, London', *Nursing Mirror*, 14 February: vii–x, 1964.

——, 'The symptomatic treatment of incurable malignant disease', *Prescribers' Journal* 4 (4), October: 68–73, 1964.

——, 'The patient's response to treatment. A photographic presentation showing patients and their families' in *Catastrophic Illness in the Seventies: Critical issues and complex decisions. Proceedings of Fourth National Symposium, 15–16 October 1970* (New York: Cancer Care, Inc., 1971).

——, 'A place to die', *Crux* 11 (3): 24–27, 1973–74.

——, 'A window in your home' in *The Light of Experience* (London: BBC, 1977).

—— (ed.), *The Management of Terminal Malignant Disease* (London: Edward Arnold, 1978).

—, 'The philosophy of terminal care' in C. Saunders (ed.), *The Management of Terminal Malignant Disease* (London: Edward Arnold, 1978).

——, 'Current views on pain relief and terminal care' in M. Swerdlow (ed.), *The Therapy of Pain* (Lancaster: MTP Press, 1981: 215–41).

——, 'The modern hospice' in W. Wald (ed.), *In Quest of the Spiritual Component of Care for the Terminally Ill* (Yale: Yale School of Nursing, 1986).

——, 'What's in a name?', *Palliative Medicine* 1 (1): 57–61, 1987.

——, 'Dame Cicely Saunders: an Omega interview', *Omega* 27 (4): 263–69, 1993.

—— and R. Kastenbaum (eds.), *Hospice Care on the International Scene* (New York: Springer, 1997).

——, D. Summers and N. Teller (eds.), *Hospice: The living idea* (London: Edward Arnold, 1981).

T. Scott, 'Chaplaincy – a resource of Christian presence', *Scottish Journal of Healthcare Chaplaincy* 3 (1): 15–19, 2000.

A. Seldon and J. Pappworth, *By Word of Mouth: Elite oral history* (London: Methuen, 1983).

H. Selye, *The Stress of Life* (New York: McGraw Hill, 1956).

——, *Stress without Distress* (New York: Signet, 1975).

P.R. Silverman, *Widow to Widow* (New York: Springer, 1986).

SMAC (Standing Medical Advisory Committee)/SNMAC (Standing Nursing and Midwifery Advisory Committee), *The Principles and Provision of Palliative Care* (London: HMSO, 1992).

N. Small, 'Spirituality and hospice care' in M. Cobb and V. Robertshaw (eds.), *The Spiritual Challenge of Health Care* (Edinburgh: Churchill Livingstone, 1998).

Specialist Palliative Care: A statement of definitions (London: National Council for Hospice and Specialist Palliative Care Services, 1995).

Spiritual Care Work Group of the International Work Group on Death, Dying and Bereavement, 'Assumptions and Principles of Spiritual Care', *Death Studies* 14: 75–81, 1990.

R. Stanworth, *Recognising Spiritual Needs in People who are Dying* (Oxford: Oxford University Press, 2004).

S. Stoddard, *The Hospice Movement: A better way to care for the dying* (London: Jonathan Cape, 1979).

M. Stoddard Holmes, '"The grandest badge of his art": Three Victorian doctors, pain relief and the art of medicine' in M.L. Meldrum (ed.), *Opioids and Pain Relief: A historical perspective. Progress in Pain Research and Management*, Vol. 25 (Seattle: IASP Press, 2003: 21–34).

M.S. Stroebe, R.O. Hansson, W. Stroebe and H. Schut, *Handbook of Bereavement Research. Consequences, coping and care* (Washington, DC: American Psychological Association, 2001).

P. Sturgess, *The Marie Curie Memorial Foundation: A brief history 1948–1984* (London: Marie Curie Memorial Foundation, 1985).

M. Swerdlow (ed.), *The Therapy of Pain* (Lancaster: MTP Press, 1981).

– T –

P. Thompson and R. Perks, *An Introduction to the Use of Oral History in the History of Medicine* (London: National Life Story Collection, British Library, 1993).

Thucydides, *History of the Peloponnesian War* (Harmondsworth: Penguin Books, 1954).

M. Torrie, *Begin Again: A book for women alone* (London: Dent, 1970).

——, *My Years with Cruse* (Richmond: Cruse, 1987).

R. Twycross, 'The Brompton Cocktail' in J.J. Bonica and V. Ventafridda (eds.), *Advances in Pain Research and Therapy, Vol. 2* (New York: Raven Press, 1979).

—— and S.A. Lack, *Symptom Control in Far-Advanced Cancer: Pain relief* (London: Pitman, 1983).

—— and S.A. Lack, *Oral Morphine in Advanced Cancer* (Beaconsfield: Beaconsfield Publishers, 1984).

—— and S.A. Lack, *Therapeutics in Terminal Cancer* (London: Pitman, 1984).

—— and S.A. Lack, *Control of Alimentary Symptoms in Far-Advanced Cancer* (Edinburgh: Churchill Livingstone, 1986).

– V –

M.L.S. Vachon, W. Lyall, J. Rogers, K. Freedman-Letofsky and S. Freeman, 'A controlled study of self-help interventions for widows', *American Journal of Psychiatry* 137: 1380–84, 1980.

– W –

W. Wald (ed.), *In Quest of the Spiritual Component of Care for the Terminally Ill* (Yale: Yale School of Nursing, 1986).

T. Walter, *The Revival of Death* (London: Routledge, 1994).

——, 'The ideology and organisation of spiritual care: three approaches', *Palliative Medicine* 1: 21–30, 1997.

——, *On Bereavement* (Buckingham: Open University Press, 1999).

C. Webster, *The Health Services Since the War. Volume II, Government and Health Care, The British National Health Service 1958–79* (London: The Stationery Office, 1996).

E. Wilkes, 'General practitioner in a hospice', *British Medical Journal* 282: 1591, 1981.

——, *No Second Chance* (1988).

J. William Worden, *Grief Counselling and Grief Therapy: A handbook for the mental health practitioner* (London: Tavistock, 1983).

Working Group on Terminal Care [The Wilkes Report], *Report of the Working Group on Terminal Care* (London: DHSS, 1980).

Working Party, *Mud and Stars: The impact of hospice experience on the church's ministry of healing* (Oxford: Sobell Publications, 1991).

World Health Organization, *Cancer Pain Relief* (Geneva: WHO, 1986).

J. Worswick, *A House Called Helen*, 2nd edn (Oxford: Oxford University Press, 2000).

M.C. Wright, 'Chaplaincy in hospice and hospital: findings from a survey in England and Wales', *Palliative Medicine* 15: 229–42, 2001.

——, 'Good for the soul? The spiritual dimension of hospice and palliative care' in S. Payne, J. Seymour and C. Ingleton (eds.), *Palliative Care Nursing: Principles and evidence for practice* (Maidenhead: Open University Press, 2004).

——, *Victor Zorza. A life amid loss* (Lancaster: Observatory Publications, in press).

– Z –

M. Zenz and A. Willweber-Strumf, 'Opiophobia and cancer pain in Europe', *The Lancet* 341, April: 1075–76, 1993.

R. Zorza and V. Zorza, *A Way to Die* (London: Sphere Books, 1981).

Index

– A –

Ahmedzai, Sam Hjelmeland 146, 199, 209
AIDS 41, 90, 115, 171
Aine, Sister 48
alcohol 137, 147–48
'all of me is wrong' 2, 19, 40, 145
Alzheimer's disease 172, 211
Anglican Society of All Saints Sisters of the Poor, Oxford 60
Antonia, Sister Mary 55–56, 67, 139–41, 199, 210
Archway Hospital, Highgate 15, 214
Association for Hospice Management 90, 109–10
Association for Palliative Medicine (APM) 97, 106, 204, 216
Association for Palliative Medicine of Great Britain and Ireland 90, 108–09
Association of Chartered Physiotherapists in Oncology and Palliative Care 90
Association of Children's Hospices 90
Association of Children with Terminal Illnesses 207
Association of Hospice Administrators. *See* Association for Hospice Management
Association of Hospice and Palliative Care Chaplains 90
Association of Hospice and Specialist Palliative Care Social Workers 90, 107–08
Association of Hospice Managers 109
Association of Hospice Social Workers 73, 94, 107–08, 111, 201, 205, 206, 215
Association of Palliative Day Care Leaders 90
Association of Palliative Medicine 73
Atkinson, Liz 66, 129, 183, 199

– B –

Baines, Mary 33, 55–56, 63, 141–42, 199, 200

Barrett, Mr 138
Barrett, Norman 134
Bates, Thelma 56, 59, 200
Baum, David 39
Beattie, Rita 33, 71, 102, 119, 200
Beetham, Ros 35, 81, 105, 163, 186, 200
bereavement 51, 64, 72, 101, 105, 177, 202, 209, 212. *See also* Bereavement Research Forum, Cruse Bereavement Care; *See also* Harvard Bereavement Study, International Work Group on Death, Dying and Bereavement
    care 101, 104, 155–74
    early influence on Cicely Saunders 18, 197
    impact of 173–74
    interest in 31–32, 101
    journals 104
    new openness about 3
    professional organisations 8
    programmes 66
    research 105, 167–69, 213
    responding to 10
    services 20, 80–82, 101, 105, 159–63, 213. *See also* St Christopher's Hospice Bereavement Service
    study of 31
    understanding 8, 10
Bereavement Research Forum 90, 98, 104–05
Berkeley, John 103, 138, 184, 194, 200, 201
Bermingham, Sister Seraphine 119, 201
Bibby, Colin 35
Bloom, Anthony (Metropolitan Anthony) 128–29
Bloomsbury Support Team 111, 205
Bonica, John 134, 140
Bottomley, Virginia, MP 111
du Boulay, Shirley 132

Bowlby, John 159, 167, 212
Box, Mary 82, 201
British Association of Social Workers 111
British Medical Association (BMA) 99–100, 115
British Medical Journal 1, 33, 35, 147
Brodribb, Carolyn 64, 94, 121, 167–68, 201
Brompton Cocktail 40, 137–38, 140–41, 147–48
Brompton Hospital, London 137, 147
Butterwick, John 201
    John Butterwick Trust 27, 201
Butterwick, Mary 26–27, 122, 155, 161–62, 192, 201, 202
Butterwick Hospice, Stockton-on-Tees 26–27, 71, 161, 202, 210

– C –

Calman, Kenneth 115, 180, 184, 199
Campalani, Sally 97, 126, 191, 202
cancer
    adult 61
    advanced 56, 84, 120, 137, 151
    care 91, 94, 202, 207
    care charities 2, 42, 69, 89. *See also* Macmillan Cancer Relief,
        Marie Curie Cancer Care
    centres 61, 171, 207
    challenge of 118
    changing character of disease 189
    control 149, 185
    coping with 27
    effects of 90
    fear of 82
    impact on poor 94
    journey 194
    local services 211
    model 61–62
    paediatric 61–62
    pain 134–35, 137–38, 142, 146, 149–50, 152
    patients 15, 21, 26–27, 29–30, 50, 56–57, 62, 75, 84, 90, 92,
        94–96, 120, 128–30, 134–35, 137–38, 146–49, 151, 171,
        185, 188–90, 194, 214
    service 48, 171
    talking about 82
    terminal 25–26, 29, 45, 48, 79, 82, 120, 138, 148, 164, 170,
        188, 214
    treatment 56, 191
    unit 211

    wards 57
    wartime casualties from 94
Cancer Care, Lancaster 211
Cancer Relief. *See* Macmillan Cancer Relief, National Society for
        Cancer Relief
Cannon, Yvonne 62
Caplan, Gerald 170, 175
Carleton-Smith, Michael 95–97, 103, 202
Carradice, Margaret 54, 142–43, 202
Carstairs, Maurice 158
Case, Sister Cecily Mary 46, 202
Cassidy, Sheila 26, 46, 64, 171, 194, 202, 203
chapels 34, 51, 70, 121, 123, 165
chaplains and chaplaincy 10, 27, 34, 37, 57, 76, 83, 90, 103, 120,
        123–29, 132, 165, 171, 177, 180, 201, 202, 204, 210, 216
Chaplains to the Queen 128
chlorpromazine 147–48. *See also* Largactil
Christianity 10, 16, 19, 35, 46, 90, 115, 117–19, 121, 123–24, 126,
        129, 131–32, 177, 203
Churchill, Winston 94
Church Missionary Society 25, 78, 203, 216
Clench, Prue 25, 75, 86, 91–92, 100, 123, 166, 203
cocaine 137, 147–48
Cockburn, Marjory 36, 40, 57, 121, 187, 195, 203, 216
community nursing 95, 111. *See also* day care, home care,
        Macmillan nurses, Marie Curie nurses
Conrad House, Newcastle 97
Cooney, Ann 53, 126, 203
Cotlands Baby Sanctuary 41
Council for Music in Hospitals 90
Countess Mountbatten House, Southampton 11, 47, 83–84, 107,
        193, 208, 215
Creative Response, The 90
Crowther, Tony 22, 24, 27–28, 58, 93, 100, 102, 145, 203
Cruse Bereavement Care 8, 27, 62, 156, 169–70, 201, 209, 212

– D –

Daly, Edward 37, 124, 191–92, 204
Day, Gloria 30, 93, 143, 204
Day and Night Nursing Service 94
day care 2, 20, 42, 45, 52, 57–60, 65, 73, 84, 93, 120, 122, 191,
        193, 202, 209, 214, 215
dementia 190
diamorphine 142–45, 147–48, 215

dignity 2, 82
district nurses 45, 47, 55, 64, 77, 93–95, 97, 135, 191, 199, 200, 204, 206, 211
Dominica, Sister Frances 38–39, 60, 198, 204
Dorothy House Foundation, Bath 92, 166, 203
Douglas House 204
Doyle, Derek 33–34, 36, 40, 104, 115, 127, 144, 183, 184, 204
Duchess of Devonshire 49
Duchess of Kent 58
Duchess of Norfolk 98–99, 115
Duffield, Madeleine 161
Duffing, Sue. See Osborn, Sue
Dufour, Prue. See Clench, Prue

– E –

Earnshaw-Smith, Elisabeth 62, 72, 107–08, 161, 163–64, 166, 173, 205
Easun, John 82, 205
Ellenor Foundation Home Care Service 52, 212
European Association for Palliative Care (EAPC) 107, 114, 204, 215
euthanasia 1, 3–4, 103, 130

– F –

faith 10, 44, 117, 119, 121–23, 126–27, 131–32, 177
faith healer 128
Faull, Christina 135
Floriani Foundation, Milan 150
Forbes, Lyn 48, 80, 191, 205
Ford, Gillian 30, 74, 83, 103–04, 114, 140, 185, 190, 199, 205
Forum of Chairmen of Independent Hospices 90
Foyle Hospice, Derry 37, 45–46, 53, 191, 204, 210, 211
Franklin, Julia 86, 101, 108, 111–12, 181, 205, 206
fund-raising 19, 30, 42, 46, 49–54, 66, 73, 80, 96, 100, 102, 106, 109, 192, 199, 202, 205, 207, 210, 211, 212

– G –

Gaffin, Jean 103
Gahegan, Janet 143, 206
Galton, Barbara (Mrs G) 19
Garnett, Major Henry 52, 90–93, 115
general practitioners (GPs) 3, 22, 30, 33, 45, 48, 52, 55, 58, 63, 97, 135, 145, 167, 174, 191, 200, 204, 210, 212, 213, 216
    acceptance from 45

    consent of 55
    cooperation of 47–48
    inexperience of 143
    involvement of 49–50, 55, 77, 93, 201, 211
    survey of 31
Gerrish, Maddy 85, 206
Gilbert, Patricia 37, 93, 206
Gilmore, Ann 31, 51–52, 206
Goldman, Ann 60–61, 207
Graham, Douglas 48
Great Ormond Street Hospital for Children, London 60–61, 204, 207
grief 14, 18, 31, 51, 62, 72, 101, 155, 156–59, 163, 171, 173, 206, 212
    acute 155
    collective 126
    expression of 155
    impact of 10, 155
    individuality of 168
    models of 167–68
    processes of 155, 167
    projecting 87
    talking about 63, 168–69
    working through 168
Griffiths, Peter 50–51, 207

– H –

Hanna, Sheila 82, 207
Hardman, Colin 148, 191, 207
Hartlepool and District Hospice 65, 71, 210
Harvard Bereavement Study 159, 167, 170, 175, 212
Helen House, Oxford 38–39, 61, 198, 204
Help the Hospices 8, 90, 96, 98–102, 111, 114, 181, 207, 213, 216
Hillier, Richard 11, 22, 24–25, 28–29, 36, 47, 83, 91, 108, 115, 208, 215
Hinton, John 31, 141, 182, 208
Hitchens, Julia 105, 208
Hockley, Jo 22, 54, 130, 208
Holland, Mary 77, 188, 208
home care 61, 65, 124, 153, 166, 193, 199, 211, 214
    nurses 46–47, 92
    programmes 41
    services 2, 20, 42, 47, 52, 55, 75, 120, 128, 200, 201, 210
    sisters 45–46, 66
    teams 27, 45, 55, 69, 73, 76–77, 84, 93, 185, 201, 209

HOPE 90
Hospice and Palliative Care Pharmacists' Association 90
hospice information 90, 114
Hospice Information Service 114, 214
Hospice Social Workers' Association 108
Hoy, Andrew 57, 59
Hoyle, Clifford 31
Hunt, John 146, 209

– I –

Independent Hospice Representative Committee 90
International Association for the Study of Pain 149
International Work Group on Death, Dying and Bereavement 170,
          172, 175, 200, 212, 214
Intractable Pain Society of Great Britain 150
InVOLve 90
Irwin, Betty 47, 190, 209

– J –

Jeremiah's Journey 171
Jessie's Fund 90
John XXIII, His Holiness Pope 46
Joint National Cancer Survey 134

– K –

Kerr, Eileen 193, 209
Kerr, Finlay 48
King's College Hospital, London 40, 203, 207, 208
King's Fund 44, 132
Kirk, Steve 98, 209
Kübler-Ross, Elisabeth 31–32, 138, 168

– L –

Lancet, The 1
Lack, Sylvia 114, 149
Laidlaw, Peter 75, 209
Lamerton, Richard 42, 54–56, 91, 100, 199, 210
Largactil 140, 148. *See also* chlorpromazine
Le Poidevin, Susan 168
Libraries in Hospices 90, 98, 105–06
Lindemann, Eric 157
London Cancer Hospital. *See* Royal Marsden Hospital, London

London Hospital Bereavement Service 171
Lovel, Tim 20–22, 65, 85, 97, 180, 187, 210
Lunn, Leonard (Len) 125, 210

– M –

Macmillan, Douglas 90, 92
Macmillan Cancer Relief 8, 10, 52, 69, 86, 89–94, 99, 101–02, 104,
          108, 114, 214. *See also* National Society for Cancer Relief
          (NSCR)
    Dorset Square (London HQ) 92
    expansion of 92
    grants and funding 52, 92–93, 204
    influence of 100
    origin of name 92
    problems faced by 92
    sponsored lectureships 94, 201, 213
Macmillan doctors 91
Macmillan Home Care Service 17
Macmillan nurses 47, 52, 77, 90–93, 97–99, 171, 188–89, 203, 206,
          209, 213
Macmillan Service 91–93, 204
Macmillan units 90, 92, 213
Maher, Robert 140
Marches, Hospice of the 70, 210
Marie Curie Cancer Care 8, 10, 89–90, 94–99, 101–03, 114, 185,
          202, 205, 206
Marie Curie Cancer Care Scotland 75, 210
Marie Curie Centre, Belfast 97, 126, 146, 183, 191, 193, 202, 209,
          210
Marie Curie Centre, Harestone, Surrey 209
Marie Curie Centre, Newcastle 209
Marie Curie centres 98, 103
Marie Curie diplomas 97
Marie Curie Foundation 97, 110
Marie Curie Homes 103
Marie Curie Hospices 98
Marie Curie Hospital, Hampstead 94
Marie Curie Memorial Foundation 94, 134, 209, 213
Marie Curie nurses 95–97
Marie Curie nursing homes 94, 97
Marie Curie palliative care centre, Newcastle 97
Marie Curie Service 95
Marie Curie teams 95
Marris, Peter 159, 167

Marshall, Sam 48
Maudsley Hospital, London 31, 157–59, 208, 212
McCreery, Ivy 146, 183, 210
McGinley, Ciaran 53, 210, 211
McGinley, Tom 29, 37, 45, 53, 124, 204, 210, 211
McIllmurray, Malcolm 48, 117, 118, 173, 211
McNulty, Barbara 55, 64, 116, 128, 172, 193, 200, 211
Medical Research Council (MRC) 28
    Social Psychiatry Unit 158–59
Memorial Sloan Kettering, New York 140
Metropolitan Anthony. See Bloom, Anthony
Michniewicz, Antoni 14, 17–18, 197
Monroe, Barbara 164
Morgan, Mrs J.T. (Olwen) 51
morphine 27, 28, 135, 137–40, 142, 144, 147–148, 215
Morris, Osmond 192, 211
Mount, Balfour 2
Mount Pleasant Chapel 51
Murphy, Michael 89, 109, 212

– **N** –

National Association of Bereavement Services 105
National Association of Complementary Therapists in Hospice and
    Palliative Care 90
National Association of Hospice Fundraisers 90
National Association of Hospice Volunteer Coordinators 73, 200
National Council for Hospice and Specialist Palliative Care Services 8,
    90, 98, 100–04, 111, 114, 204, 214, 216
National Forum for Hospice at Home 90
National Health Service (NHS) 36, 44, 49, 68, 94, 101–03, 123, 146,
    209, 214, 215
    changing concerns of 68
    cutbacks 92
    discrimination against 70
    funding 2, 42, 68–69, 74, 92, 180
    guidance 68
    hospices 83–85, 102
    initiatives 99
    partnership with 65
    provision 36
    relationship with 42, 74, 89, 180–81, 183
    separation from 14, 20, 36, 49, 94, 103, 113, 180
    units 108, 178, 208, 215
National Hospice Council 97, 181, 189

National Network for the Palliative Care of People with Learning
    Disabilities 90
National Organisation for the Widowed and their Children. See Cruse
    Bereavement Care
National Society for Cancer Relief (NSCR) 50–51, 69, 84, 90–91, 115,
    203, 207. See also Macmillan Cancer Relief
Newcastle General Hospital 97
Newry Hospice. See Northern Ireland Southern Area Hospice Services,
    Newry
Nicholson, Alexander 135
non-cancer diseases 3, 11, 188–90, 198. See also AIDS, Alzheimer's
    disease, dementia
Northern Ireland Cancer Nursing Research Group 98
Northern Ireland Hospice, Belfast 47, 66, 79, 102, 129, 183, 190,
    199, 200, 209, 214
Northern Ireland Southern Area Hospice Services, Newry 53, 126,
    192, 203, 211
Nurse Link 96
Nuttall, Derek 170, 175

– **O** –

Osborn, John, MP 49
Osborn, Sue 49, 50, 212
Our Lady's Hospice, Dublin 109, 212

– **P** –

pain 10, 21, 25–26, 38, 82, 162, 208
    chronic 72
    control of 2–3, 28–29, 35, 55–56, 61, 71, 91, 93, 116, 134–52,
        177, 197, 199, 207
    finding peace in 125–26
    ladder 150–52
    meaning of 127
    relief of 10, 29, 32, 177, 211
    responses to 8
    spiritual 22
    'staff pain' 72, 163
    'total pain' 2, 10, 22, 72, 137–38, 145–47, 152, 160, 177
    understanding nature of 19, 22, 147–52
    unrelieved 120
Paintings in Hospitals 90
palliative care 3, 5–6, 10, 20, 22, 65, 82, 95, 101, 103–04, 107, 131,

137, 149, 171, 179–80, 188–90, 193, 195, 202, 207, 208, 209, 211, 213, 215
activists 103, 177
and non-cancer diseases 10, 62, 188, 190
approach 146, 212
availability of 3
benefits of 3
centre 201
changing nature of 177, 183
Christian roots of 123
consultants 86
development of 1, 10, 89, 110, 152, 197
dissemination of 188, 191
education and research 4, 84, 94, 97, 101, 103, 106, 138, 148, 153, 188, 195, 200, 215
ethos of 3, 194
expansion of 72, 195
facilities 212
'for all' 3
funding of 69
history of 3, 4, 147, 195
home-based 60–61
hospital 130
hospital service 97, 203
hospital teams 2, 42, 60, 73, 77, 143, 208, 209
innovation in 191
integration of 3
literature 73, 131
movement 117
multidisciplinary 197, 208
multiprofessional 84
neglect by government of 69
outreach 76
paediatric 60, 61, 62, 207
professional associations 10, 89–113, 177, 215
provision of 76
services 3, 11, 66, 101, 148, 209
specialist 77, 102–04, 182–86, 190–91, 216
specialist nurses 66, 77, 188
standards of 188
teams 55–56, 73, 77
units 33, 97, 146, 178, 181
use of term 2, 56
workers 101
Palliative Care Research Forum 73, 105, 107, 215

Palliative Care Research Society 90, 98, 106–07
Parker, Lucy 48
Parkes, Colin Murray 20, 31–32, 62, 127, 148, 156–60, 166–72, 175, 179, 207, 212
Payne, Malcolm 73, 78
Payne, Sheila 105
Perolls, Graham 52, 212
Petrie, Gillian 94–95, 111, 213
Pets as Therapy 90
Pilgrims Hospice, Ashford, Kent 205
Pincus, Lily 168
Prince and Princess of Wales Hospice, Glasgow 51–52, 184, 206
Princess Alice Hospice, Esher 57, 71, 105, 200
psychiatry 31, 157–59, 206, 208, 212

– Q –
Queen's Chaplains. See Chaplains to the Queen
Quilliam, Peter 98

– R –
Radcliffe Infirmary, Oxford 21
Radley, Jean 20, 37, 213
Raigmore Hospital 48
Ramsey, Roland 85
Rapson, Malcolm 74, 110, 213
Reece, Dorothy 41
Regnard, Claud 187–89, 213
Relf, Marilyn 62, 65, 80–81, 104, 162, 167–68, 171, 213
religion 9, 14, 32, 34, 37–38, 44–47, 64, 116–17, 119–23, 126–27, 129, 131–32, 141, 177, 182, 194–95, 201, 202
Richards, Donald 77
Richard Dimbleby Cancer Trust 59
Rosetta Life 90
Rossi, Paul 98–99, 101, 213
Rourke, Bill 79, 214
Royal College of General Practice 109
Royal College of General Practitioners 3
Royal College of Nursing (RCN) 114, 188
    Palliative Nurses Group 90
Royal College of Paediatrics and Child Health 39, 207
Royal College of Physicians 3, 35, 103, 190
Royal Hospital, Sheffield 202, 204, 206
Royal Infirmary, Edinburgh 34, 205

Royal Infirmary, Manchester 215
Royal Marsden Hospital, London 147, 153, 199
Royal Northern Hospital, Holloway 215
Royal Pharmaceutical Society of Great Britain 207
Royal Society of Medicine 135
Royal United Hospital, Bath 203
Royal Victoria Hospital, Belfast 199, 200
Royal Victoria Hospital Palliative Care Service, Canada 11
Rupert Fund 61
Ryder, Sue (Lady Ryder of Warsaw) 114

– S –

St Ann's Hospice, Cheadle 49
St Barnabas Hospice, Lincoln 207
St Barnabas Hospice, Worthing 206
St Benedict's Hospice, Sunderland 71, 85, 210
St Christopher's Hospice, Sydenham 33, 50–51, 72, 103, 105, 107,
        128, 153, 162, 172, 176, 178, 183, 200, 207, 208, 209, 210,
        212
    acquisition of land for 44–45
    advances at 160
    and non-cancer diseases 190
    approach of 42, 54
    architects 69, 75
    bereavement service 20, 62, 160–61, 163–67, 173–74
    building of 43
    calling towards 32
    chapel at 132, 165
    Chaplain 124–25, 165, 210
    Community Pharmacist 201
    Coordinator of Studies 215
    courses at 50, 210
    Deputy Medical Director 25, 216
    Director of Studies 205
    early team at 7, 55–56, 63–64, 74, 78, 82–83, 193
    education at 74, 83
    founded by Cicely Saunders 2, 29
    'founding patients' of 18, 44
    Friends of 63
    fund-raising for 19, 30, 63
    history of 20, 214
    home care 55, 128, 209, 211
    Honorary Consultant Psychiatrist 212
    Hospice Information Service 114
    hospital support team 56–57
    ideas developed at 2
    improvements at 149
    inspiration to others 49, 62, 75, 92
    international conferences 214
    multidisciplinary 72, 83
    multidisciplinary approach 78
    multidisciplinary courses 163
    multidisciplinary team 54, 164
    opening of 56, 63, 135, 141, 150, 214, 215
    origin of name 19
    outside the NHS 20, 74
    Pilgrim Club 166
    placements at 26, 203
    planning committee 64, 211
    plans for 159–60
    promotion of 214
    relationship with the community 82
    reputation of 20, 33, 61
    research at 137, 148
    Research Fellow 215
    risk assessment model 62
    social work at 160–61, 205
    spiritual and medical foundation of 16, 117
    spiritual care 119
    steering group 159
    Vice-Presidents 129
    vision for 44
    visitors to 2, 22, 34, 56, 63, 199, 207, 208
St Clare's Hospice, Jarrow 65, 71, 210
St Columba's Fellowship 90, 123, 203
St Columba's Hospice, Edinburgh 33–34, 48, 115, 130, 204, 208
St Francis Hospice, Romford 105
St Gemma's Hospice, Leeds 27, 37, 46, 79, 93, 98, 119–20, 202,
        206, 209, 216
St Helena Hospice, Colchester 105
St John's Hospice, Lancaster 48, 211
St Joseph's Hospice, Hackney 2, 16–18, 22, 27–29, 32, 37, 55, 67,
        69–70, 91, 99, 114–15, 132, 135–36, 139–41, 149, 171, 199,
        210, 211, 214, 215
St Luke's Hospice, Bayswater 153, 214
St Luke's Hospice, Plymouth 46, 64, 201, 203
St Luke's Hospice, Sheffield 22, 74–75, 85, 92, 100, 129, 142, 145,
        162, 195, 202, 203, 206, 213
    architects 69

bereavement care at 162
changes at 110
chapel at 121
Chaplain 124–25, 216
Day Hospice 75
Day Unit 57–58
donation of land for 49
financial stability 74
founded by Eric Wilkes 5, 49, 69, 216
founding of 28, 35, 49, 54, 212
Friends of 35
fund-raising for 49
home care 75
library 105
volunteers 35, 81, 105, 163, 186–87, 200, 204, 208, 215
St Luke's Hospital, New York 56, 200
St Michael's Hospice, Basingstoke 105
St Michael's Hospice, Hereford 210
St Oswald's Hospice, Newcastle 213
St Peter's Hospice, Bristol 92
St Thomas's Hospital, London 15, 44, 56–57, 59, 64, 138, 176, 199, 200, 205, 211, 214, 216
Saunders, Barbara 57
Saunders, Cicely 5, 13, 34–35, 39, 55–56, 63, 109, 124, 134, 137, 140, 144, 156, 166, 177, 188, 193, 196, 200, 205, 212, 214, 215, 216
    'total pain'. See pain, total
    and Antoni Michniewicz 14, 17–18
    and David Tasma 14–16, 18
    and Mrs G 19
    as innovator 32
    at St Joseph's 17–18, 27–28, 32, 135–36, 141, 199
    back problems 15
    contacted for advice/assistance 25–26, 49, 60, 96
    correspondence of 7, 114, 117
    early patients of 18, 25
    evolving ideas of 29, 116, 135, 140
    founder of St Christopher's 2, 20, 29, 44
    highly motivated 30
    influence of 15, 108, 164, 197
    listening to patients 22, 145
    management of pain 135
    multidisciplinary 137
    nature of pain 19, 22
    opposition to euthanasia 3
    patients' needs 19
    pioneer of the hospice movement 68, 170, 197
    President of Help the Hospices 98, 115
    publications by 28, 44, 72, 134, 137, 142, 214
    religious calling 32, 124
    setting up St Christopher's 43–45, 67, 159, 160, 214
    training as doctor 16, 25, 33, 134, 138, 199, 214, 216
    training as nurse 15
    vision for hospice care 44, 116, 160
    work of 2, 14, 37, 49, 61, 135, 214
Scott, Nicholas, MP 113
Scott, Patricia 76–77, 84, 120, 122, 214
Scott, Tom 103, 184
Scottish Partnership for Palliative Care (Scottish Partnership Agency for Palliative and Cancer Care (SPAPCC)) 75–76, 90, 98, 103–04, 201, 204
Selye, Hans 157
Shaw, Brian 187, 215
Sheldon, Frances 94, 106–08, 185, 195, 215
Shepherd, David 128
Silverman, Phyllis 167
Sir Michael Sobell House, Oxford 62, 65, 76, 80, 84, 104, 120, 162, 213, 214, 215
Snow, Herbert 137
Soldiers', Sailors' & Airmen's Families Association 216
spirituality 2–3, 8, 10, 14, 17, 19, 22, 32, 38, 57, 79, 116–131, 137, 152, 160, 177, 179–80, 197
Stevens, Mike 57
Stevens, Robin 105
Stevenson, Margaret 76
Stjernsward, Jan 149
Stokes, Julie 105, 175
Stoke Mandeville Hospital 84, 214
Strathcarron Hospice, Denny 48, 104, 184
Sue Ryder Care 90, 101–02
Summers, Dorothy 83, 142, 215
Support After Murder and Manslaughter (SAMM) 172, 212
Sweetser, Carleton 70
Swerdlow, Mark 150

– T –

Takeda, Fumikazu 150
Tasma, David 14–16, 18, 44, 138, 214
Tavistock Clinic 40, 159, 193

Tavistock Institute of Human Relations 174, 212
Thames Valley Hospice 203
Thorpe, Graham 11, 107–08, 193, 215
Thucydides 7
Torrie, Alfred 175
Torrie, Margaret 169–70
Trinity Hospice, Clapham 200
Tudor Trust 53, 212
Twycross, Robert 26, 32, 34, 36, 84, 100, 106–08, 114, 118, 138, 142, 147, 149–51, 213, 215, 216
Ty Olwen Pallative Care Service, Swansea 50, 207

– U –

United Nations 31

– V –

Vachon, Mary 167
Valleys, Hospice of the, Tredegar. *See* Marches, Hospice of the
Vanier, Jean 176
Vanier, Therese 174
Vatican Council, Second 46, 120
volunteers 1, 3, 6, 27, 42, 57, 62, 65, 79, 116, 187, 202, 204, 205, 207, 208, 210, 214, 215, 216. *See also* InVOLve
    becoming 26, 35, 163
    integration of 81
    in bereavement care 62–64, 104, 155, 160, 162–63, 165, 167–70, 174
    in libraries 105
    numbers 80–81
    support for 82, 162–63, 167, 207, 213
    teamwork 75, 80–81, 87
    training 81, 105, 162, 167–68, 170, 200, 207, 213
Volunteer Centre 62
volunteer coordinators 65, 80–82, 104, 163, 186, 200, 207, 213.
    See also National Association of Hospice Volunteer Coordinators
volunteer teams 73

– W –

Walter, Tony 132, 169
Walton, Wilf 124, 129, 216
Warren, Miriam 79, 216
Weatherill, Ann 33–34, 204
Welfare Grant Scheme 95

Welldon, Ron 41
West, Tom 25, 78, 120, 125, 160–61, 199, 203, 216
Widow-to-Widow Project 167
Wilkes, Eric 5, 30, 35, 58, 68, 85, 93, 96, 105, 110–11, 120–21, 125, 162, 181, 187, 203, 204, 206, 210, 212, 216
    and Help the Hospices 98, 100, 115
    and National Council for Hospice and Specialist Palliative Care Services 101
    as GP 20, 30, 49–50
    founder of St Luke's 5, 50, 216
    medical training 21
    setting up St Luke's 49–50, 68–69, 75
    training GPs 143
Wilkes Report. *See* Working Group on Terminal Care
Williment, Paul 27, 216
Winner, Albertine 49, 205
Winner, Dame Albertine 49
Winston's Wish 171
Worden, William 62, 167
Working Group on Terminal Care (Wilkes Report) 68, 75, 182, 216
World Health Organisation (WHO) 31, 41, 73, 149–50, 152, 154, 198, 216

– Y –

Yorkstone, Paddy 62

– Z –

Zorza, Jane 66
Zorza, Victor 214
Zorza, Victor & Rosemary 66

Observatory Publications

Innovative Writing on End-of-Life Issues

Human mortality is a rare constant in a changing world. Yet how we die is a matter of growing social, medical and moral complexity and creates one of the major challenges of our times. Observatory Publications promotes the understanding of death, dying and bereavement; seeks to improve care at the end of life; fosters interdisciplinary perspectives; and encourages the most innovative writers, editors and researchers in the field.

Observatory Publications focuses on the following areas:

- Historical and cultural studies of hospice, palliative care and related end of life issues

- Studies of current issues in the development of palliative care both nationally and internationally, focusing on service development, policy factors and reimbursement

- Empirical and theoretical contributions on mortality and end of life issues from anthropology, sociology, social psychology, ethics, religious studies and the clinical disciplines

Founded in 2004 by the sociologist Professor David Clark, Observatory Publications is a non-profit venture located within the International Observatory on End of Life Care at Lancaster University. Proceeds from the sales of Observatory Publications are used to support the work of the Observatory.

Please see our website for full details of current and forthcoming titles and how to purchase Observatory Publications books.

OBSERVATORY PUBLICATIONS

International Observatory on End of Life Care, Institute for Health Research,
Lancaster University, Lancaster, LA1 4YT, UK

observatory-publications@lancaster.ac.uk
www.eolc-observatory.net